*He has we...*
*now...*

# Her Tycoon Lover

Three glitzy, contemporary romances from
three favourite Mills & Boon authors!

In March 2010 Mills & Boon bring
you two classic collections, each
featuring three favourite romances
by our bestselling authors

## HER TYCOON LOVER

*On the Tycoon's Terms* by Sandra Field
*Her Tycoon Protector*
by Amanda Browning
*One Night with the Tycoon*
by Lee Wilkinson

## HER PREGNANCY SUPRISE

*His Pregnancy Bargain* by Kim Lawrence
*The Pregnancy Secret* by Maggie Cox
*Their Pregnancy Bombshell*
by Barbara McMahon

# Her Tycoon Lover

SANDRA FIELD

AMANDA BROWNING

LEE WILKINSON

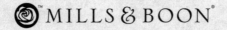
MILLS & BOON

All the characters in this book have no existence outside the imagination of the author, and have no relation whatsoever to anyone bearing the same name or names. They are not even distantly inspired by any individual known or unknown to the author, and all the incidents are pure invention.

All Rights Reserved including the right of reproduction in whole or in part in any form. This edition is published by arrangement with Harlequin Enterprises II B.V./S.à.r.l. The text of this publication or any part thereof may not be reproduced or transmitted in any form or by any means, electronic or mechanical, including photocopying, recording, storage in an information retrieval system, or otherwise, without the written permission of the publisher.

This book is sold subject to the condition that it shall not, by way of trade or otherwise, be lent, resold, hired out or otherwise circulated without the prior consent of the publisher in any form of binding or cover other than that in which it is published and without a similar condition including this condition being imposed on the subsequent purchaser.

® and ™ are trademarks owned and used by the trademark owner and/or its licensee. Trademarks marked with ® are registered with the United Kingdom Patent Office and/or the Office for Harmonisation in the Internal Market and in other countries.

First published in Great Britain 2010
Harlequin Mills & Boon Limited,
Eton House, 18-24 Paradise Road, Richmond, Surrey TW9 1SR

HER TYCOON LOVER © by Harlequin Enterprises II B.V./S.à.r.l 2010

*On the Tycoon's Terms, Her Tycoon Protector* and *One Night with the Tycoon* were first published in Great Britain by Harlequin Mills & Boon Limited in separate, single volumes.

*On the Tycoon's Terms* © Sandra Field 2002
*Her Tycoon Protector* © Amanda Browning 2005
*One Night with the Tycoon* © Lee Wilkinson 2004

ISBN: 978 0 263 88098 4

05-0310

Printed and bound in Spain
by Litografia Rosés S.A., Barcelona

# ON THE TYCOON'S TERMS

BY
SANDRA FIELD

Although born in England, **Sandra Field** has lived most of her life in Canada; she says the silence and emptiness of the North speaks to her particularly. While she enjoys travelling and passing on her sense of a new place, she often chooses to write about the city which is now her home. Sandra says, "I write out of my experience; I have learned that love with its joys and pains is all important. I hope this knowledge enriches my writing and touches a cord in you, the reader."

# CHAPTER ONE

"LUKE! Good to see you, did you just arrive?"

"Hi there, John," Luke MacRae said, shaking the older man's hand. "Got in an hour ago. Jet-lagged, as usual." And remarkably reluctant to be here, he added to himself although he had no intentions of telling John that. "How about yourself?"

"Earlier in the day.... There's someone here I'd like you to meet, he's got some holdings in Malaysia that might interest you."

"Inland?" Luke asked, and to his satisfaction heard the slight edge to his voice, the intentness that had brought him to where he was today: owner of a worldwide mining conglomerate. He and John were two of the delegates at an international conference on mining being held at a resort beside one of Manitoba's vast lakes.

"You'll have to ask him the exact location." John signaled to the nearest waitress. "What'll you have, Luke?"

"Scotch on the rocks," Luke said crisply, sparing a moment to wonder why the waitress was wearing such ugly glasses. She might be rather pretty without them.

He was deep in conversation with the Malaysian, who did indeed interest him, when an exquisitely modulated voice to his left said, "Your drink, sir."

The voice didn't in the least match the dark-framed glasses or the blond hair strained back under a frilly white cap. Uptight about her femininity and deadly dull into the bargain, Luke decided. Despite that very intriguing voice.

It was a game of his to make instant assessments of people; he was very rarely wrong. One thing was certain. The

5

waitress wasn't the kind of woman who turned his crank. "Thanks," he said briefly, then forgot her right away.

Three-quarters of an hour later they all moved into the dining room; his table, he noticed automatically, had the best location as far as the view of the lake was concerned, and its occupants were the real powers behind this conference. He had long ago trained himself not to feel any self-satisfaction from such arrangements. He was good. He knew it and didn't dwell on it. Power for the sake of power had never interested him.

Power was security. Security against the kind of childhood he'd had.

Luke took his seat, running his fingers around his collar. Dammit, he never thought about his childhood. Just because Teal Lake, where he'd been born, was in nearby northern Ontario was no reason to indulge in maudlin memories. The proximity of his old home was, of course, the reason he was reluctant to be here. Although *home* was the laugh of the century. Neither of his parents had provided him with much of a home in the little mining town of Teal Lake.

Quickly Luke picked up the leather-bound menu and made his choices; then his eyes flicked over the other occupants of the table.

The only surprise was sitting directly across from him: Guy Wharton. Inherited money without the requisite brains to manage it had been Luke's opinion of Guy the first time he'd met him, and any subsequent encounters hadn't caused him to change his mind. Unfortunately Guy's wealth was coupled with a tendency to throw his weight around.

The bartender took their orders, then the waitress started at the other end of the table. The waitress with the glasses and the beautiful voice, Luke thought idly. Guy had brought his drink to the table, and was now ordering a double, as well as a bottle of very good wine that would be wasted on him. Guy drinking was several steps worse than Guy sober. Luke turned his attention to his neighbor, a charming Englishman with an unerring nose for the commodity market; then heard that smooth contralto voice again. ''Sir? May I take your order?''

''I'll have smoked salmon and the rack of lamb, medium rare,'' Luke said. She nodded politely, then addressed his companion. She wasn't writing anything down; her eyes behind the overlarge lenses, he saw with a little jolt, were a clear, intelligent blue. Not dull at all. Somehow Luke was quite sure she'd keep all the orders straight.

Well, of course she'd be good at her job; a resort like this wouldn't hire duds.

Waitresses and Teal Lake…he was losing it. ''Rupert,'' he asked, ''what are your thoughts on silver over the next couple of months?''

The Englishman launched into a highly technical assessment, to which Luke paid close attention. Wine was poured into his glass; he sipped it sparingly, noticing that Guy's face was already flushed and his voice overloud. The smoked salmon was excellent; the rack of lamb tender and the vegetables crisp. Then Luke noticed Guy signaling the waitress. She came instantly, her severe black uniform with its white apron effectively hiding her figure. But nothing could hide a certain pride of bearing, Luke thought slowly; although she wasn't a tall woman, she walked tall, like someone who knew who she was and liked herself. Yet he'd categorized her as deadly dull…was he going to prove himself wrong for once?

''The steak,'' Guy said loudly. ''I asked for medium. You brought rare.''

''I'm so sorry, sir,'' she said. ''I'll take it back to the kitchen and bring one more to your liking.''

But as she reached down for his plate, Guy grabbed her

by the wrist. "Why didn't you do it right the first time? You're being paid to bring me what I ask for."

"Yes, sir," she said. "If you'll let go, I'll make sure your steak is brought to you immediately."

There were faint pink patches in her cheeks; her mouth, Luke noticed, was set, her whole body rigid. But Guy didn't let go. Instead he twisted her wrist, leering up at her. "You should take those stupid glasses off," he said. "No man in his right mind'll look at you with those on."

"Please let go of my wrist."

This time, she hadn't said *sir*. Without stopping to think, Luke pushed himself partway up from his chair and said in a voice like a steel blade, "Guy, you heard the lady. Let go of her. Now," and noticed from the corner of his eye the maître d' heading toward their table.

"Only kidding," Guy said, running his fingers over the woman's palm, then releasing her wrist with deliberate slowness. The waitress didn't even glance at Luke as she quickly removed Guy's plate and hurried away from the table.

"I didn't find it funny," Luke said coldly. "Nor, I'm sure, did anyone else. Including her."

"For Pete's sake, she's just a waitress. And we all know what they're after."

Luke was quite sure the waitress with the ugly glasses wasn't after anyone. If she were, she'd wear contacts, and make the most of eyes that could be truly startling were they not framed by thick plastic. Pointedly he turned to the man on his other side, an Italian goldminer. A few minutes later the maître d' brought Guy another plate. "Please let me know if that's not to your satisfaction, sir," he said with meticulous politeness.

"She chickened out, did she?" Guy smirked.

"I beg your pardon, sir?"

"You heard," Guy said. "Yeah, this is okay."

Brandishing his knife as he talked, he began telling an off-color story to his neighbor.

When they'd finished their entrées, it was the waitress who removed their plates. Her name tag said Katrin. Luke had read that the resort was near a village that had been settled over a hundred years ago by Icelandic immigrants; with her blond hair and blue eyes, she certainly fit the stereotype. Then, as she reached for his plate, he saw on her wrist the red mark where Guy had twisted her skin, and felt an upsurge of rage that was out of all proportion.

Because he'd always loathed men who picked on those who were weaker, or otherwise powerless to defend themselves? Because basic justice was a tenet he held no matter what the class distinctions?

He said nothing; the woman had already made it all too clear she hadn't been grateful for his intervention. In no mood for dessert, he ordered a coffee.

"Join me in a brandy?" John murmured.

"No, thanks," Luke replied. "Jet lag's catching up on me, I'm going to call it a day very shortly."

This was true enough. But Luke had never been one for alcoholic excess; his father had drunk enough for five men. One more reason why Guy's drunken pronouncements had gotten under his skin. He and John talked briefly about the abysmal markets for copper and nickel; then Luke saw Katrin approaching their table with a loaded tray of rich desserts. She lowered it skilfully onto the dumbwaiter and started distributing tortes and cheesecakes with scarcely a pause. She had a very good memory and was extraordinarily efficient, he thought with reluctant admiration. So what else had he missed in his initial assessment?

Guy had ordered a double brandy. As she started to put it on the table, he deliberately brushed his arm against her breast. "Mmm...nice," he sneered. "You hiding anything else under that uniform?"

So quickly he wondered if he'd imagined it, Luke saw a flash of blue fire behind her ludicrous glasses. Then the brandy snifter tipped as though the stem had slipped through her fingers. The contents drenched Guy's sleeve and trickled down his pale blue shirt. "Oh, sir," she exclaimed, "how careless of me. Let me get you a napkin."

As Guy surged to his feet, his face mottled with rage, Luke also stood up. She'd done it on purpose, he thought, and suppressed a quiver of true amusement: the kind he rarely felt. "Guy," he said softly, "you cause any more trouble at this table, and I personally will see that the deal you're working on with Amco Steel gets shelved. Permanently. Do you hear me?"

There was a small, deadly silence. Guy wanted that deal, everyone at the table knew that. Wanted it very badly. Guy snarled, "You're a bastard, MacRae."

Technically Guy was telling the exact truth: Luke's father had never bothered marrying Luke's mother. But Luke had long ago buried any feelings around the circumstances of his birth. "I'll kill the deal before it even gets to the table," he said. "Now sit down and behave yourself."

Katrin had reached for a serviette from the shelf below the dumbwaiter. As she straightened, she gave Luke a withering look which said more clearly than words that she neither needed nor appreciated his help, and passed the crisply folded linen to Guy. "The resort will, of course, look after the dry cleaning of your suit, sir," she said, and very calmly passed out the remainder of the drinks and desserts, as if nothing had happened.

Adding a formidable self-control to his list of the shapeless and bespectacled Katrin's qualities, Luke drained his coffee cup and said flatly, "Good night, all. According to my time zone it's 2:00 a.m., and I'm going to hit the pit. See you all in the morning."

On the way out, he stopped to speak briefly to the maître d'.

"I trust there'll be no repercussions for the waitress at our table," he said. "If he were working in my office, Mr. Wharton would be slapped with a sexual harassment charge. And I'd make damn sure it stuck."

The maître d', who was at least five years younger than Luke's thirty-three, said noncommittally, "Thank you, sir."

"I'm sure there'll be no further trouble from Mr. Wharton."

"Certainly, sir."

Luke said pleasantly, "If she's fired or otherwise penalized, I'll file a complaint with the management."

"That won't be necessary, sir."

Suddenly Luke was tired of the whole game. Why was he wasting his time on a woman who patently couldn't care less about him, and had resented his help? Bed, that was where he should be, he decided, and marched toward the elevators.

In bed. Alone. As he'd been for rather too long.

Once he got back to San Francisco, he must do something about that.

# CHAPTER TWO

LUKE slept well, went for an early morning run, then returned to his room to shower and dress. After straightening his discreet silk tie, he shrugged into a jacket and ran a comb through his black hair; he'd had it trimmed last week in Milan, although nothing could subdue its tendency to curl. He glanced quickly in the mirror, meeting his own dark brown eyes, so dark as to be almost black. He'd do. He looked his usual self: well-groomed, single-minded and totally in control.

Not bad for a kid from Teal Lake.

Luke grimaced irritably. He didn't want to think about Teal Lake. Now or ever. So why was he standing here admiring himself when he should be downstairs? There were some valuable contacts he could cement in the next few days.

He took the elevator to the main floor. The resort might be situated in the wilderness but there was nothing remotely backwoods about it. The dining room had tall, velvet-draped windows and a magnificent stone fireplace, flanked by striking oil paintings of the prairie wheatfields. It was mid-July, the lake as smooth as the mirror in his room, the eastern sky a limpid blue.

He'd like to be out there, Luke thought. Capturing the sky's serenity with his digital camera.

But not right now; there were more important things to do. As he started across the room to his table, Katrin the waitress emerged from the kitchen. She was wearing a peasant skirt and an embroidered blouse. He said cheerfully, "Good morning, Katrin."

12

Her steps didn't even falter. "Good morning, sir."

In three words she managed to imply that although being polite to him was part of her job, it was far from her personal preference. Again Luke felt that wayward flash of true amusement. He'd been insulted many times in his life, both as a raw kid working the mines of the Arctic and as a ruthless entrepreneur. But rarely with such finesse. Not one wasted word.

He'd like to pluck those god-awful glasses off her nose.

He'd reached his table. Guy was noticeable by his absence. No loss, thought Luke, and sat down so that his back was to the lake. He didn't want to look at water. He had work to do.

And work he did, all day. Lunch was served buffet-style in the foyer to the conference rooms; Katrin was nowhere to be seen. Before dinner, Luke went to the fully equipped exercise room to get rid of the pressures of the day. On the whole, he was pleased with the way things were going. He had Malaysia hooked; and could feel himself backing off from a strip mine in Papua New Guinea. Long ago he'd learned to trust his instincts, and they were all screaming beware. Labor troubles, gangsters and environmental destruction: not his cup of tea.

An hour later, feeling both relaxed and alert, Luke was crossing the lobby toward the dining room. A smartly dressed woman walking in the opposite direction gave him an assessing glance, followed by a smile that was rather more than casual. Luke was used to this; it happened to him all the time. His own smile back was courteous, nothing more.

As he waited for the maître d', he wondered idly what it was about him that attracted women. His suit and shirt were custom-tailored, his shoes Italian; both outward signs of wealth. But lots of other men were similarly garbed. So it wasn't just his money. He wasn't blind to his height, his athletic build and the regularity of his features; and had always assumed that they were what drew women to him. What he was unaware of was his aura of decisiveness, of hard-won power, of sheer male energy and banked sexuality; unaware also of the impact of his rare smile, that softened his deep-set, enigmatic eyes and the hewn masculinity of his jaw.

He was the last to arrive at his table. Katrin was once again wearing her unflattering black uniform; for the first time, Luke noticed how thick the bundle of straight blond hair was under her cap. Loose, it would fall past her shoulders…he suddenly realized she was speaking to him. "What can I get you to drink, sir?"

"Rye and water, no ice, please."

"Certainly, sir."

At what point did politeness turn to parody, he wondered; and decided Katrin knew that point precisely, and wasn't above using it. He sat down.

No one else had noticed anything; perhaps his imagination was working overtime. The odd thing was that, elusively, she reminded him of someone; he'd figured this out while he was doing his routine of bench presses. He'd already searched through all the old Teal Lake contacts, and knew she didn't belong there. So where else could he have met her? Nowhere that he could think of. And yet something about the tilt of her chin, her carriage, set off signals in his brain.

Once again the food was excellent; once again Guy was gulping a fine Shiraz as though it were water and eating Châteaubriand with the appreciation hamburger deserved.

The conversation turned to the vagaries of the stock market. Guy, to do him justice, had one or two insights about insider trading that were worth listening to. As Katrin poured coffee from a sterling pot, moving efficiently from seat to seat, Guy said with overdone bonhomie, "Well,

Katrin, I don't suppose you earn enough to consider investing. But if you did, would you buy into the Alvena bond fund?''

She said woodenly, ''I wouldn't know, sir.''

''Of course not,'' Guy said in a voice as smooth as cream. ''Let's try something a little closer to your level. How about two-minute portfolios, they're all the rage for people with no smarts who know zilch about the market…is that how you'd invest your money?''

For a split second she hesitated, as though making an inner decision. Then she looked right at Guy, coffeepot suspended, and said crisply, ''A two-minute portfolio isn't a bad strategy. When you play the market, you're going to get some duds no matter how careful you are. So by picking from the TSE's top blue-chips, you'll also get enough high-earners to more than offset your losses.'' She gave him a bland smile. ''Would you agree with me, sir?''

Guy flushed an unbecoming brick-red. ''This coffee tastes like it was brewed yesterday,'' he snarled.

''I'll make you some fresh, sir,'' she replied, deftly removing his cup, and with that same unconscious pride of bearing that Luke had noticed the day before, headed for the kitchen.

Luke drawled, ''That woman's wasted as a waitress…so what's the prognosis for the S&P over the next six months, Guy?''

For a moment he thought Guy was going to jump across the table at him, and felt all his muscles tighten in anticipation. Then Guy subsided, mumbling something about low percentiles, and the conversation became general again. Luke lingered over a second coffee and was the last to leave the dining room, timing his departure just as Katrin was clearing off a nearby empty table. Soft-footed as a cat, he stepped up behind her. ''It'd be a shame if you had to cash in your investments, Katrin,'' he said, ''but you'll lose your job if you go dumping expensive brandy over every customer who insults you.''

She turned to face him, her hands full of dirty wineglasses, her face expressionless. "I have no idea what you're talking about, sir.''

"Last night you spilled brandy all over Guy Wharton on purpose.''

"Why would I do that? Waitresses don't have feelings—they can't afford to.''

"Then you're the exception that proves the rule. I wish to God you'd take those glasses off…then I might have some idea what you *are* feeling.''

She stepped back in sudden alarm. "My feelings, or lack of them, are none of your business…sir.''

She was right, of course. "I also wish you'd stop calling me *sir*.''

"It's one of the house rules,'' she said frigidly. "Another of which is that guests and staff don't fraternize. So if you'll excuse me, sir, I have work to do.''

"You're wasted in a job like this, you're far too intelligent.''

She said tightly, "My choice of job is just that—*my* choice. Good night, sir.''

She had turned away. Short of grabbing her by the arm, a move he had no intention of making, Luke knew the conversation was over. Score: Katrin, one; Luke, zero. He said pleasantly, "If you are investing, steer clear of Scitech—it's going down the tubes. Good night, Katrin.''

But, just as he was turning away, he heard himself add, "You know, I have the oddest feeling—you remind me of someone, and I can't think who.'' He hadn't planned to tell her this. Not before he'd pinned down the memory that was teasing his brain.

Her whole body went still: the stillness of prey faced with a predator. She said so quietly he could hardly hear her, "You're mistaken. You're quite wrong—I've never seen you before in my life."

His senses sharpened. Her shoulders were stiff with tension, the same tension that had underlain her voice. So there *was* something mysterious about her. The ugly glasses were nothing to do with hiding her femininity, and everything to do with another kind of disguise. Katrin didn't want to be recognized because she was other than she appeared. He said, thinking out loud, "Right now I can't pin down where I might have seen you...but I'm sure it'll come to me."

Two of the wineglasses slipped through her fingers. As they fell to the carpet, one hit the table leg, shattering into pieces. With a tiny exclamation of distress, Katrin bent to pick them up.

"Careful," Luke exclaimed, "you could cut yourself."

He grabbed a napkin from the table and knelt beside her, wrapping the shards of glass in the thick linen. Her perfume drifted to his nostrils, something floral and delicate. The red mark on her wrist hadn't completely faded; her veins were blue against her creamy skin, her wrist bones fragile. She said raggedly, "Please go away—I'll clean this up."

Jerkily she reached for a splinter of glass. Blood blossomed from her fingertip; she gave a gasp of pain. Luke said urgently, "Katrin, leave this. Here, stand up."

He seized her by the elbow, pulling her to her feet. Then he gently rested her fingers on his sleeve, probing at the wound. She said breathlessly, "Stop, you're hurting."

"There's glass in it, hold still," he ordered, and as carefully as he could extracted a small shard of glass from the cut. "There, that's better. Is there a first-aid kit in the kitchen?"

A male voice said authoritatively, "What's the trouble here, sir?"

The ubiquitous maître d', thought Luke, and wished the man a hundred miles away. "She's cut her finger," he said with equal authority. "Will you please show me where the first-aid kit is?"

"I'll look after—"

"Now," said Luke, transferring his gaze from Katrin's finger to the young man's face. As Luke had known he would, the young man backed off.

"Certainly, sir. This way, please."

The kitchen was in a state of controlled chaos from having produced gourmet meals for two hundred people. The maître d', whose name tag said Olaf, led Luke to a square box in a secluded corner of the kitchen. "Thanks," Luke said briefly, "I can manage now. Perhaps you could see that the remainder of the glass gets picked up."

Without another word, Olaf left. Katrin tried to tug her hand free, saying with suppressed fury, "Who do you think you are, throwing your weight around like this? Giving everybody orders as if you owned the place. It's only a cut, for heaven's sake—I'm perfectly capable of looking after it myself."

Luke rummaged in the kit. "Here, I'm going to douse it with disinfectant, hold still."

"I don't—ouch!"

"I did warn you," Luke said, giving her a crooked grin as he ripped open a pad of sterile gauze. "There, that's better."

Under the black uniform her chest was rising and falling; her eyes, very close to his, were a brilliant blue. On impulse, Luke reached up and snatched the glasses from her nose, putting them down beside the first-aid kit. His heart skipped a beat, then started a slow, heavy thudding in his chest. She had the most beautiful eyes he'd ever seen.

He'd always thought of blue eyes as being open, unguarded, not potentially secretive as gray eyes could be, or his own dark brown. Once again, he'd been wrong, for Katrin's eyes were so deep a blue he'd never be able to fathom them. Her brows were arched; her cheekbones, which had been hidden by the plastic frames, were exquisite. Even as Luke watched, color mounted in her cheeks, subtle as a rosebud unfolding in summer.

He was still holding her by the hand. As he let his finger drift to rest on the pulse at her wrist, it speeded up, fluttering like a frightened bird's. Had he ever in his life felt anything so intimate as those tiny thrusts against his skin? Had he ever allowed himself to?

He wasn't into intimacy; he'd sworn off it years ago. But right now it was as though a chunk of lead had found a flaw in the bulletproof vest he was wearing and had gone straight for the heart. Hitting him where it hurt the most.

Scarcely knowing what he was saying, Luke muttered, "So you feel it, too."

Her lashes flickered. Yanking her hand free, she cried, "I don't know what you're talking about—I don't feel anything! Please…just go away and leave me alone."

Luke made a huge effort to regain control. A control he was famous—or infamous—for maintaining in any situation and at any cost. His voice sounding almost normal, he said, "I'm going to tape your cut. Then I'll go."

"I can do it!"

She sounded desperate. Desperate to be rid of him. And he was no nearer to pinning her down in his memory than he had been at the dining table. "It'll take ten seconds," he said in a hard voice. "Quit arguing."

"You're sure used to having people do what you say." She raised her chin. "I'm not going to cause a scene in the place where I work, you're not worth it. But get on with it—and then get out."

He stripped the paper lining from a plaster. "You don't sound very grateful."

"I don't feel grateful."

"You've made that plain from the start."

"I can look after myself," she snapped. "I don't need some high-powered business type fancying himself as a knight in shining armor and then trotting up five minutes later to claim his reward. Thanks but no thanks."

Luke felt his own temper rise. "You think I did this so we could have a quickie in the corner of the kitchen?"

"You bet."

"That's not the way I operate!"

"You could have fooled me."

Using every bit of his restraint, Luke taped the bandage over her cut. Then he took three steps backward and said with intentional crudity, "No feeling you up, no kisses behind the refrigerator. And—by the looks of you—no thanks, either."

Scarlet flags of fury stained her cheeks. She reached for her glasses and thrust them back on her nose. "You got that right. I don't thank people who insult me."

Making a very determined effort to get his heart rate and his temper back to normal, Luke said dryly, "I've noticed that already. I'll see you at breakfast, Katrin."

"I can wait."

Suddenly he laughed. "How would I ever have guessed?" Then, before she could respond, he turned on his heel and strode along the narrow aisle between ranks of stainless steel refrigerators. The kitchen door swung shut behind him. He crossed the deserted dining room, took the four flights of stairs to his suite, and slammed the door behind him.

For a man who'd made it a mission in life to keep his distance and his cool, especially with regard to the female portion of the population, he'd made a total fool of himself.

Well done, Luke. Tomorrow, at the breakfast table, you'd better concentrate on eating your cereal and minding your own business. So a waitress has gorgeous eyes. So what?

Gorgeous eyes, obvious intelligence and a fiery temper. As well as a healthy dose of independence.

And who in the world did she remind him of?

# CHAPTER THREE

At 3:00 a.m. Luke woke to the black silence of his bedroom punctuated by the pounding of his heart in his ears.
He swung his legs over the side of the bed, breathing hard.
He'd had his usual nightmare about Teal Lake, the one
where his dad had him slammed against a wall and was
brandishing a broken beer bottle in his fist. His mother, as
always in these dreams, was nowhere to be seen.

She'd left when he was five.

Stow it, Luke told himself. It's only a dream. And you're
thirty-three, not five. But his heartbeat was still thumping
like a drum, and he knew from experience that it was useless to try and go back to sleep right away. Getting up, he
pulled the drapes open and gazed out over the lake, where
a half-moon traced a glittering path from horizon to shore.
Teal Lake was a tenth the size of this lake; but the moon
had been equally beautiful on Teal Lake, and equally indifferent.

With an exclamation of disgust, Luke picked up a financial magazine from the mahogany coffee table and buried
himself in an analyst's prediction of the future of OPEC.
At four he went back to bed, sleeping in snatches and finally getting up at five-thirty. He decided to go for a run
along the lakeshore. Anything was better than being cooped
up in this room until the dining room opened.

The breeze was pleasantly cool, the morning sky a pale,
innocent blue. Birds chirped in the willows; he startled two
deer on the golf course. Far out on the lake he could hear
the low growl of boats: fishermen catching pickerel and
goldeye, for which the lake was famous. He must have

some for dinner tonight; the goldeye in particular was considered a delicacy. He'd have to ask Katrin her opinion, he thought sardonically. Sure. Good luck.

Pushing himself, Luke jogged for nearly an hour, sweat soaking his hair and gluing his T-shirt to his chest. He started to slow down when he reached the wharf that was just inside the resort's high cedar fences. He should take time for some stretches, he thought, watching absently as a small daysailer came into sight through the trees. The sail was scarlet against the blue water, luffing as the sole crew member smartly brought the boat around the end of the wharf.

It was a woman, her long blond hair blowing free in the breeze. She was wearing shorts and a brief top, white sneakers on her feet. With smooth expertise she docked the daysailer, throwing a line over the cleat on the wharf and tightening it before leaping ashore.

It couldn't be.

It was.

His mouth suddenly dry, Luke loped the last few yards toward the wharf. The woman had her back to him as she finished mooring the boat, her spine a long curve, her hair gleaming in the sun. Stepping onto the gently swaying wooden planks, he said, "Good morning, Katrin."

She gave an exaggerated start. Then she tied a couple of untidy half hitches, dropped the rest of the rope and stood up, turning to face him. She pushed her dark glasses up into her hair; her eyes, a glacial blue this morning, fastened themselves on his face. "What are you doing here?"

"You're a pro," he said easily. "You handled the boat beautifully—is it yours?"

"My question came first."

He swiped at his forehead with the back of one hand, and said with a winning smile, "I'm trying to work off last night's pork tenderloin. Not to mention the orange mousse.''

As though she couldn't help herself, her gaze skidded down his chest, its pelt of dark hair visible through his wet top, to the flatness of his belly. She took a sudden step back. Luke grabbed at her arm. "Watch it, you don't want to fall in.''

Her skin was warm from the sun. She shook her elbow free, patches of color in her cheeks. "I've got to go,'' she muttered. "I'll be late for work.''

His glance flickered down her body. Her breasts pushed against her thin green top, the faint shadow of her cleavage visible at the scooped neck; her legs were slim and lightly tanned. It wasn't an opportune moment to remember Guy's question…*you hiding anything else under that uniform?* Luke now knew what she'd been hiding. Trying to gather his wits, he repeated, "Do you own the boat?''

"Yes,'' she snapped, "I bought it with my investments.''

Ignoring this, Luke said tritely, "Nice lines.'' The same, of course, could apply to her. "Do you do much sailing?''

"Whenever I can.'' She lifted her chin. "It gets me away from the dining room. In more ways than one. Keeps my sanity, in other words.''

"There are a great many other jobs that would suit you better.''

"You're repeating yourself.''

"You're not getting it.''

"Life isn't quite as simple as you seem to think it is. Sir.''

If anyone knew life wasn't simple, it was himself. Holding tight to his temper, Luke said more moderately, "I'm sorry, I'm being tactless. I'd hate to see you stuck here year after year when there are wider horizons, that's all.''

"Fine. I get the message.''

"I'm also sorry about Guy," Luke went on. "He's a grade-A jerk who shouldn't go near a bottle of booze."

"I can look after types like him."

"So I noticed."

"The brandy was an accident."

"And the sail on your boat's purple."

For a brief moment laughter glinted in her eyes. He'd already decided she had beautiful eyes. Now add the rest of her, he thought. Although *beautiful* was a much overused word that didn't really encompass her grace, femininity and unconscious pride; the luster of her skin, the smooth flow of her muscles; the sexual pull she was exerting on him without—he was almost sure of this—in any way intending or wanting to.

But wasn't this all irrelevant? He met lots of beautiful women, so many that he should be immune to outward appearances by now; and the only reason his heart was thumping in his chest was that he'd been running for the better part of sixty minutes. Nothing to do with Katrin. He said abruptly, "I don't even know your full name."

"You don't need to."

Smiling broadly, Luke held out his hand. "Luke MacRae."

Katrin looked down at his hand, her own firmly at her sides. The wind blew a strand of hair across her face. "I already told you, staff and guests don't fraternize. I could get in real trouble if someone sees us talking like this."

"Then it's too bad there isn't a bottle of brandy close by."

Again wayward laughter briefly warmed her blue irises; and was as swiftly tamped. Her whole face changed when she laughed, becoming vibrant and full of mischief. Luke discovered that he very badly wanted to make her laugh again, although he had no idea how to go about it. He said, reaching for her right hand, "How's your cut, by the way?"

Her fingers lay tense in his palm. The bandage was still in place. He said flatly, "The mark is gone where Guy grabbed you."

This time there was no mistaking the emotion in her voice: it was panic. "Let go...I'll be late!"

"Why do I scare you?" Luke said slowly.

"I don't know. You don't! Why should you?"

He watched her swallow, the tendons moving in her throat where sunlight gilded skin like satin. He wanted to rest his fingers there. Feel the pulse in that little hollow race to his touch. Then let them drift across the delicate arch of her collarbone to the soft swell of her breast...he felt his own body tighten, every nerve on high alert.

He'd felt desire before. Many times. But never quite like this. So instinctual and imperative. So all-encompassing. He said with a deliberate lack of emphasis, "I think you're by far the loveliest woman I've ever seen."

If he'd expected Katrin to be flustered by his remark, or pleased, he was soon disappointed. She folded her arms across her chest, her eyes narrowing. "Do you?" she said. "Perhaps you're beginning to understand why I wear those awful glasses in the dining room—to discourage cheap compliments from men like you."

"Every word I said was the literal truth."

"And the sails on my boat are purple," she mocked.

"It's no crime to be beautiful, Katrin."

"Maybe not. But it's sure a liability in a job like mine. This conversation proves my point."

"You're stereotyping me!"

"Deny that you gave me the once-over a moment ago."

He couldn't. Trying to iron any emotion out of his voice, Luke said, "You're a very desirable woman. You know it, and so do I."

She hugged herself tighter. "I hate flattery."

Suddenly it was blindingly obvious to Luke. He said with

all the subtlety of a fourteen-year-old, "You want me just as much as I want you. That's why you're scared."

His words hung in the air; waves lapped the wharf, and overhead a gull wailed mournfully. Katrin whispered, "You're out of your mind."

He was. No question of that. "But I'm right. Aren't I?"

"No! You're the one who's after me—not the other way around. And it's because I'm just a waitress," she added with a depth of bitterness that shocked him. She snatched her hand free. "I'm yours for the asking. Cheap. Available. It's fine for you—you can jet in and jet out. But I'm stuck with—"

"This has nothing to do with how you earn your living," Luke said fiercely.

"Yeah, right." She pushed her hair back; in the sunlight, it gleamed like ripe prairie wheat. "You asked my name. It's Katrin Sigurdson. My husband's name is Erik Sigurdson. He's a fisherman. He's out there on the lake right now."

It was as though she'd punched Luke hard in the solar plexus. He rasped, "You don't wear a ring."

"My wedding band's antique gold, very finely engraved... I choose not to wear it at work. Or sailing."

Was she telling the truth? She was staring straight at him, conviction in every line of her body. Conviction, defiance, and something else: a trace of the panic he'd seen before?
"Are you from here?" he asked, trying to gather his wits.

"Yes. I've lived here all my life."

"So I haven't seen you anywhere else..."

"Not unless you've been here before. How could you have?"

How indeed? Baffled, frustrated and at some deep level frightened in a way he wasn't about to admit to himself or her, Luke said bluntly, "Then I was wrong. You don't remind me of anyone. If you don't want to be late for work, you'd better go.''

Her expression was guarded; certainly he could discern not the slightest trace of relief. She said, ''One more thing. Leave me alone from now on. Strictly alone. That way maybe I'll believe you're not just another tourist on the make.'' Then she turned on her heel and walked away from him.

She moved with a lissome grace: something else her shapeless uniform had disguised. As she entered a grove of poplars, sunshine and shadow played in her hair, sprinkling the curves of her hips and slender lines of her thighs. Luke discovered his fists were clenched at his sides, his breathing trapped in his throat. What was wrong with him?

She was married. Unavailable.

Her ugly glasses and unflattering hairdo were to deflect unwanted male attention. She wasn't in disguise. There was no mystery after all.

Luke pulled first one heel then the other to his buttocks, stretching his quads. He never behaved like this around a woman. Pushing her for answers. Wanting to know everything about her. Pursuing her. For one thing, he never needed to: the women came to him. For another, his whole focus since he'd run away from Teal Lake at age fifteen had been work. Unrelenting work. Be it underground in mines in the north, then aboveground everywhere else. He'd spent years reading, making contacts, investing his carefully hoarded savings and traveling the world over. He'd endured late hours and setbacks. There'd been times when he thought he was going under, so close to it he could taste defeat, smell the sourness of failure. But he hadn't gone under. He'd made it to the top, to the sweet smell of success.

And all because he'd driven himself unmercifully. If his expectations for his staff were high, his expectations for himself were astronomical. Work was central to his life, its driving force. Women were peripheral. Decorative, pleasant, but definitely on the sidelines. And that's where he intended to keep them.

There'd been women during those years, of course. He was no monk. But they had to be the kind who'd accept his conditions. No commitment with nothing long-term.

Although there hadn't been nearly as many women as some of his colleagues might think.

And now, for no reason that he could discern, a mysterious, argumentative, independent blonde had gotten through all his defenses. A married woman, no less.

He never involved himself with anyone married. He abhorred infidelity. Besides, he thought meanly, his preference was for tall brunettes, and Katrin Sigurdson was of average height and blond into the bargain.

Would he ever forget the way the sun had threaded her hair with gold? Or the delicate shadows under her cheekbones? And then there was her body, so graceful, so exquisitely curved. Calling to him in a way that made nonsense of all his self-imposed rules and defenses.

Because defenses they were. His childhood and adolescence had killed something in him. The ability to love, to reach out to another human being and show his vulnerability. All the gentler emotions, like tenderness and protectiveness, had gone underground. He could add to the list, he thought savagely. But why bother? He was the way he was. And that was that.

He wasn't going to change now.

Not for anyone. And certainly not for a married woman who didn't even want to pass the time of day with him.

Luke thudded his foot back on the wharf, stretching his calf. Enough, he thought. More than enough. Right now he was going back to his room to shower, then he was heading for breakfast. And not once at breakfast or dinner was he going to make as much as eye contact with Katrin Sigurdson.

Luke made sure he walked into the dining room that morning accompanied by John, Akasaru and Rupert, who were engaged in an animated discussion about pollution control. Katrin was waiting on their table, wearing her plastic glasses. As if she weren't there, Luke sat down and ordered his standard breakfast. "And coffee," he finished with an edge of impatience. "Right away."

"Certainly, sir."

*Certainly, sir.* Luke gritted his teeth, and started discussing the effectiveness of the scrubbers a couple of refineries were using in Hamilton area. Gradually he became aware that Martin and Hans, across the table, were talking about a fishing expedition that had taken place that very morning, during which Martin had landed several pickerel. "We spoke to Katrin," Hans said in his heavy German accent. "The chef, he will cook them for us for supper. That is right, not so, Katrin?"

"That's right, sir. He does an excellent job with fresh fish."

"I'm planning to try the local goldeye this evening," John intervened. "I hear it's very tasty."

Olaf, the maître d', was just arriving with a new pot of coffee. Luke said in a carrying voice, "I gather Katrin's husband is a lake fisherman—perhaps we'll be sampling his catch this evening."

Olaf stopped in midstride, giving Katrin a puzzled look. She glared at him, her cheeks pink, took the sterling silver pot from him, and said dismissively, "Thanks, Olaf."

"Married, eh?" Guy said, as she reached over to refill his cup. "Lucky fellow...so when did you tie the knot, Katrin?"

Several drops of coffee spilled on the immaculate linen tablecloth. She said evenly, "I'm so sorry, sir...oh, it was quite a while ago."

"Like two years?" Guy persisted.

She flinched, her fingers curled tightly around the handle of the coffeepot. "Several years ago, sir."

"And you did say he was a fisherman, didn't you?" Luke asked with deliberate provocation, looking right at her even though he'd sworn he wasn't going to.

She held his gaze. "Yes, I did."

If she was lying, she was a pro. And if she wasn't, he had to give her full marks for poise. For a wild moment Luke played with the idea of jumping up, pulling the glasses from her face and kissing her with all his pent-up frustration. Would that tell him the truth about Katrin Sigurdson?

John said casually, "I hear the storms can be very dangerous on the lake."

"That's correct, sir. It's because the lake's so large and the water's shallow—consequently, big waves can arise very quickly. A south wind is particularly bad. But the fishermen know all the weather signals, and head for shore before they run into trouble."

Luke said nothing. He wasn't going to kiss her in full view of a roomful of his peers. Of course he wasn't. He wasn't going to kiss her anywhere. He gulped down his excellent Colombian coffee, thinking very fast. Katrin's husband had been news to Olaf, Luke would swear to that on a stack of Bibles. So had she produced an entirely fictional husband for Luke's benefit down on the wharf? And was she now continuing that lie at the breakfast table?

There were ways he could find out. Although asking Olaf wasn't one of them. A guest asking questions about the marital status of a waitress would be a sure way to get that waitress in trouble. No, he wouldn't ask Olaf. However, there was a two-hour break in the proceedings right after lunch. He'd planned to corner the delegates from Peru; but that could wait until this evening.

He had to know if she was telling the truth. Because if she wasn't, then it raised the very interesting question of why she'd bothered lying to him.

Why would Katrin invent a husband who didn't exist? Was she afraid of Luke? Or of herself?

Either way, he wanted the answer.

# CHAPTER FOUR

AT TWO o'clock that afternoon Luke unlocked his rental car and got in, dropping his camera on the passenger seat. It was a perfect summer day, warm with a breeze from the lake, fluffy white clouds skudding across a sky as blue as Katrin's eyes. He had no real plan in mind, other than driving to the nearby village and looking around, asking questions of anyone he happened to meet. The village of Askja was small. Everyone must know everyone else.

Certainly he could find out if a fisherman called Erik Sigurdson existed; and whether he had a wife called Katrin.

He'd played with the idea of asking the desk clerk where Katrin lived, and had abandoned it because he couldn't think of a plausible reason why he should want such information. Whether she was married or not, he didn't want to cause her any problems at work. She must have her reasons for taking a job that didn't use her intelligence and caged her spirit; it wasn't up to him to upset that particular apple cart.

He left the grounds of the resort, taking the turnoff to the village. The road was narrow, following the lakeshore. Little whitecaps dotted the water like seabirds; a lighthouse, brightly striped in red and white, stood guard over a long, tree-clad promontory where gulls soared the air currents. It was a peaceful scene. But Luke had grown up at much the same latitude, and knew how long and brutal the winters could be; for the early Icelandic settlers, this must have been a cruel and unforgiving landscape.

He took a couple of photos of a weathered gray barn, of sheep munching the grass in a fenced field and a solitary cow chewing her cud. A small stone church stood watch over lichen-coated gravestones and neatly mowed grass; along the village wharf, fishing boats were rocking at their moorings, their white flanks gleaming. He didn't want to take a photo of the boats. What if he found out Katrin wasn't lying? That one of those boats belonged to her husband Erik? What then?

He'd turn around and go back to work. That's what he'd do. And he'd forget her existence in three days' time when the conference ended and he flew to New York for a series of meetings.

The houses were small, set apart in a long curve that followed the shoreline, most with a fenced garden. He'd drive the length of the village first, then he'd turn around and go into the general store. Or into that tearoom.

The last house was painted pale yellow, with a rhubarb patch, hills of potatoes, and neat rows of peas and beans. On the sand beach in front of the house, a woman and two children were playing with a Frisbee. Luke jammed on the brakes. He'd have known the woman anywhere, even though her hair was hidden under a baseball cap. She was wearing the same shorts and top that she'd had on this morning.

She hadn't said anything about children.

His heart beating in thick, heavy strokes, Luke looped the camera around his neck, got out of his car and walked through the trees toward the sand. He felt overdressed in his lightweight slacks and cotton shirt; he felt like a kid on his first date.

He stopped and, using his zoom lens, brought Katrin into focus, her legs a blur of movement, her teeth a dazzling white as she laughed. She was so intent on the game that she hadn't seen him yet. In quick succession he took three photos of her, hating her for being so carefree when he felt anything but.

As he lowered the camera, one of the children yelled something to her, and Katrin pivoted to face him. Her body went rigid. Then she tugged at the strap of her tank top and swiped at her forehead. "Are you looking for someone?" she called in a voice no one would have described as friendly.

Okay, Luke. Go for it.

He plastered a smile on his face, hung his camera over the branch of a small apple tree, and loped down to the beach. "Hi, Katrin," he said. "I had a couple of hours off, so I decided to check out the village…it's a gorgeous day, isn't it?" Without waiting for a reply, he grinned at the nearest child, a girl of about seven with pale blond hair in two long pigtails. "I'm staying at the resort. It's been a long time since I've played with a Frisbee…do you mind if I join you?"

She gave him a gap-toothed smile. "You can be on my team," she said. "What's your name?"

"Luke. What's yours?"

"Lara," she replied, and tossed him the plastic disc.

Lara Sigurdson? Daughter of Katrin? Discovering he wasn't ready for the answer to that question, Luke watched the Frisbee whirl toward him in a graceful arc. His muscles seemed to have seized up. Awkwardly he grabbed for it, then with a wicked twist of his wrist threw it toward Katrin. For a split second she stood stock still, glaring at him.

"Get it!" the little boy shouted. He also was blond, about five, thin as whip.

The same age Luke had been when his mother had left.

Katrin leaped sideways, her arm upstretched, and caught the Frisbee. She tossed it to the boy. "Run, Tomas!"

Tomas ran the wrong way, doubled back and clutched the Frisbee to his shirtfront. When he threw it toward Lara, it smacked into the sand. Lara said gleefully, "Our point."

She aimed it at Katrin, who then with the strength of

fury whipped it through the air straight at Luke's chest. He began to laugh, a helpless belly laugh, jumped to his right so it wouldn't break his ribs, and snagged it from midair. His shoes weren't intended for the beach; he skidded on the sand, saving himself at the last minute from falling to the ground. "Good shot," he said appreciatively, and sent the Frisbee to Tomas with just enough spin to be a challenge, but not so much that the little boy couldn't catch it. Tomas's hand closed around it; this time his throw was to Luke, a wildly off-course throw that somehow Luke managed to land.

He was enjoying himself, Luke realized, laughing at the little boy. How long since he'd done something like this?

Not since he'd played with his friend Ramon's children in the spring, back in San Francisco.

In quick succession Katrin scored two points on Luke, who then proceeded to gain them back; she was playing in deadly earnest, he could tell, and laughed at her openly as she missed an underhanded shot he'd flashed her way. Then Tomas snaked a shot at him that he hadn't been expecting; his eyes glued to the white disc, he ran for it, his hand outstretched. Lara shouted a warning. And Luke ran smack into Katrin.

The two of them tumbled to the soft sand in a tangle of arms and legs. Somehow Luke ended up with his cheek jammed into her chest, one leg under her, his other thigh flung over her hip. She was breathing rapidly, her breasts enticingly soft. She smelled delicious, a dizzying combination of sunshine and that same delicate floral scent he remembered from the dining room.

His body hardened. He shifted hastily, not wanting her to know how instantly and fiercely he wanted her; and felt, as he moved against her, the tightening of her nipples. With all his self-control he fought against the urge to take her in his arms and find her mouth with his. Kiss her so he could taste the sunshine on her skin, the heat of her flesh.

Footsteps padded across the sand toward them. "Are you guys okay?" Tomas huffed. "You look kind of funny—all tangled up like an octopus."

Swiftly Luke rolled over on his stomach, distancing himself from Katrin, who leaped to her feet and said breathlessly, "We're fine. That was a great shot, Tomas."

"It was our point," Tomas said complacently. "Whose turn is it now?"

Luke hauled himself to his feet, grabbed the Frisbee and flung it with very little finesse at Lara. He felt as though he'd been hit with a ton of bricks. He felt punch-drunk, wired and lustful.

Just as well the kids were here, he thought with a crazy edge of laughter. Or he'd have rolled Katrin onto her back on the sand, fallen on top of her and kissed her until neither one of them could breathe; until making love with each other was the only possible option. Then, out of the corner of his eye, he saw the Frisbee coming at him; catching it, he whipped it toward Tomas.

He didn't dare look at Katrin.

Five minutes later, the little boy plunked himself down on the sand. "Time out," he puffed. "I'm too hot."

"Me, too," Lara echoed.

Katrin smiled at them. "Why don't you both go up to the house and get yourselves ice-cream cones? You know where they are. Don't forget to shut the freezer afterward."

"Two scoops?" Lara said, her blue eyes calculating.

Katrin grinned. "Two scoops. But not three, you know what happened last time."

"Splat," said Tomas.

"Exactly," Katrin said. "Off you go, and look both ways before you cross the road. I'll be up in a minute."

The two children, forgetting they were tired and hot, ran

for the house, obediently stopping on the grass verge and checking for traffic. By the time they were out of earshot, Katrin had turned her back on them to face Luke. Her smile had vanished. "How dare you invade my private life?" she blazed. "You've got no right to be here, forcing yourself on my children like that."

A cold fist squeezed his heart. "So they're your children?"

"Who else's would they be?" she retorted. "I don't want you anywhere near here—I keep my work life and my personal life totally separate. Besides, I told you to leave me alone, remember?"

He said reluctantly, "They're fine kids."

"Yes, they are. And if you think I'm going to have some kind of a two-day fling with you and jeopardize my whole life, you're crazy."

Luke's tongue felt thick, and his brain seemed to have stopped working altogether. Katrin was married, the mother of two children. What the hell was he doing here? He swallowed, clearing his throat. "Let's keep something straight. I've not once suggested I wanted a fling with you."

She flushed, shoving her hands into the pockets of her shorts. "Don't insult my intelligence—I can read the signals."

"Then you're quite intelligent enough to know that some very basic chemistry's operating between us. It's not just me."

"It is just you!"

Her cheeks were now a bright pink. Luke drawled, "We could have one of those exchanges best suited to Tomas and Lara. It's not. It is. It's not. It is…is that what you want?"

"I want you gone from here. And I don't want you to come back," she said with deadly precision.

He had the same sinking feeling in his gut that had overcome him ten years ago when he'd been outwitted by a broker whose financial wizardry had been exceeded only by his lack of morals. Now, as then, there was no way to recoup. His only recourse was to get out as gracefully as he could and accept his losses. He said with a sudden raw honesty that took him by surprise, "Okay. I'll leave and I won't come back. But I won't find it easy to forget you...don't ask me to explain that, because I can't. And don't for one minute think I make a habit of hitting on women when I'm at a conference. Nothing could be further from the truth—and that holds whether they're waitresses or CEOs."

He'd run out of words. There was nothing else to say that could make any difference. Game over.

As though he were taking another photograph, Luke found himself trying to memorize every detail as Katrin stood before him: the elegant lines of her cheekbones, the sudden uncertainty in her sky-blue eyes, the push of her breasts against her thin green top. Storing it all in his brain against the time when he'd be gone from here. When he'd never see her again.

She said stiffly, "Give me one good reason why I should believe you."

"I can't! Either you believe me or you don't. And what does it matter anyway?"

"You're right, it doesn't matter." She bit her lip. "Please leave now, Luke—I should go up to the house and make sure the kids are all right. Besides, Erik will be home shortly."

The last person in the world Luke wanted to meet was Katrin's husband. The man who shared her bed. The father of her children. With one small part of his mind he realized that this was the first time Katrin had called him by name, and would also be the last. "Goodbye, Katrin," he said, turned on his heel and wound through the poplars toward his car, remembering on the way to snag his camera from the apple tree.

Just as he opened the car door, Lara and Tomas emerged onto the front step of the house, each clutching an ice-cream cone. They waved at him. "Bye, Luke," Lara called.

"Goodbye, Lara. Bye, Tomas," he called back, turned around in the road and drove north along the shore. In his rearview mirror he watched Katrin cross the road and walk toward the house.

Game over, indeed.

Except it didn't remotely resemble a game. Rather, Luke felt like that little five-year-old boy in Teal Lake who'd finally realized his mother wasn't going to come back home; that she hadn't just gone to the store, or into Kenora for a visit. Then, as now, he had the same sensation that the earth had shifted, that there was nothing firm to stand on.

Katrin was married, the mother of two children. No matter how much he desired her, she belonged to someone else.

Once Luke was out of sight of the pale yellow house, he pulled up by the side of the road and gazed out over the lake. Its serenity mocked him, so placid was it, so much in harmony with the graceful willows that draped its shoreline.

He felt cheated. As though he'd caught a glimpse of beauty beyond his imagining, only to have it snatched away before he could grasp it.

A couple of teenage boys were slouching along the road toward him. Luke edged off the shoulder and drove on. But five minutes later, when the tearoom came in sight, he slowed down again. He didn't want to go back to the resort and be convivial. He didn't want to play golf or lift weights, and he'd already jogged this morning. While tearooms weren't priority on his list, he could do with something cold to drink. And maybe a piece of chocolate pie, he thought wryly. The basic cure for a bruised ego.

Because that's all this was. It wasn't a major tragedy. He'd merely made a fool of himself for reasons he didn't want to analyze, with a woman far too acute for his own comfort. Yeah, he thought, turning into the driveway between rows of pink and scarlet petunias. Chocolate pie. That's what I need.

The tearoom wasn't designed with six-foot-two men in mind: the tables were small, the curtains frilly, the wallpaper with more flowers than a Hollywood funeral. But in the cooler by the door there was a chocolate torte with thick layers of dark chocolate icing, and the proprietress gave him a friendly welcome. Luke smiled back. "I'll have a big slice of the torte," he said, "and iced tea with extra lemon, please."

"Coming right up," she said, her brown eyes twinkling at him. Her name tag was inscribed in such elaborate calligraphy that he had difficulty deciphering it; he was almost sure it said Margret. Her hair was the orange of marigolds, her eyeshadow blue as delphiniums, and she had no pretensions to youth. But something in her smile said that a tall, athletic-looking man could brighten her day anytime.

Luke picked up a newspaper from the stand by the door and sat down by the window. Six women were sharing a table on the far side of the room, and two more were seated nearer to him; he was the only man. Feeling minimally more cheerful, he unfolded the paper. When his iced tea arrived, he took a sip; it was exactly as he liked it. Then Margret arrived with a flowered plate bearing a huge slab of torte surrounded by swirls of chocolate sauce, sliced strawberries and whipped cream. He grinned. "No calories in that."

"You're in fine shape, you don't need to worry," she said, giving him a flirtatious wink. "You must be staying at the resort?"

"That's right, there's a mining conference going on."

Deliberately he added, "I was just driving through the village and met Katrin, who's our waitress in the dining room."

"Katrin Sigurdson, that's right. She lives in the pink house two down from the church."

Luke's fork stopped in midair. "No...she was at the very end house in the village. Playing with her kids."

Margret frowned. "Kids?"

"Lara and Tomas. Blond like her."

"Katrin doesn't have any children." Margret's brow cleared. "Those are Anna's children." In a carrying voice she addressed one of the two women seated nearby. "Anna, is Katrin looking after your kids today?"

Anna, who had a cluster of blond curls and light blue eyes, smiled at Margret. "She offered to take them to the beach for an hour so Fjola and I could meet here and have an uninterrupted visit." Her smile encompassed Luke. "Katrin's such a lovely person. So kind. And the children adore her, they'd do anything for her."

Anna, he could tell, was the sort of woman who'd grown up in a small place and trusted everyone, including himself. Striving for just the right touch of lightness, he said, "Then it's to be hoped she has children of her own someday."

Anna chuckled. "First she has to find a husband."

Luke's heart jolted in his chest. "She's a pretty woman," he said with deliberate understatement. "That shouldn't be a problem."

"But Katrin is very choosy, too choosy for a little village like Askja." Anna shrugged. "She is talking of leaving here. That will be our loss, but no doubt her gain." She gave Luke another of her generous smiles. "Now, if you will excuse me..."

She went back to her conversation with her friend Fjola. Luke said, "Margret, I've heard that a fisherman called Erik Sigurdson takes tourists out in his boat, is that right?"

"Erik? Yes, but only on weekends. He's too old now to do it every day, he says." Her smile had a touch of malice. "Too fond of the rum bottle if you ask me."

"Too bad... I'll be gone by the weekend."

"Jonas takes out tourists every day, the resort would have his phone number."

"Thanks," Luke said. "I'll probably look him up."

Three more women came in the door and Margret left to show them to a table. Luke stared unseeingly at the newspaper. So Katrin was neither a married woman nor a mother.

She'd lied to him.

For her own protection? Because she was afraid of him, and put him in the same category as Guy? Or because he'd been reading her correctly all along, and Katrin wanted him as badly as he wanted her?

The latter couldn't be true. She'd been doing her level best to discourage him ever since they'd met.

His initial assessment of her as deadly dull had been way off the mark. So maybe when it came to her sexuality he was misreading her again.

Luke gazed at his torte, discovering that he'd entirely lost his appetite. However, he had the feeling Margret would take it personally if he didn't finish every morsel on his plate. He picked up his fork, his thoughts marching on. He now knew where Katrin lived and that she was thinking of leaving Askja.

He could invite her to San Francisco.

Sure, he jeered. You're really into rejection, Luke MacRae. She'd laugh in your face. And if by any chance she did agree, she'd turn your life upside down, you can be sure of that. Is that what you want?

No. Definitely not. His life was fine as it was.

The torte was moist with chocolate, the strawberries slightly tart. Luke began to eat, trying simultaneously to

make some sense out of the latest financial predictions; but
when he left the tearoom twenty minutes later, after a serious overdose of chocolate, he realized he was in a foul
mood. Oh, he'd been all very clever the last couple of
hours. Chief Detective MacRae in action, ferreting out the
truth about the marital status of a waitress in a little fishing
village in Manitoba. But what good did his new knowledge
do him?

Katrin Sigurdson spelled danger. And what was a sensible tactic when face-to-face with danger? Avoid it. He
wasn't a reckless eighteen-year-old anymore, he had no
bent toward self-destruction; and he'd proved himself often
enough in the past, he didn't need to do so again. Not with
a blue-eyed blonde who could tear apart everything he'd
so carefully constructed.

Stay away from her. That was all he needed to do.

It was so simple.

# CHAPTER FIVE

FOR twenty-four hours Luke did stay away from Katrin. He got back to the lodge that afternoon late for a panel discussion, which did nothing to improve his state of mind. He then set up a private consultation with the Peruvian delegates in his suite, ordering room service for dinner. Afterward, he worked far into the night, fell into an exhausted sleep, and was also late for breakfast because he'd forgotten to set his alarm.

At least he hadn't dreamed about her. He'd been spared that.

When he took his seat in the dining room, he soon discovered it was Katrin's day off; a young man called Stan waited on them. Again Luke drove himself hard all day. But by four-thirty he'd done everything that needed to be done, and he was in no mood to drift to the bar and exchange small talk. He decided to go for a run instead.

He jogged for the better part of an hour, watching distant purple-edged clouds move closer and closer, until they merged into a dark mass that spread all the way to the horizon. When he passed the wharf below the resort, he noticed with an edge of unease that the daysailer was gone from its mooring.

The wind had come up in the last few minutes. A south wind, he realized, his unease growing. Hadn't Katrin said that was the most dangerous wind on the lake?

It was her day off. Wasn't it all too likely that she'd gone sailing?

What had she said? It kept her sanity?

When he needed a break from the pressures of work, he jogged, played tennis and skied. It was the same principle.

A sudden gust whipped through his hair. Fear lending wings to his feet, Luke ran back to the lodge, changed in his room into jeans and a T-shirt, and raced for his car. First he checked the resort wharf again, but there was still no daysailer. Then he drove fast to the village wharf. Again, no slim white boat with a furled scarlet sail. By now, waves were lashing the wharf, the spray driven against the thick boards.

An old man was climbing the metal ladder from his boat to the dock. Luke strode over to him, raising his voice over the gusts of wind. "I'm looking for Katrin Sigurdson—she uses a small boat with a red sail. Do you know if she's out on the lake?"

The old man had red-veined cheeks and bleary blue eyes. "Katrin? That's my niece…I'm Erik Sigurdson."

"Luke MacRae," Luke said, shaking hands. How it must have amused Katrin to posit her disreputable uncle as her husband. He repeated urgently, "I'm worried about her, surely she wouldn't stay out in weather like this?"

"Katrin?" The old man gave an uncouth cackle. "Too smart for that. Although she likes pushing herself, I must say. I've said to her more than once, you'll go too far one day, my girl, and then what'll—"

"Then where is she?"

"You're in a right state, young feller," Erik said, spitting with careless accuracy into the churning water.

Luke said tightly, "Yes, I am. So why don't you answer the question?"

"She ain't interested in guys from the resort. Here today and gone tomorrow, that's what she says."

Each word dropping like a chip of ice, Luke said, "I may be staying at the resort, but even I can tell there's a storm brewing on the lake. No one, but no one, should be out there in this kind of wind, especially in a skimpy little daysailer. So will you for God's sake tell me if you know where she is?''

"If she's not home and the boat's gone, she likely docked on the far side of the island. In the lee."

"How do I get there?"

Erik took a square of tobacco from one pocket of his flannel shirt, a jackknife from the other, and with its viciously sharp blade cut off a chunk of tobacco. "You got designs on my niece, Mr. Luke MacRae?''

"No. But I sure don't want her drowning while you and I stand here passing the time of day!''

"Okay, okay, no need to get antsy. Get in your car, turn right, take the next left and keep going to the end of the road. And I'll bet my entire supply of 'baccy that she's there."

"I hope you're right," Luke snarled, and ran for his car. In a screech of tires he turned right. The first drop of rain plopped on his windshield. The limbs of the birches were tossing in the wind; clouds skudded across the lurid sky. Then he was suddenly enveloped in a downpour as a flash of lightning split the horizon in two.

Strong winds and lightning were deadly enemies of sailors. Fear knotting his muscles, Luke drove as fast as he dared through the rain and the gathering gloom. He should have asked how far before he turned left, he thought, furious with himself for the oversight. But he'd been so desperate to get away from Erik Sigurdson, he'd overlooked that all-important question.

She had to be at the dock. She had to be.

He shoved his foot on the brake, then backed up ten feet. He'd almost missed the turnoff, a narrow road flanked by spruce and poplar, rain pelting its gravel surface and running in rivulets into the ditches. He turned onto the road beneath shadowed trees. Slowing down, flicking the wipers to high speed, Luke drove on. Rocks rattled under his wheels.

As suddenly as it had begun, the road opened into a clearing, then snaked down a short, steep hill toward the water. Almost miraculously, the wind had dropped: the broad bay that he'd glimpsed from the top of the hill was in the lee. Lightning ripped the sky apart, followed by a clap of thunder that made him wince. He took the slope as fast as he dared, then parked beside a tangle of boat cradles and overgrown shrubbery. His was the only car in sight.

Thrusting his door open, Luke got out. Earth and rocks had been heaped to make an artificial barrier from the lake, barring his view. He ran down the last of the slope, rounded the corner and saw in front of him a dark stretch of water, pebbled with raindrops, and a small wooden jetty.

A daysailer was moored at the jetty. Katrin was kneeling on the wet boards, searching for something in her duffel bag. Her back was toward him.

She was safe.

For a moment Luke stood still, all his pent-up breath whooshing from his lungs. She wasn't out on the lake. She hadn't drowned. She was right here in front of him. Safe.

She was also quite alone, and without any visible means of transportation.

Slowly he walked toward her, his hair already plastered to his skull, his T-shirt clinging to his chest. Another spectacular jag of lightning lit up the whole scene; her shirt was pink, her cap a fluorescent green. Like a drumroll, thunder ushered him onto the wharf.

Enter the hero, Luke thought. Although Katrin would more likely categorize him as the villain; and she had clearly no need of rescue, which is what heroes were supposed to do. As he stepped across the first couple of planks, the vibrations of his steps must have alerted her. She lifted her head sharply, gazing right at him; for a moment he saw

the exhilaration still on her face, her wide smile and dancing eyes.

The terror that had kept his foot hard on the accelerator
all the way across the island fled, replaced by a tumultuous
rage. He grated, "Why are you looking so damned pleased
with yourself?"

The laughter vanished from her face. She pushed herself
upright, swinging her bag in one hand. "If you really want
to know," she said coldly, "I was congratulating myself
on how well I handled the boat once the wind came up."

"You were a fool to be out in this weather!"

"Thank you for that resounding vote of confidence."

He stepped closer, water gurgling beneath the boards.
"A south wind and a lightning storm—are you crazy? Or
just plain suicidal?"

"Neither one," she flared. "Why don't you go back to
the resort where you belong, Luke MacRae? Where, in theory at least, you know what you're talking about."

He took her by the arm, rain sluicing his face. "It so
happens that right now I do know what I'm talking about—
if you'd gotten in trouble out there, someone would have
had to rescue you. You'd have been risking the lives of
other people just so you could get some cheap thrills. I used
the wrong word—that's not crazy. It's totally irresponsible."

She tried to pull free, her blue eyes blazing. "You seem
to be forgetting something—I got back ahead of the storm
and I didn't risk anyone's life. Including my own. Anyway,
what the *hell* are you doing here? I can't tell you how much
I dislike you following me around like this."

Luke's answer was to grab her by the shoulders, pull her
toward him and kiss her hard on the mouth.

Her response was instant and unmistakable. She flung
her arms around his waist and kissed him back.
Passionately. Generously. Recklessly.

As the contact ripped through him, another stroke of lightning lit the wharf with an eerie blue light. Thunder rattled through the trees, where the wind moaned like a creature in distress. But Luke scarcely noticed.

Katrin was soaked to the skin; he circled her waist, drawing her closer, trying to shelter her. One hand moved up her spine until her long ponytail hung like wet rope over his forearm. Then her lips opened to the urgent probing of his tongue. She pressed herself against him, her fingertips digging into his back, kneading his muscles. In a dizzying surge of pure lust, Luke felt her tongue dance with his.

She wanted him just as much as he wanted her. He'd been right all along. Fiercely and wondrously grateful, he grasped her by the hips and pulled them toward him, so that she could be in no doubt of his response. The wet fabric of her jeans was clammy and cold beneath his palms; yet inwardly Luke was on fire.

She was moving against him with a kind of coltish awkwardness that was eager, yet somehow untutored. She couldn't be a virgin, he thought distantly. Of course not. Anna had said Katrin was choosy…but surely not to that extent? He muttered against her mouth, "Let's run for the car—you're soaked."

"So are you," she whispered, cupping his face in her palms, her eyes brilliant as stars, as eerily blue as the lightning.

She'd bewitched him, he thought. She could have been a spirit from the depths of the lake; yet simultaneously she was flesh and blood, wholly and utterly desirable.

With a muffled groan Luke kissed her again, moving his lips over hers in a voyage of discovery that he wanted never to end. Her cheekbones, the sweep of her forehead, the firm line of her jaw…he wanted to know them all, to put his mark on them so that they were his alone. "You're so beautiful,'' he whispered hoarsely, ''so incredibly responsive…you taste of raindrops.''

She gave him another of those passionate kisses, her fingers running through his wet hair and down his nape. She couldn't have missed his shudder of response. Again he felt the thrust of her hips against his groin. Overwhelmed by a hunger as primitive as the thunder that was shaking the sky, Luke said, ''Let's go to the car.''

Katrin suddenly pulled her head back, her breasts rising and falling against the hard wall of his chest; as the rattle of thunder died away, he watched her struggle back to a different reality. ''My bag,'' she muttered, ''I've got dry clothes in it.''

''Then we'll take it,'' Luke said, grinning at her with something of her own recklessness. ''Although I like that shirt just the way it is.''

She glanced down. Her nipples were tight, the thin cotton outlining them as though she were naked. She bit her lip. ''Luke, I—''

He leaned down, grabbed her bag, put his arms around her and lifted her from the ground. Luxuriating in her weight, he growled, ''Enough talk,'' and kissed her again, his blood thrumming through his veins.

''I can feel your heartbeat,'' she said, twisting in his arms as she rested her hand against his chest, her face rapt.

Had he ever wanted a woman the way he wanted Katrin? It was as though that first kiss had opened floodgates too long closed, loosing a torrent of desire Luke was helpless to resist. He took the slope in long strides, the runoff saturating his sneakers, rain lashing his face. With his chin he tried to tuck Katrin's head into his chest, craving to protect her; a far part of his brain noted that protectiveness. Noticed also that it was new to him. Completely new. Inexplicable. But very much there.

He shoved his thoughts away. This wasn't the time for

analysis. Reaching the car, he fumbled with the passenger door, and eased her onto the seat. Then he hurried around to his side, searching for the keys in his wet pocket. He'd get some heat in the car first.

He got in and slammed his door. In the sudden silence, shielded from the onslaught of the storm, Luke looked at the woman in the seat beside him.

In the few moments it had taken him to walk from one side of the car to the other, Katrin had retreated from him. Her bag was on her lap; she was hugging it to her chest as though to ward him off, her eyes wideheld in the gloom. At a loss, for this wasn't what he'd expected, Luke said with a lightness that didn't quite succeed, "It's okay—I don't bite."

"I must have been mad," she cried. "It was the storm, and fighting the waves on the lake, and then getting into the bay and knowing I'd made it—"

"Katrin," he said evenly, "we want each other. There's nothing wrong with that."

"There's everything wrong with it!"

"Look, before we get into a big discussion, I think you should get out of those wet clothes. Right now."

She gave him a hunted look. "Oh, no—I'm fine."

"I'll close my eyes," he said, exasperated. "Or I'll wait outside the car with my back to you. For Pete's sake, what do you think I am?"

"I don't know what you are. Who you are. How could I?"

"You don't trust me."

With an intensity that entranced him, she said, "I don't trust myself! Surely that must be as obvious to you as it is to me."

Laughter welled in his chest. He fought it down; Katrin would not, right now, appreciate being laughed at. He turned on the ignition and the fan, to get some heat in the car, and said deliberately, "Is that why you lied to me? About your husband, Erik, and your two lovely children, Lara and Tomas, blond-haired and blue-eyed just like you? Because I have something to tell you—in Margret's tearoom, your friend Anna informed me the children were hers...and then I met your uncle Erik on the wharf when I was looking for you half an hour ago. His shirt needing washing, his boots belonged in the garbage, and he was about to chew on a large lump of tobacco, no doubt using the lake as a spittoon. I must say I'm very glad he's not your husband."

Katrin glowered at him, if anything clutching her bag even tighter. "I had to tell you something! You think I was about to admit to you that ever since that first evening in the dining room I've been dreaming about you every night? X-rated dreams. Not the kind I could tell Lara or Tomas."

His jaw dropped. *"What?"*

"You heard what I said. I'm not going to repeat it."

Dazedly Luke said, "Is honesty your middle name?"

"Stupidity, more like."

She looked as edgy as a wild creature, as though she'd bolt if he made the slightest wrong move. "That kind of honesty's rare," Luke said.

Her grimace was endearing. "I never usually tell lies...it goes against the grain, so I'm very bad at it. I was amazed when you fell for all that stuff about my husband and my two kids. I figured you'd see through it right away."

"Maybe I'm the stupid one," Luke said dryly. "How about making me a promise? No more lies."

"Promises are made between people who mean something to each other."

He looked her straight in the eye. "This particular promise has to do with your own integrity."

She was the first to look away. "Okay," she said grudgingly.

"Good," said Luke. "Change your clothes, I'll be back in five minutes."

He got out of the car. The storm was moving off as fast as it had arrived, the lightning had abated, and even the rain had let up. He scrambled down the slope and sat down on some old boards, reflecting on what had happened.

He'd lost control down there on the wharf, when Katrin had so unexpectedly and wholeheartedly kissed him back. Lost it instantly and completely and uncharacteristically. He never lost control. No matter who the woman was or how long he'd been without one. Oh, physically he could let go, that wasn't the issue. But he always kept his emotions under wrap.

Not with Katrin. In the space of five minutes he'd felt passionately grateful, hugely protective, and fiercely possessive. Grateful? Because a woman had kissed him? Protective of a woman entirely capable of looking after herself? As for possessive, he neither wanted to possess another human being nor to be possessed by one. If honesty were Katrin's middle name, independence was his. He'd come to that conclusion at fifteen, and had seen no reason to change it since.

It was a good thing she'd been too shy or too frightened to change her clothes in front of him. He'd needed to get away from her. To take time out, to think with his brain cells instead of his hormones.

Danger. That was what Katrin spelled. He already knew that.

Danger or not, he still wanted her. More than he'd wanted anything or anyone for a very long time.

As a stray gust rustled through the shrubs behind him, a shower of raindrops trickled down his neck. Luke swiped them off, thinking furiously. If he really wanted Katrin, why couldn't he have her? On his terms?

She hadn't needed any persuading on the wharf.

He could persuade her again. Of course he could. Although he'd have to tell her what his terms were; it wouldn't be fair to deceive her on that score.

But if she accepted them, he could take her to bed.

How else was he going to get rid of this obsession with Katrin Sigurdson?

## CHAPTER SIX

A LAST flicker of lightning lit the sky. Far across the lake thunder growled in a halfhearted way. Luke's thoughts marched on. Once he'd gone to bed with Katrin, he'd be leaving here. Flying to New York, then back home to San Francisco. He'd forget her.

Easy.

Was the five minutes up? He hoped so. It was cold sitting here, his shirt clinging to his back. Luke got to his feet and walked up the hill. Katrin was sitting bolt upright in the front seat, a pale yellow sweater swathing her body. Luke got in the car.

The sudden blast of heat made him shiver involuntarily. In quick distress, she said, "You're cold. Here, I've got an extra sweater."

"I'm fine," he said roughly. "Quit feeling sorry for me."

"I wasn't aware that I was."

"I don't need mothering!"

The words had come from nowhere, and instantly Luke wished them unsaid. Katrin said in an unfriendly voice, "If I felt the slightest bit motherly toward you, I wouldn't be having X-rated dreams."

"So tell me about them," he said.

"Are you kidding? Luke, take me home. Then you should go back to the resort and have a hot shower."

"I could have one at your place."

"Look, I know I—"

"Katrin," he said softly, "come here."

"No! We can't—" Then she gave a strangled yelp, for

Luke had leaned over and, with exquisite gentleness, pressed his mouth to hers. Her lips were soft and yielding, warmer than his. His head began to swim.

She shifted in her seat, nibbling very gently at his lower lip, her hands drifting down his throat to his shoulders. In every nerve in his body he was aware of these small movements, of her quickened breathing and the pliancy of her body as she, in turn, leaned toward him. Control, Luke thought. Control. Technique, not emotion. And deepened his kiss, easing closer to her. Then he let one hand move from her shoulder to the swell of her breast, tracing its fullness, feeling the shock ripple through her slender frame. He cupped her breast in his hand, his groin hardening imperiously.

"Katrin," he whispered, "I want you so much."

She was trembling very lightly. "I want you, too," she whispered. "But I don't do this, Luke…I never have affairs with the guests. It's nothing to do with the resort, it's one of my own rules."

"You think I don't know that?" Trying to banish the strain from her face, he added, "Those glasses you insist on wearing, and your hair pulled back tight as a halyard in a hurricane…they're not exactly a come-on."

She smiled weakly. "Self-defense."

"Very effective," he replied; and knew now was the time to be as truthful to her as she'd been with him. Feeling as though he were tossing dice with no idea how they'd fall, Luke said, "I should make something clear to you— I'm not into any kind of commitment. If we make love tonight, that would be that. I fly to New York the day after tomorrow, and I won't be back."

She said in a strange voice, "That's okay…I wouldn't want commitment. It's not a word in my vocabulary, either."

"Why not?" he flashed.

She stared down at the fingers, intertwined in her lap. "To be blunt, Luke, if we go to bed together it'll have nothing to do with making love. I want you out of my system—I'm sorry if that sounds crude, but that's the way it is. For some reason you get past every one of my defenses. I can't explain that, and I'm not going to try. But I need to get on with my life…and I don't need a man in it. It's time I left Askja. Past time, and for reasons that are nothing to do with you. So if you have conditions, so do I—no confidences and no questions. And no—to use your word—commitment."

Luke sat back in his seat. He didn't like having his own words thrown back at him. Didn't like it all. Because he wasn't used to it? Was it that simple?

A couple of women in the past had taken his usual spiel about commitment as a challenge, figuring they could change his mind. Katrin, obviously, wouldn't be like that. Katrin didn't want commitment any more than he did.

Nevertheless, didn't her stance suit his purposes admirably? He could make love with her and leave.

She'd be out of his system, too.

Precisely what he wanted.

He said flatly, "I accept." Quickly he put the car in gear, turned around in the clearing and drove up the hill toward the woods.

The road needed all his attention because the heavy rain had turned some sections to a glutinous mud, and dug deep channels into the ditches. Keeping his eyes straight ahead, Luke said, "At least tell me how old you are."

"Twenty-seven. And you?"

"Six years older. Were you born here?"

"I said no questions, Luke."

"Secrets in your past?" he said lazily.

"Of course not!"

All his senses on high alert, he heard the tension in her

voice, noticed the tightening of her hands in her lap, her sudden wariness. So she did have secrets. He said without inflection, "I have secrets, too. Don't we all?"

"I wouldn't know."

End of that conversation, thought Luke, and found he was intensely curious to know what secrets in Katrin's past would prevent her from even telling him where she was born. None of your business, he told himself; then found himself wondering if it could have anything to do with that elusive sense of recognition he'd had for a while, as though somewhere he'd seen her before. He said out loud, "Good, there's the main road."

Katrin said nothing. He flicked a glance at her. She was staring out the window at the wet trees and gleaming pavement, just as though he didn't exist. He felt a quiver of pure rage, and forced it down. What was he complaining about? Once again he'd found a woman who was willing to warm his bed—or in this case, her bed—on his terms. Nothing wrong with that, and everything right.

He drove on, in a silence that seemed to thicken with every minute. After he passed the lane to the resort, he had to navigate all the turns and twists of the road to the village. The church loomed out of the dusk, followed by a weathered clapboard house and then a small bungalow painted pale pink with white trim. Luke turned in the driveway and parked level with the back door.

"Let's go in," he said, striving to sound matter-of-fact. "If you've got a drier, maybe I could put my jeans and shirt in it for a few minutes."

"Luke, I can't do this," Katrin said in a strangled voice.

"It's perfectly normal to be nervous, Katrin. I'll use protection, and I'll be as good to you as I can be, I promise you that."

"Protection?" she snapped, glaring at him. "You mean you walk around with it all the time?"

He said, an ugly note in his voice, "I've already told you I'm not in the habit of picking up women at conferences…and I have a clean bill of health. But the last thing I ever want to do is start an unwanted child. There are enough of those already in the world."

"Were you one?" she said.

"Lay off!"

"I hit a nerve there, didn't I?" She gazed at him thoughtfully. "You mean you never want to have children?"

"You said no questions and no confidences. That works both ways."

"Okay, okay. But whether or not we've got protection is beside the point." She looked right at him. "I've changed my mind. I'm sorry, but I can't go to bed with you—no matter what kind of dreams I've been having."

A cold lump had settled in the pit of Luke's stomach. He said nastily, "Do you do this often—lead a guy on, then say no at the last minute?"

"No! I never do!"

"You could have fooled me."

"Are you one of those men who think a woman isn't allowed to say no?"

"Katrin, I know you want me and you know I want you. So what's the big deal if we go to bed together? We're not talking marriage and three kids."

"No," she said, her voice unreadable, "we're talking a one-night stand."

"That's right. Which suits both of us just fine."

"Down on the wharf, and then in the car, I thought it would suit me. So that I'd get you out of my system, isn't that what I said? But now I've realized the absolute last thing I need is a one-night stand. With you or anyone else. I've never gone to bed with anyone casually, as if sex were in the same league as a game of Frisbee or an afternoon sail on the lake. And I'm not going to start now."

Luke looked over at her. Her lower lip was set mutinously, her wet ponytail was trailing down her neck, and her bulky sweater almost completely hid the fact that she had breasts. She was as different from his usual women as a woman could be, he thought with uncomfortable honesty. No makeup, no fancy hairdo, no designer clothes. No sophistication. Quite possibly, very little experience. Because if there was one thing he'd stake his fortune on, it was that Katrin Sigurdson was speaking the truth.

She didn't deal in fancy footwork. In coyness or manipulation. Just the truth, no matter whether he wanted to hear it or not. Keeping her promise that she wouldn't lie to him again.

He said harshly, "I'm not sure casual is the right word for what happens when we kiss each other. For me, it's like the combination of an earthquake and a volcanic eruption...you wouldn't exactly call those casual." Then he gave an exasperated sigh. "I had no intention of saying that—the truth must be catching. Like the flu."

She said with suppressed violence, "I've never in my life kissed anyone the way I kissed you."

Luke looked at her in silence, emotion clogging his throat. Once again, Katrin was telling the truth. And once again, just by being herself, she'd knocked him sideways. Warning bells rang in his brain. If he was half as smart as he thought he was, he'd push her out of the car and drive hell-bent for leather in the opposite direction.

Any other woman he'd had an affair with had treated bed as just another playground. Like a game of tennis with no clothes on. But Katrin wasn't like that.

"Katrin," he said with sudden intensity, "why don't we go for it? Is life about running away from risk, taking the safe route time and again until finally you're buried under the ground and there aren't any more risks to take? Is that all there is to it?"

She said bitterly, "I took a big risk once, with a slick businessman like you. It backfired and I paid for my mistake. Paid and paid and paid. The answer's no, Luke. No."

"Who was he?"

"That's irrelevant."

Luke made one more try. "Listen, I'm going back to San Francisco—"

*"Where?"*

The color had drained from her cheeks; she looked suddenly older. Older, and horribly frightened. "What's the matter?" he demanded.

"You said you lived in New York!"

"I said I was flying to New York from here—I've got a couple of meetings there early in the week. But once they're over, I'll be heading home. Which is San Francisco. What's the big deal about that?"

Her struggle for control was painful to watch. Her knuckles bone-white with strain, she said tonelessly, "Luke, I'm exhausted, I've got to go in. I'm sorry if you thought I was leading you on, truly I wasn't. What happened on the wharf was more than I could have imagined…it did away with all my common sense and my rules. But I've had time to think now, and I know I'd regret it if we went to bed together. I have rules for a very good reason, and they've always stood me in good stead."

He wanted to know that reason, and knew better than to ask. His gaze trained on her face, he said softly, "If I kissed you again, you'd change your mind."

Her jaw tensed. "Please don't!"

"You don't have to worry—I've never once forced myself on a woman, and I'm not going to start with you."

"Anyway," she said with a flash of spirit, "can you imagine how I'd feel tomorrow morning when I'd have to take your order for breakfast? *Cream and sugar with your coffee, sir?* No way!" She leaned down and picked up her bag from the floor of the car. "Thank you for the drive," she added in a muffled voice. "Good night."

He could have stopped her. Very easily. Luke sat still, watching as she ran for the side door of the little bungalow, took a key out of her pocket and turned it in the lock. Then she slipped inside the house. A moment later he saw the dim glow of light through the chinks in the blinds.

He put the car in reverse and backed onto the road. Which did he need more, a hot shower because every garment he had on was wet, chilling him to the bone? Or a cold shower, to take his mind off sex? Sex with Katrin.

That's all it would have been, he thought furiously. Sex. Nothing less and nothing more.

How long since a woman had turned him down?

Too long, obviously.

The sun was setting behind the last of the storm clouds in a stunning display of orange, magenta and purple. He scowled at it, wishing he could fly home tomorrow. Or tonight. One thing was certain. He didn't care if he ever saw Katrin Sigurdson again.

Because he was a stubborn man who rarely allowed himself to acknowledge a setback, Luke went to breakfast early the next morning. The morning paper was folded under his arm. He was the first one at his table. He started reading the front page, and when an all-too-familiar voice said, "Coffee, sir?" he didn't even look up.

"Black, please," he said, and ostentatiously rustled the pages.

His coffee was poured without a drop being spilled. He added, "A large orange juice, waffles with strawberries and an order of bacon, no toast. Thanks."

"You're welcome," Katrin said in a voice that implied the opposite.

He forced himself to continue reading the latest story of

political patronage, not even looking up when she'd left the table. Rupert arrived, then John, and slowly Luke relaxed. When she brought his waffles, he saw in one glance that she looked as different from the passionate woman on the wharf as she could; her ugly glasses were firmly in place and her hair scraped back ruthlessly. Good, thought Luke. He didn't want any reminders of those shattering kisses in the rain.

He'd dreamed about her last night. Explicitly and at considerable length.

The sooner he left here, the better.

The day dragged on. Luke had both contributed to and gained from the conference; but now he couldn't wait for it to be over. Dinner was a full-fledged banquet and seemed to last forever. Guy drank far too much and in a distant way Luke was amused to see that the whole table was united in making it clear that Guy had better behave himself. As for Katrin, she was efficient and polite and a thousand miles away.

Which is where he'd be tomorrow.

The meal wound down, Luke was called on to add to the impromptu speeches, and people began drifting toward the bar. Guy, however, was taking his time. As though he were waiting for everyone else to leave, Luke thought uneasily, and moved over to have one last chat with the Japanese delegation. Then he went back to the table and said with a friendliness he was far from feeling, "Come on, Guy, I'll buy you a drink."

"I could tell you something," Guy mumbled.

"Oh?" Luke said casually. "What's that?"

Guy shot him a crafty look. "I'm going to tell her first," he said, swaying on his feet.

"Her?"

"Our esh-esteemed waitress."

"What about her?"

"Nope. Her first."

Under cover of the hum of conversation and laughter, Luke said very quietly, "You leave Katrin alone, Guy. Remember what I said about Amco Steel?"

"Thish-this is for her own good," Guy said, blinking owlishly.

"Then tell me about it."

"Tomorrow. At breakfast." Guy chuckled. "You'll have to wait, Luke."

"Fine," Luke said, as though it were of no interest to him whatsoever. "Let's go to the bar, that's where the action is right now."

For well over an hour, Luke wandered from group to group in the bar, never staying long, always trying to keep Guy in sight. But Andreas and Niko from Greece wanted to show him a fax they'd just received and when Luke looked up, Guy had vanished. He said, "Andreas, that's good news. I think we should have a talk about this once I get back to San Francisco, can I call you? And now will you excuse me, I want to talk to Guy Wharton for a moment."

When he questioned one of the waiters, the young man said he'd seen Guy heading for the side door of the resort. As Luke hurried along the corridor, he was stopped by an elderly statesman from Japan, who with impeccable courtesy wished him a protracted goodbye. Holding his impatience rigidly in check, Luke replied with equal good manners. Then, almost running, he headed outdoors.

The side door opened onto a walkway that split into two, one to the guest parking lot, the other to the staff lot. Trusting his intuition, Luke took the path to the staff area. To muffle his steps he kept on the grass, simultaneously wondering if he was overreacting. Was he really going to find Guy and Katrin together? He did know one thing: he didn't trust Guy, sober or drunk. Especially not drunk.

Then he stopped in his tracks as he heard voices, Guy's slurred, Katrin's quiet, but edged with panic. So they were together. Although not, by the sound of it, from Katrin's choice.

He was going to do his level best to protect her from whatever threat Guy posed.

But first he hoped to find out exactly what that threat was.

# CHAPTER SEVEN

LUKE skirted the dogwood and tall shrub roses, whose scent teased his nostrils, and saw that Guy had cornered Katrin several feet away from the staff parking lot. Her back was to a clump of birch; Guy was looming over her, one hand clamped around her elbow. Although his stance was far from steady, he was talking with relative coherence.

"I e-mailed a friend of mine this afternoon," he was saying. "Wanted to be sure of the facts before I said anything. It was a friend in San Francisco."

Katrin flinched as though he'd physically struck her; with desperate strength she tried to tug her arm free. "I don't want to hear this," she said, "it's got nothing to do with me."

"Oh, yes, it does. We both know what I'm talking about." He gave an uncouth burst of laughter. "A stain on your reputation. How's that for starters?"

To Luke's puzzlement, Katrin suddenly sagged against the white trunk of one of the birches. She looked defeated, he thought. Broken. What the hell was going on?

Guy laughed again. "I see you understand what I'm talking about. Well, I've got a little proposition for you. You come to my room, say in ten minutes, and we'll forget the whole thing. But if you don't, I'll make sure before I leave here tomorrow morning that you don't have a job—they wouldn't want someone with your little secret working for them, now would they?"

Katrin said nothing. It wasn't just defeat, Luke thought. It was despair. As though Guy had pushed her too far, to a place where she was defenseless. What was her secret?

And why did she react like a startled deer whenever San Francisco was mentioned?

As though her silence infuriated him, Guy said nastily, "Room 334. In ten minutes—you be there, okay? If not, I'll smear your name over every newspaper in Manitoba and you won't get a job anywhere."

He dropped her elbow and started weaving along the path toward the lodge. Luke sank back into the shadowed bushes, thorns scratching his neck and hands. Then he stayed very still, scarcely breathing. Guy stumbled past, never once glancing at the rosebushes. When he'd vanished around a bend in the path, Luke carefully extricated himself from the branches. His suit would never be the same again, he thought, and in a few long strides reached the woman who was still cowering under the birch trees.

"Katrin," he said, "are you all right?"

She stared at him as though she'd never seen him before, as though he were some kind of apparition. She was trembling all over, Luke saw with a surge of compassion that rocked him to the roots. "What's wrong?" he said gently, and reached out for her.

She shrank from him. "Don't touch me," she quavered, "I can't stand it! Just go away. *Please.*"

"I can't do that…you're in some kind of trouble, aren't you? Tell me about it, and perhaps I can help."

Help? he thought blankly. Get involved? Him? Normally he never got involved in the lives of others.

"No one can help," Katrin said with such a depth of hopelessness in her voice that Luke was chilled to the bone.

"What was Guy talking about? What's this secret all about?"

Her shoulders drooped. "So you heard him."

"He let it drop after dinner that he had something to say to you. He's a bad actor, we both know that. Hell, the whole conference knows it. So I followed him here."

With none of her usual grace, Katrin pushed herself away from the tree. "Luke, this has nothing to do with you. Stay out of my life... I keep asking you, and you just don't get it."

"Are you going to his room?"

"So that's what's bothering you," she flared. "If you can't have me, then no one else can?"

Luke winced. Then he said in a hard voice, "Guy Wharton's a sleaze. You can do better than him, Katrin...and no, I'm not referring to myself."

"Oh, Luke, I'm sorry," she cried, "I shouldn't have said that. I hurt you, didn't I? I know I'm doing this all wrong. But I—"

"I sure don't like being put on a par with Guy Wharton."

"I'm not going to his room," she said rapidly. "I don't care what he tells the management, he can tell them anything he likes. I've been feeling like a caged bear for the last six months, and I'm sick to death of this job anyway. If I got fired it would be no great loss."

"A caged bear—strong language. Is that why you go sailing on the lake in a south wind?"

"Well, of course."

Luke let out his pent-up breath in a long sigh. "I'll deal with Guy. I've got enough leverage that I could ruin him if I chose to."

"I don't need your help! Let him say what he wants— I'm leaving here by the end of the summer, so why should I care? My friend Anna knows who I really am, and the rest don't matter."

"And where am I in that?"

"I've already told you," she said stonily. "Whatever my secrets are, they're nothing to do with you."

"I do wish you'd tell me," Luke said with such intensity that he was taken aback.

"Too bad."

"You're one heck of a stubborn woman!"

"If I weren't, you'd be trampling all over me."

She had a point. Taking a moment to gather his thoughts, Luke said, "Katrin, you egged Guy on in the dining room—if you were really scared of him, you wouldn't have spilled the brandy, or showed him you knew your way around the financial pages. But when he was threatening you a few minutes ago, you looked...despairing, I guess, is the closest I can get. Beaten."

The words tumbled from her lips. "Have you never had anything so awful happen to you that when you go back there, even in your imagination, all the old emotions overwhelm you? Just as they did when it was going on?" She drew a ragged breath. "Or are you immune from all that, Luke?"

As though time and space had collapsed, Luke was suddenly back in the shack at Teal Lake the day his mother had left, never to return. His father's drunken rampage, smashing glasses and crockery, the flames from the old woodstove flickering crazily over the ceiling. And in one corner, clutching an old teddy bear, cowered a little boy with black hair and dark eyes, terrified and alone.

Katrin said slowly, "So you do know what I'm talking about. What happened to you, Luke?"

With a shuddering breath, Luke hauled himself back to the present, away from an abyss that he'd fled years ago, a nightmare filled with noise and fire and unending fear. God knows what he looked like. He raked his fingers through his hair. "Nothing happened. Your imagination's working overtime."

"I don't think so." With sudden violence she cried, "What's wrong with admitting you're vulnerable? Just like the rest of the human race?"

Had he ever, wittingly or unwittingly, revealed as much

of himself to anyone else as he had to Katrin in the last few seconds? And how he hated himself—and her—for that revelation. Not knowing what else to do, Luke went on the attack. "What if Guy goes to the media? What then?"

She hugged her arms around her chest, lines of strain bracketing her mouth. "He won't. He'll be so hungover in the morning, he'll do well to get out of bed."

It was painfully obvious she was trying to convince herself as much as Luke. Luke said savagely, "In effect, he's blackmailing you."

"Don't be so melodramatic!"

"I'm telling it like I see it."

"You're overreacting," she said coldly. "Luke, I've got to go home, I'm really tired."

She looked more than tired. She looked at the end of her rope, with faint blue shadows under her eyes, her face haunted and unhappy. His only desire to comfort her, to somehow let her know that she wasn't alone with her secrets, he awkwardly rested his hand on her wrist.

She looked down. In a strange voice she said, "You have such beautiful fingers. Long and lean…"

By mutual compulsion they fell into each other's arms, Luke's hands locking around her waist, her mouth straining upward to his. Her palms were flat to his chest, burning through the fabric of his shirt; the first touch of her lips enveloped him in a tumult of desire. He thrust with his tongue, pulling her hard against his body. As she melted into him, tinder to his flame, she fumbled with the buttons on his shirt. Then, like a streak of fire, Luke felt her touch his bare chest, almost shyly, with a tiny tug at the tangled hair on his torso.

He groaned with pleasure, aching to feel her naked breasts, warm and soft and yielding against his flesh. His kiss deepened. Then he reached for the clasp that held her hair, wanting to free its silken flow over his wrist. Nibbling at her lips, he said huskily, "You should never wear your hair like this. I want to see it loose on a pillow, Katrin, I want to bury my face in it. I want you naked in my bed…"

As precipitously as she'd reached for him, Katrin pulled back. Her hands pressed to her cheeks, she whispered, "What's *wrong* with me? I'm doing it again, kissing you as though I'm in love with you, as though I can't get enough of you—oh God, I can't bear this."

In the dim light, Luke was sure he could see the glimmer of tears in her eyes. "Don't cry…"

"I'm not! Two years ago I swore I—" She stopped, aghast.

"What happened two years ago?" Luke said with dangerous quietness.

A shudder rippled through her body. Fear and pain flashed across her features so fast Luke might have imagined them. But he hadn't. They were real. Her voice cracking, she said, "If you have the slightest feeling for me, Luke, leave me alone. Go back to the resort. Go to New York, go to San Francisco, go anywhere in the world. You'll forget me by the time you arrive at the airport, I know you will—your normal life will catch up with you and take over. That's all I ask—that you forget about me."

She bit her lip, and for a moment he thought she was going to say something else. Then she struck his hands from her waist, whirled and ran away from him toward the staff parking lot, her black uniform blending into the night.

Luke took one quick step after her. Then he stopped dead. He could chase her and force his way into her car. Or he could let her go. It was his choice.

For a crazy moment that was outside of time, Luke felt as though his heart were being torn apart; as though every choice he'd ever made had been leading to this one. To a woman who'd been swallowed by the darkness. A woman with a secret.

He took a deep, harsh breath. He had no use for such fanciful guff. Woman of darkness, woman of secrets. He was losing his marbles. It was time he went back to civilization, to the sophisticated types he dated who knew the score. In fact, he was going to do precisely what Katrin had suggested: get on his plane tomorrow morning and forget all about her.

The quicker the better.

But first he had one piece of unfinished business.

Luke marched back to the lodge and took the stairs two at a time to the third floor. Then he halted outside Room 334. He tapped gently, rather as Katrin might have tapped, and waited.

Nothing happened. He knocked again, louder this time, again without result. Pressing his ear to the door, Luke could have sworn he heard a guttural snoring coming from Guy's room. So Katrin had been right; she had nothing to fear from Guy. Not tonight, anyway.

He'd make double sure of that. Taking a piece of paper from his pocket notebook, Luke scrawled a very succinct message on it, knelt down and inserted it under the door, and then headed upstairs to his suite.

Guy wouldn't be telling the management or the media anything tomorrow. Not if he valued his own skin.

If only he, Luke, could fix the turmoil in his gut as easily. Or did he mean his heart, not his gut?

Back in his own bedroom, he packed quickly, then went to stand by the window, gazing out over the black waters of the lake. If this were a story, and not real life, he'd be at the airport right now. That would be a tidy finish to an episode that had totally unsettled him. Unfortunately real life required him to get up in the morning, go to breakfast, say goodbye to his cohorts, including Guy; and face Katrin again.

Luke knew a good many swearwords, having grown up

in a rough and tumble mining town in the bush. Not one of them seemed remotely adequate to his feelings. All he hoped was that he wouldn't dream about her again. That would really be the final straw.

Luke did dream, tangled and distorted dreams in which Katrin, in a ridiculously ruffled wedding dress and her ugly glasses, was arm in arm with his father, who was equipped with snorkel gear and the financial section of the newspaper. Then Katrin and Guy were out on the tarmac accompanied by a trio of Icelandic ponies draped in peasant skirts. Katrin was jeering at Luke as he boarded his plane. He woke with that ugly laughter echoing in his ears.

He rubbed his eyes. At least she'd been wearing clothes; another night of erotic dreams would have finished him off. He had no idea what the dream was trying to tell him, or why Guy was in it. But he'd stake his bottom dollar that Guy was nothing to Katrin. She was genuine, every emotion she'd ever shown Luke coming straight from her heart.

Not that this made any difference.

Luke climbed out of bed, restlessly working the muscles in his bare shoulders. The best thing in this whole mess was her advice. Forget me, she'd said. And he had every intention of doing so, just as soon as he could.

If he pushed it, he could leave the resort in an hour and a half. Go for it, Luke, he thought, and headed for the shower. He checked out on his way to the dining room, leaving his bag at the front desk, and took his seat at the table. The young man called Stan was pouring Rupert's coffee. With an uncomfortable mingling of relief and pure rage, Luke saw that Katrin was taking someone's order over by the far wall.

She'd gotten her tables changed so that she wouldn't have to talk to him.

We'll see about that, thought Luke, and asked for black

coffee. When he'd finished eating, he said a quick round of goodbyes and crossed the width of the room. Katrin was gathering the used dishes from one of her tables. He stopped beside it, aware that several people were within earshot, and said pleasantly, "I just wanted to say goodbye, Katrin, and thank you for everything you've done all week." A statement that should leave plenty to her imagination.

She straightened, holding a heap of dirty plates; she looked as though she'd had as little sleep as he had. She said politely, "Goodbye, sir. Have a safe journey."

Her eyes didn't look polite. Far from it. He said, "I've already told you you're wasted as a waitress—you're far too intelligent. You should leave here, go to a city and get a job more suited to your IQ. Go to New York, for instance. Or to San Francisco."

Her breath hissed between her teeth; her fingers tightened around the pile of plates. He added softly, "I dare you. To throw them at me, I mean."

"That might jeopardize my tip, sir," she said, giving him a brilliant, insincere smile. "And now, if you'll excuse me, I have work to do."

"Goodbye, Katrin," Luke said; and heard, to his inner fury, the edge in his voice. The hint of rawness that said, more clearly than words, that this was no ordinary goodbye.

He turned on his heel, nodded at a couple of Italians and left the dining room. It was an anticlimactic ending to an episode as inconclusive as it had been unnerving: his last contact with a woman who had aroused him sexually and emotionally in ways he could only deplore.

Temporary madness. That's all it was. And the cure? To get as far away from here as he could and never come back.

To forget Katrin Sigurdson. Her beauty and laughter, her adventurous spirit and her independence. Her body. Her unspoken secrets.

To get his life back on track. Where it belonged.

Luke picked up his bag from the front desk and went outdoors to the parking lot. As he drove toward the road, his back to the resort and the glimmering lake, he told himself he was glad to be leaving. Of course he was.

He'd worked very hard to construct his life. He wasn't going to allow a blue-eyed blonde, no matter how beautiful, to disrupt it.

And that was that.

# CHAPTER EIGHT

FIVE days after he'd left the resort, Luke parked his sleek silver sportscar in the garage of his ultramodern house in Pacific Heights, and went inside. As always when he'd been away, he was struck by how impersonal and stark the rooms were, with their angled white walls, designer furniture, and the cold gleam of highly polished parquet. Not for the first time, he thought he should sell the house.

What had possessed him to buy it in the first place?

To show that he'd arrived, he thought dryly. That Luke MacRae from Teal Lake had a prestigious address in San Francisco, a city many considered America's most beautiful. And, of course, to cut any last ties with Teal Lake. No one from there would have lived in a cement and glass box painted white and trimmed with metal.

He'd outgrown the house; which had nothing to do with its vast floorspace. What he should do is purchase some land outside the city and build a house out of cedar and stone, with a view of the beach and the rolling surf of the Pacific. Yeah, he thought. He might just do that. He'd check out the acreages that were available, and find an architect who dealt in anything other than postmodern.

Luke opened the mail, turned on his computer to scan his emails, and listened to the four messages on his telephone; three were from women he'd dated. Then he wandered over to the huge expanse of plate glass in the living room and gazed out. Another reason he'd bought the house was for the spectacular view of the city. Sailboats dotted the turquoise waters of the bay; the distant hills were a misty, cloud-shadowed blue. It was midafternoon. He should go to his office headquarters, housed in the elegant spire of the Transamerica Pyramid. Show his face and make sure everything was ticking over the way he liked.

There'd been no messages from Katrin.

How could there be? For one thing, she didn't have his address; for another, she had no reason to get in touch with him and every reason not to.

So far, he hadn't succeeded in forgetting her.

He'd gone out with two different women in New York, both ambitious and successful women, each of whom had let him know she'd be happy to warm his bed.

He hadn't asked. Because neither had made him laugh like Katrin? Because each took the expensive dinner, and the waitress who served it, for granted? Because he couldn't care less if he ever saw either of them again?

He could get a date for this evening, if he wanted one. Go dancing in one of the clubs south of Market, find a jazz bar, or see what was playing at the Geary Theater. If he tried, he could probably even find someone to play Frisbee with him on Ocean Beach.

And it was then that Luke remembered the three photos he'd taken of Katrin playing Frisbee by the lake with Lara and Tomas. He'd get them developed. That's what he'd do.

As he was unlocking his suitcase, the telephone rang. He grabbed the receiver. "Hello?"

"Luke, Ramon here. I wasn't sure if you were back today or tomorrow."

Again Luke was aware of a crushing and utterly illogical disappointment that the person on the other end wasn't Katrin. Get a life, Luke MacRae. "Hi, Ramon," he said, "I just got in half an hour ago. It was a good conference, I made some useful contacts. How've you been?"

Ramon Torres was a high-ranking police officer whom Luke had met several years ago at the indoor tennis club he belonged to. On the court, they were more or less evenly matched, Ramon with a tendency to an erratic brilliance, Luke somewhat stronger and more consistent. From a series of hard-fought games, they'd moved gradually and naturally to an undemanding friendship. At least every two weeks they had lunch together, sparring over politics, learning from each other's areas of expertise; occasionally Luke had dinner with Ramon, his wife Rosita and their three children. Somehow, over the years, it had become clear that both men had pulled themselves upward from backgrounds of poverty and deprivation: Luke from Teal Lake, Ramon from the slums of Mexico City. They never spoke directly about this. But it was there, an unspoken bond between two laconic men.

"I've got a court booked at noon tomorrow," Ramon said. "Want a game? We could have lunch afterward, if you've got time."

"Sure. Sounds like a good idea. As always at these shindigs, I ate too much... I'll meet you there."

They rang off. Luke changed into casual clothes and drove downtown to the nearest camera shop. The prints would be ready the next morning; he could pick them up on his way to the tennis club.

So at eleven-forty the next morning, Luke walked out of the shop with an unopened envelope in his hand. He got in his car, drove to the club, and parked a little distance away from all the other cars. It was one of those summer days of thick fog, a heavy white blanket spread over the city, cooling the air.

Appropriate, thought Luke, realizing he was reluctant to open the envelope. He'd been in a fog ever since he'd left Manitoba. Oh, at his meetings in New York he'd functioned at top efficiency, and he was doing the same at the office here; there was nothing new about that. But the rest of the time he felt as though his feet weren't quite on the ground. As though part of him was still back in Askja.

His normal life had taken over; but he hadn't forgotten Katrin. Far from it.

She was even more real to him here, hundreds of miles away, than she'd been at the resort, Luke thought, tugging at the tape on the flap of the envelope. He had the eerie sense that if he turned around quickly enough, she'd be standing there, her brilliant blue eyes gazing straight at him.

Ridiculous. Get a grip. He didn't need a woman turning his life upside down, he reminded himself. Not now or ever.

With sudden decision Luke pulled the flap open, took out the prints and leafed through them. His heart jumped in his chest. There she was, on the beach, her hair swirling around her head, her slim legs bare to the sun as she reached for the Frisbee. In the other two photos she was laughing, Tomas grinning back at her, their shadows striping the sand.

She looked young and carefree, and very beautiful.

He shoved the photos in his gym bag and hurried into the club. He was late. He was never late.

Ramon was tossing balls into the air and practising his serves when Luke joined him on the court. *"Buenos días, amigo,"* Ramon said. His gaze sharpened. "You okay?"

Luke should have remembered Ramon had a law officer's ability to assess people with just a glance. "Sure," he said, jogging on the spot to warm up. "Want to rally for a few minutes?"

What would Ramon have thought of Katrin in her shapeless uniform and ugly glasses? Would he have discerned the woman of passion—and secrets—behind her disguise? Or would he have been as obtuse as Luke had been?

Grimly Luke forced himself to concentrate. They rallied for five minutes, then settled into the game. But Luke's focus was off. He lost the first set 6-4, won the second by sheer brute force, and lost the final set 6-2. He and Ramon headed for the locker room, showered, then walked to a little Greek restaurant they both liked. Once they'd ordered, Ramon said, "What's up, Luke? Was business off-kilter for you up there in the wilds of Canada?"

"It went fine."

"You've never played so badly before."

"Thanks," Luke said dryly. "How's Rosita? And the family?"

Rosita, Ramon's gorgeous and flamboyant wife, had had three children since their marriage, and to everyone's surprise, including her own, settled into motherhood as though made for it. "She's in decorating mode," Ramon said, wiping the froth from his beer off his moustache. "Tearing the rooms apart, painting up a storm. The kids are fine. Usually covered in paint by the time I get home. So you don't want to tell me what's wrong."

"I met this woman," Luke blurted.

"About time."

"Marriage isn't for everyone, Ramon," Luke said forcefully. "One of these years I'll settle down. But until then, I like playing the field."

"This woman...she wanted marriage?"

"No."

Ramon smiled at the waitress as she put his spanakopita in front of him. "So," he said amiably, once they were alone again, "she was immune to your charm and your undoubted good looks?"

"Yeah. Well, no. Sort of. I guess."

Ramon gave him a quizzical look. "One thing I've always admired about you is your decisiveness. Yes. No. Always you know which one to choose. Except now."

"It's not that simple," Luke said edgily. "She wasn't one of the delegates. She was working as a waitress at the resort."

Ramon raised his brows. "So she was after your money? I thought you were used to that by now."

"She wasn't! I swear she wasn't."

"You went to bed with her?"

Luke ate a black olive. "I feel like I'm in the dock," he said, scowling. "No, I did not."

"But you wanted to. Some women say no just to keep a man interested. On the hook."

"She wasn't like that."

"You've got it bad, *amigo*," Ramon chuckled. "She was beautiful, yes?"

"Oh, yeah, she was beautiful." Luke frowned. "She reminded me of someone, but I can't think who. And she had a thing about San Francisco, reacted like a startled deer every time it was mentioned."

"What was her name?"

"Katrin." Impulsively Luke fumbled in his gym bag, took out the envelope of prints and passed the three of Katrin across the table. Ramon took them carefully by the corners, his total attention focussed on the laughing woman on the beach. When he looked up, he was no longer smiling.

"What's her last name?" he asked in a clipped voice.

"Sigurdson. What's the matter?"

"Sigurdson…that's right. Although I knew her as Katrin Staines. Widow of Donald Staines. That mean anything to you?"

Luke's nerves tightened like overstretched wire. Katrin a widow? He said brusquely, "Not a damn thing—and I have a pretty good memory for names. What do you mean, you knew her? When? And where? And who was this Donald Staines?"

"There's no easy way to tell you this," Ramon said. "She used to live in San Francisco. About two and a half years ago, her husband was murdered."

*"Murdered?"* Luke repeated dazedly. "Are you sure we're talking about the same woman?"

Ramon flicked the photos with his finger. "I recognized her immediately...she's not exactly forgettable. It came out at the trial that she was of Icelandic descent, from northern Canada. I don't forget these details, it's part of my job."

"Trial?" Luke said sharply. "What trial?"

"She had a motive. Money. A great deal of money. The prosecution made the most of that, of course. But she also had an ironclad alibi. In the end, although they did their best to suggest she hired someone to kill Donald Staines, they couldn't make it stick. There was absolutely no record of her paying out any large sums of money in the preceding few months."

Luke stared at his companion, his brain whirling. "Am I dreaming?" he demanded. "Are we actually sitting here having this conversation?"

"Unfortunately, yes."

Out of the blue, Luke was transported back to Askja on his last evening there. Under the birch trees, Guy had said something to Katrin that had made her sag with despair. What exactly had he said? It had had to do with a stain on her reputation.

Her married name had been Staines.

So that was why she'd looked so upset. And no wonder she'd reacted so strongly to any mention of San Francisco, the city where she'd lived; where her trial had taken place.

He said at random, "I was out of the country for several months two years ago. But I must have seen a photo in the newspaper, and that's why I had that strange feeling that I recognized her."

"Are you in love with her?" Ramon asked very quietly.

"No. Of course not! But it's a shock, nevertheless." Trying to gather his scattered wits, Luke ploughed on. "You know, I'm listening to every word that you're saying.

Words like *murder* and *trial* and *alibi*. But I can't connect them with the woman I know. I just can't. I keep thinking there must be a mistake. Or this is some kind of sick joke.''

''Not on my part,'' Ramon said pithily.

Luke gave him a rueful smile. ''Sorry, you know I didn't mean you. You've knocked me sideways, that's all.''

''I can see that… Why are you so sure that the Katrin you know couldn't have murdered her husband? Who by all accounts was a very nasty piece of work.''

Scarcely aware of what he was doing, Luke buttered a piece of crusty white bread. ''She couldn't have. The woman I met at that resort wasn't capable of murder.'' He gave a baffled laugh. ''I know that's not a rational response. But that's the way I see it. Dammit, I know I'm right.''

''Ah,'' said Ramon. ''How very interesting.''

''Don't play games with me, Ramon.''

''I'm not. But I'm glad you said what you did. Rather than asking me if I thought she was guilty.''

''Guilty of murder? *Katrin?* I don't care what the prosecution said, Katrin Sigurdson couldn't possibly have killed her husband. And to say she hired someone else to do it is laughable. There's not an underhanded bone in that woman's body—her honesty was one of the things that first attracted me to her. Even if I didn't always like being at the receiving end.''

Ramon took a healthy bite of spanakopita. His mouth full, he mumbled, ''Her alibi was real. She was with friends overnight, and the murder happened in the small hours of the morning. But she most certainly had a motive, and that was what caused the most difficulty.''

''Okay,'' Luke said, tension hardening his jaw. ''So now I'll ask you the question. Do *you* think she did it?''

''Nope. Never did. I have very good radar for liars, and she wasn't anywhere near my screen. But her motive…she and Donald Staines had had a huge fight that evening. The servants heard it, and she freely admitted to it. He was a wealthy man, and—this is off the record, my friend—the scum of the earth. As well as being an unfaithful husband he was an embezzler, not to mention a highflyer in some very dubious circles.''

Ramon paused to take a long pull at his beer. ''Eat up, Luke,'' he added, a smile crinkling the lines around his eyes. ''I want you in better shape for our next game.''

Luke's heartbeat had finally settled down to normal; but his hands were cold, and he still hadn't quite taken in that this was Katrin they were talking about. Manfully he took a mouthful of salad.

''During the course of their disagreement, Katrin told her husband she was leaving him. That very evening. He said he'd cut her out of his will first thing the next morning if she did so. She said go right ahead, she couldn't care less...then she left the house by taxi with the clothes she was standing up in, and went to her friends' house. They were a highly respected couple, he was a chief attorney, she was a hospital administrator. The three of them stayed up most of the night, talking.''

''A cast-iron alibi,'' Luke said thoughtfully.

''Indeed. In my opinion, the case was mishandled from the start. It should never have gone to trial. But it had too many of the right ingredients: money, corruption, scandal, and a beautiful woman as the defendant. When you put all that together with murder and a possible hit man, you can imagine what happened. The press had a field day.''

Belatedly Luke's brain was now working at top speed. ''So that would explain why Katrin buried herself in Askja. There are no major newspapers there. And who would connect a waitress with Katrin Staines?''

''Not you. Obviously.''

Guy had. But Katrin hadn't really cared. She'd been

ready to leave Askja anyway. "What a terrible ordeal for anyone to go through," Luke said.

"I felt very sorry for her. She had enormous dignity and courage...both before and during the trial. But you could see it wearing her down, day by day, month by month. By the time it was over, she was on the verge of collapse. She got her lawyers to sell the house, packed her bags and left town. I lost track of her after that. But every now and then I'd wonder what had happened to her."

Briefly Luke described Katrin's situation. "She's ready to leave Askja," he finished. "But I can't imagine she'd ever come back here."

"Not unless she had a reason to," Ramon said, his eyes twinkling.

"Don't go there," Luke said harshly.

"Warning me off?"

"You said it." Then Luke grimaced. "I haven't asked the obvious question. Did they ever find out who did murder Donald Staines?"

"Case unsolved." It was Ramon's turn to frown. "And you know how I love those."

Luke dug into his salad. Ramon was his closest friend, but right now he needed to be by himself. Alone. So he could think. Take in all the implications of what he'd learned.

Half an hour later, after settling on a time for their next game, the two men parted in the parking lot of the sports club.

Luke walked toward his car, his gym bag in his hand. For the space of ten minutes he sat in the car, staring straight ahead at the brick wall.

His lunch with Ramon had cleared up so many unanswered questions, things he hadn't understood about Katrin. He now knew why she lived in a remote village, worked at a job that in no way fulfilled her potential, and was wary of wealthy men. She had very good reasons; furthermore, after an ordeal that must have tested her to the limits, she'd had the sense to retreat and lick her wounds.

He couldn't bear to think of her going through a protracted trial conducted in full gaze of the press and the public. Living day after day with flashbulbs bursting in her face, the prosecution ascribing to her things she would never have contemplated, the ceaseless and remorseless prying into her private life; add to that the terror she must have felt that justice might miscarry and she be held responsible for something she hadn't done...

He banged his palm on the steering wheel. No wonder she'd looked so utterly despairing when Guy had confronted her that night.

Wishing he could take on Ramon in the tennis court right now and get rid of some of his pent-up energy, Luke looked around him. The fog had lifted; the car was starting to warm up. So what was he going to do? Go back to work?

He had no reason not to. Perhaps now that he knew Katrin's secret, he could forget about her. For hadn't that tantalizing air of mystery been one of the things that had drawn him to her? That, along with all the contradictions that had now been so neatly explained.

Where would she go when she left Askja? Return to the States? Stay in Canada? And how would she earn her living?

Hadn't she inherited her husband's money? But if so, why was she working as a waitress?

His jaw set, Luke put the key in the ignition. None of these questions was any of his concern. The resort in Askja and his brief sojourn there were history. Over and done with. Along with the woman who had caused him, briefly, to forget all his hard-won control.

Luke turned left out of the parking lot, toward the distant spire of the Transamerica Pyramid, the city's tallest building and a notable landmark. Once he got there, he must phone Andreas in Greece.

That was the final piece of unfinished business from the mining conference at the Askja resort.

# CHAPTER NINE

FOUR days later, Luke was on a flight to Manitoba.

He'd made a phone call before he left, to book his room at the resort. Very casually he'd said, near the end of the conversation, "I'd like a table in the dining room with the same waitress I had before... I believe her name was Katrin." And then waited, with a dry mouth, to be told she no longer worked there.

"No problem at all, sir. We'll see you tomorrow evening."

It was seven-thirty that evening by the time Luke climbed out of his rental car at the resort. He took a deep breath of the cool air. He could smell the lake. The trees rustled companionably behind him. He felt simultaneously very tired and totally wired.

He was here. In only a few minutes, he'd see Katrin again.

Beyond that, he couldn't go. He didn't know why he was here, or what he was going to say to her; nor did he have any idea how she'd react to his presence.

He wanted to make love to her. That much hadn't changed.

Grabbing his overnight bag, he walked to the lobby, checked in and went to his suite. He took a quick shower and dressed in casual cotton trousers and a short-sleeved shirt, combing his hair into some kind of order. He should have gotten a hair cut, he thought absently. His heart was racing, as though he'd been jogging. He felt about as suave as a twelve-year-old.

In the lobby, he grabbed the daily paper; he needed

something to do with his hands. Or somewhere to hide his face. He'd never thought of himself as a coward.

What was he doing here?

He'd come on impulse, after that equally impulsive visit to the library in San Francisco yesterday afternoon, where he'd read the reports of the trial. Or had he come because he couldn't forget Katrin, no matter what he did?

He'd tried. For two whole days, after his lunch with Ramon, he'd pushed any thoughts of her out of his mind as soon as they surfaced.

Forty-eight hours. It didn't seem like much.

On Saturday night he'd even had dinner with a tall brunette, an architect from Sausalito. A move that had proved equally ineffective.

Taking a deep breath, Luke walked into the dining room. Olaf, the maître d', said politely, "Good evening, sir. Let me show you to your table."

Luke was given a table by the window, which gave him a view of the wharf and of a daysailer bobbing gently in the breeze, its red sail furled. He buried his nose in the wine list.

Then, as though a magnet had drawn his attention, he looked up. Katrin was crossing the dining room, carrying a loaded tray, her attention on the table nearest his. He noticed immediately that she was no longer wearing her ugly plastic glasses; her hair was in a loose and very becoming knot on the back of her head, a few strands curling on her nape. Then he saw how pale and tired she looked. Dispirited, he thought slowly. Sad. What could be wrong?

Just before she put the tray down, she glanced over at his table. For a moment frozen in time, she stood like a statue, staring right at him as if he were a ghost. The color fled from her cheeks. The tray tilted sideways; the loaded plates slid gently and inexorably toward the edge.

She suddenly realized what was happening and shifted

her grip in a valiant effort to straighten the tray. But she was too late. One after another, four platefuls of roast beef with all the trimmings inscribed graceful arcs in the air and landed on the carpet, the food with an uncouth squelch, the plates with a loud clatter. A Yorkshire pudding rolled under the table, coming to rest by a guest's sandal. The broccoli, Luke noticed, was the same shade as the carpet.

There was a moment of dead silence. If Katrin's cheeks a moment ago had been white as paper, they were now as red as the sails on her boat. She put the empty tray down on the dumbwaiter and looked helplessly at the congealed mass of gravy and rare roast beef at her feet. It was quite clear that she had no idea what to do next.

Luke stood up. Into the silence he said, "You didn't hurt your wrist?"

His voice sounded like it was coming from another man, one who had nothing to do with him. Discovering that his one urge was to pick her up, carry her bodily out of the room and put her on the first plane to San Francisco, he added without any tact whatsoever, "You don't look so hot...what's the matter?"

"What are you doing here?" Katrin croaked.

She'd asked the one question to which, basically, he didn't have an answer. As he sought for words, Olaf arrived on the scene with two waiters in tow, equipped with brooms, cloths and a pail of soapy water.

"Our apologies, ladies and gentlemen," Olaf said smoothly to the four people whose roast beef was on the floor rather than on the table, and who had been listening in fascinated silence to the exchange between Katrin and Luke. "Your meals will be replaced as quickly as possible," he went on, "and they will be, of course, compliments of the chef." Subtly his voice changed. "Katrin, perhaps you could take the plates back to the kitchen and reorder immediately...Katrin?"

She gave Luke a hunted look, then bent to pick up the plates. Plunking them on the empty tray, she almost ran across the dining room. As throughout the room the hum of conversation resumed, Olaf and his crew cleaned up the mess with remarkable efficiency. Then Olaf walked over to Luke's table. "Perhaps I could take your order, sir?"

Luke hadn't even looked at the menu. "Soup of the day and whatever fresh fish you have," he said.

"Wine, sir?"

"Perrier, thanks." He needed all his wits about him if he was going to talk to Katrin tonight. He should have phoned her yesterday evening and told her he was coming. But deep down he'd been afraid that if he did so, she'd vanish.

Very soon one of the waiters brought the second round of roast beef, passing a plate to each of the four guests. Then Katrin came out of the kitchen carrying Luke's soup. She walked straight toward him. With a quiver of inner laughter, Luke could tell that she'd progressed from shock and embarrassment to rage. All her movements jerky, like a wind-up toy, she put a basket of rolls on his table and the bowl of soup. Spinach soup, by the look of it. He'd never liked spinach.

He supposed it served him right. He said, trying not to sound overly familiar, and as a result sounding indifferent, "I'm sorry I startled you."

Between her teeth, she gritted, "Why are you here?"

"To see you," Luke said.

Her lashes flickered. Once again her cheeks paled, until they matched the white linen cloth on his table. She whispered, "You know. About Donald. Don't you?"

"You didn't do it," Luke said, putting all the force he could behind his words. "You were totally innocent. I knew that the moment I heard about it."

"I inherited all his money," she said flatly.

"I don't care if you inherited a billion dollars—you had nothing to do with his death."

To his horror Luke saw tears flood Katrin's eyes and tremble on her lashes. "Oh God," she said, "I've got to get out of here."

With a huge effort Luke stayed sitting in his chair, his fingers wrapped like manacles around the arms. "I'm really sorry," he said, and this time could hear the emotion in his voice. "Taking you by surprise like this was about the dumbest move I could have made."

She drew a long, shaky breath. "For once we're in complete agreement."

"Well, that's something. And now you'd better go back to the kitchen… Olaf's glaring at me. He probably thinks we're having a rip-roaring affair."

"There's not a chance in the world of that," she retorted with a trace of her usual spirit. Then she pivoted and hurried back to the kitchen, ignoring Olaf as if he were just one more oak chair.

Hoping she didn't mean it, Luke buttered a slice of crusty French bread and took the first mouthful of soup. It smelled like and tasted of spinach. Naturally. Trying to think of it as penance, he unfolded his newspaper.

Why had Katrin been so shaken up by her first sight of him?

The fish was excellent. He followed it with a maple syrup mousse that more than made up for the soup, and two cups of coffee. After she'd poured the second one, Katrin said politely, "Can I get you anything else, sir?"

The four guests who'd had the roast beef had just left. Luke said forthrightly, "Can I meet you somewhere after work? Do you have your car here?"

"My bike. Why do you want to meet me?"

"I need to talk to you!"

She looked at him coldly, rather as if he were a fly she'd

just discovered in his spinach soup. "You came all this way to talk to me? You expect me to believe that?"

"Yes, I did. And yes, I do."

"I'd have thought you had better things to do with your time. More profitable, anyway."

"I came here to see you, Katrin," Luke repeated, his voice rising in spite of himself.

"Short of hiring a bouncer, I'm not going to get rid of you, am I?"

"Not before you and I sit down and discuss everything I found out."

"You're boxing me in!"

"I know I'm not doing this right," Luke said in exasperation. "Please, Katrin, let me come to your place later on, will you do that much?"

For a moment it hung in the balance. Then she snapped, "No earlier than ten-thirty."

Her eyes were now filled with a mixture of hostility and terror; Luke wasn't sure which he disliked more. "I'll be there," he said. "Tell Olaf to jump in the lake if he gives you a hard time."

"My pay gets docked the price of four plates of roast beef," she said. *"C'est la vie."*

"That's disgraceful—the resort shouldn't be allowed to get away with it."

"I'm not a labor lawyer," Katrin said sweetly, "I'm a stockbroker. See you later."

Somehow—once again—Luke was quite sure she was telling the truth. Guy had known her background; that's why he'd goaded her with talk about investments. She'd be very good at her job, Luke would be willing to bet. Although most people might steer clear of a beautiful female broker who had a murder trial in her past.

Had he really categorized her as deadly dull the first time

he'd laid eyes on her? He couldn't have been more off base if he'd tried.

It was five to nine. He had an hour and a half to kill.

He went for a stroll along the lakeshore, listening to the shrill chorus of frogs and the soft lap of waves on the sand, the hands on his watch moving with agonizing slowness. He should have been on a jet to Whitehorse today, to look after a contract dispute; instead he'd delegated the job. Early this morning he ought to have been talking to a foreman in Texas. But yesterday afternoon had put paid to all his plans and schedules. Yesterday afternoon he'd gone to the library.

Against his better judgment Luke had spent a couple of hours there, reading through the accounts of the trial. The flash photos of Katrin had cut him to the heart. Her dark suit and silk shirt, her smooth, sophisticated chignon, her elegant pumps and gold jewellery: none of these were familiar to him, showing him another side to a woman who was still, in her essence, mysterious. But her air of reserve and her pride of bearing came across even in the grainy newsprint; these he knew all too well.

The headlines were cheap and degrading; her privacy had been mercilessly invaded for months at a time. As for her dead husband, Luke loathed him on sight, with his heavy jowls and thin, rapacious mouth. Why on earth had Katrin married him?

Even now, on the lakeshore, Luke couldn't get those photos out of his mind.

At ten twenty-four he was in the parking lot unlocking his car. At precisely ten twenty-nine he turned into Katrin's driveway. The lights were on in the house. A bicycle was parked by the side door. He walked up the steps, wiped his damp palms down the sides of his trousers, and rang the doorbell.

The door was pulled open immediately. Katrin ushered

him in and shut the door with an aggressive snap. Then she stood a careful three feet away from him and said brusquely, "We can't talk for long. I'm on the breakfast shift."

As an opener, thought Luke, this wasn't encouraging. She looked as though she'd just gotten out of the shower, her hair still in its loose knot, damp strands curling by her ears. Her cheeks were pink, her eyes guarded; her jeans and loose sweater hadn't been chosen with seduction in mind. He said, "I like your hair like that."

"You didn't come here to talk about my hair."

He said calmly, "May I sit down?"

She flushed. "Do you want something to drink?"

"No, thanks." He looked around, trying to get a sense of her surroundings. He was standing in an old-fashioned kitchen, panelled in pine, with colorful woven rugs on the softwood floor and plants on the wide sills. There were dishes in the sink, papers on the oak table, mail thrown on the counter. It was a room as different from his immaculately tidy stainless steel kitchen as could be imagined. He pulled out a chair and sat down at the table. With obvious reluctance, Katrin sat down across from him.

As far away from him as she could get.

Luke cleared his throat and said the first thing that came into his head. "Why did you drop the plates when you saw me?"

"You were the last person I was expecting to see."

"Come on, Katrin, there was more to it than that."

"If you just came up here to interrogate me," she said tautly, "you can turn right around and go back."

He leaned forward. "Yesterday I went through all the newspaper accounts of the trial… I can't imagine how you survived such an ordeal."

She tilted her chin. "I knew I was innocent and I had the support of good friends."

This wasn't going the way he'd hoped. Hadn't he pictured her falling into his arms as soon as she opened the door? "Why did you marry him?" Luke asked quietly.

"For his money, of course."

Luke held hard to his temper. "I don't believe you."

"Then you're one of the few."

"I never did like going along with the crowd," he said with a crooked smile, trying to lighten the atmosphere.

"I was young. Naive, if you're feeling charitable. Stupid, if you're not."

She was scowling down at the table, digging at the grain in the wood with one fingernail, the light from the Tiffany lamp shining on her wheat-gold hair. Wanting her so badly he could taste it, Luke said, "I don't mean to be interrogating you—you've had more than enough of that. But after I saw those photos of you in the papers—your dignity and courage, the strain in your face—I can't explain it. I booked a flight and here I am. I should have let you know, I guess. But I figured if I did, you might take off."

"You were right. I probably would have."

"Why?"

"We've got nothing to say to each other."

He suddenly reached across the table and stilled her restless fingers. She snatched her hand back. "Don't touch me!"

Pain knifed him; followed by jealousy, hot and imperative, clawing at his entrails. "You've got me out of your system, haven't you?" he snarled. "Who with, Katrin?"

She glared at him. "There's one thing you should know about me, Luke MacRae—I don't have affairs."

Slowly his body relaxed. "I've dated three different women since I left here and they all bored me to tears."

"Hurray for you."

"Why did you marry him?" Luke repeated.

For a long moment she gazed at him across the table. "If I tell you, will you go away?"

His eyes met hers, refusing to drop. "I'm not making any promises."

"You only want me because I'm not falling into your arms!"

"Give me a little more credit than that."

"I don't know what makes you tick—how could I? You're an enigma to me."

"You know you're important enough that I flew all the way up here once I found out what your secret was," Luke said forcefully. "And if you don't have affairs, Katrin, I don't chase women who don't want me around. Neither do I indulge in bed-hopping, it's not to my taste." His throat tight, he asked the second crucial question. "Do you still want to go to bed with me? Because in New York and San Francisco I couldn't forget you, day or night. Although the nights were worse. I should be in the Yukon right now dealing with contract negotiations—but I'm here instead." He gave a wintry smile. "I don't neglect business for anyone. You should be flattered."

"You frighten me," she whispered. "You're like a rockslide—nothing in your path will stop you. And that includes me."

He was losing, Luke thought, his mouth dry. And how could he push himself on a woman whose boundaries had been cruelly invaded by police, lawyers and the avaricious appetites of the public? Not to mention her husband. "Katrin, let's get a couple of things straight," he said in a clipped voice—a voice that belonged to a high-powered businessman rather than a man attempting seduction. "Yes, I want to go to bed with you. But I'm not the marrying kind. No commitments, no permanence. In other words, I won't hang around pestering you."

"We already discussed that," she said frostily. "I'm

thinking of going to law school, so I don't want any complications in my personal life.''

Luke thoroughly disliked being seen as a complication. He said flatly, ''Right now, if you tell me you really don't want me anymore, I'll leave and I won't come back.''

His words echoed in his ears. Did he mean them? Could he do it—simply leave, and never know exactly what Katrin meant to him? Surely she did still want him, just as badly as he wanted her? She couldn't have changed that quickly, not in the few days that he'd been away. So he was now trusting her innate honesty; gambling that she'd tell him the truth.

She said evenly, ''You mean that, don't you?''

Luke nodded, reminded of that long ago day when he was negotiating for his first mine. When his whole life had lain in the balance.

Ridiculous, he told himself. We're talking bed here. Seduction. Nothing else.

And waited for her reply.

# CHAPTER TEN

KATRIN said without a trace of emotion in her voice, "Yes, Luke, I still want you. That's why all that roast beef went flying. I hadn't been able to get you out of my mind and then there you were. Sitting at one of my tables."

His breath hissed between his teeth. "I knew I could count on you to be truthful."

She said rapidly, "I'll tell you why I married Donald...why I made the worst mistake in my whole life. If you still want to hear about it."

"Of course I do. That's what I came here for."

"I was born in Toronto," she said. "My father left when I was seven. I still don't know why, my mother would never talk about it. She was heartbroken. A few months later she got very sick and she died. Young as I was, I knew she didn't want to go on living without him. I was brought to Askja to live with Great-aunt Gudrun...other than Uncle Erik she was my only remaining relative, and he was hardly suitable as a surrogate parent for a little girl just turned seven."

So Katrin's father had run away from his family responsibilities, just as Luke's mother had from hers. Not that Luke was going to tell Katrin that. "Go on," he said softly.

"At first I hated it here. We'd lived in the heart of the city and all of a sudden I was living in a village where everyone knew everyone else and there wasn't as much as a toy shop." Her smile was rueful. "But my great-aunt was patient and kind, and gradually I came to love the place...she died when I was seventeen, and left me this house."

"You came back to your roots."

For the first time since he'd arrived, Katrin smiled. "Yes, I did. But I wanted more than my Icelandic heritage—I wanted to know about my father. He left here when he was young, after a fight with his father, who was Great-aunt Gudrun's elder brother. He never got in touch with his parents again, and they knew nothing about where he'd gone. After my great-aunt died, I tried to trace him. Eventually I discovered he'd died just the year before, picking grapes in the Napa Valley in California."

"So you went there."

She nodded. "I found out very little. He was a wanderer, never stayed long at any job. He had no friends and no money. So I guess he'll always remain a stranger to me…it was while I was searching through some old records in San Francisco that I met Donald."

Wishing he'd accepted her offer of a drink, Luke waited for her to continue. She said in a rush, "It's such a trite story. Donald was years older than me, and I was, of course, looking for a father figure. Classic, isn't it? Besides, I was alone in a strange country, and he could be very charming when he chose. I fell in love. Or thought I did. We were married, I trained to be a broker, and for a while everything was more or less okay. I was very busy, first as a junior in a big firm, then moving to a better position in another firm, you know how it goes. But busy as I was, I couldn't be oblivious forever. Gradually I realized Donald was being unfaithful to me. Not just once, but on a regular basis. But even worse than that were the people he'd bring into the house. His friends and business associates. Men I didn't want to be in the same room with."

Again she dug at the table with her nail. "Well, you know the rest. Things went from bad to worse, especially after he informed me he had no intention of changing his ways. Then one night we had this blazing row. I told him

I was leaving him, he threatened to cut me out of his will, and I left.''

''So he still wanted you as his wife.''

''I guess so. I was good cover, being so trustworthy and respectable.''

''Don't be bitter, Katrin,'' Luke said gently.

''You don't know how angry I've been at myself for being so trusting for so long. Anyway, after I left the house I went straight to Susan and Robert's. Thank goodness I did that. I still shudder to think what might have happened if I hadn't had that alibi.''

So did he. ''It's a tribute to you that you had such good friends…are you still in touch with them?''

''We write regularly. They moved to Maryland last year.''

So he couldn't suggest she come to San Francisco to visit her friends Susan and Robert. ''I can't believe I didn't meet you somewhere in the city during those years,'' Luke said.

''I kept a very low profile. First I was studying like a fiend, then I started dissociating myself from Donald and his friends.'' She shrugged restlessly. ''I should have left him months before I did. But one of my great-aunt's precepts was to believe the best of everyone until you had evidence to the contrary. I guess I kept looking for the best in Donald. He wasn't altogether bad—he could be very witty, and not unkind, as long as I didn't interfere with his plans.''

''Not much of an endorsement,'' Luke said dryly. He wanted to ask what sex had been like for her; and found he couldn't get his tongue around the words. He was jealous, he thought incredulously. Jealous of a dead man.

She said in a low voice, ''I finally found out about his ventures on the wrong side of the law, and that was the end of it. I should never have married him! But even now, I hate to think of the way he died. That someone hated him enough to kill him.''

"You're a good woman, Katrin," Luke said.

"Not really," she muttered. "When I came back here, I felt so battered and ashamed. I couldn't tell people about the trial, I just wanted to put it behind me. So all I said was that I was widowed. Only Anna knows the real truth." She ducked her head. "I lied, in effect."

"You looked after yourself," Luke said strongly. "The trial was no one else's business."

"I suppose." Picking at a loose thread in the sleeve of her sweater, her eyes downcast, Katrin said in a strangled voice, "So now what do we do, Luke?"

The sixty-four-thousand-dollar question. "Have you made love with anyone other than Donald?"

She shook her head. "I've been wary of men ever since I left San Francisco. And on Askja, there's not a whole lot of choice."

Knowing he was ridiculously pleased by her answer, making no move to touch her, Luke said, "I've got a suggestion. Hear me out and think about it before you reply."

She nodded, looking very wary. Luke said evenly, "Let's spend the night together. Here. Then in the morning I'll drive back to the airport and we'll go our separate ways."

Her lashes flickered. "And what will that accomplish?"

"There's something going on between us, we both know that. This way we can have the best of two worlds...find out what it is without any messy complications."

"Without any emotions, is that what you mean?"

"Without us getting entangled in a relationship neither of us wants!"

"You have it all figured out."

"You can say no, Katrin," he said in a hard voice.

She glared at him, tilting her chin. "I'm not going to do that."

"So is that a resounding yes?"

"You don't want a resounding anything!"

"At least I'm honest about it."

"There are times," Katrin said trenchantly, "when you make me extraordinarily angry."

"Yes or no," Luke said.

"Yes," she blurted.

The bravado died from her face. She looked appalled; she looked as though she might change her mind any moment. Luke pushed back his chair with a jarring scrape of wood on wood. "Don't look so frightened...it'll be fine. You'll see." He walked around the table, took her cold hands and chafed them within his warmer ones. "Where's your bedroom?"

"Down the hall."

He pulled her to her feet and led the way, still clasping her by the hand. If ever there was a time for him to keep a lid on his own needs, it was now. No matter that Katrin had said Donald wasn't unkind; Luke would be willing to swear in any court in the land that her husband had been an inconsiderate and ungenerous lover. After all, he'd seen photos of the man. So it was up to him, Luke, to undo any damage that had been done. He was used to subduing his needs; it wouldn't be a problem.

The bedroom faced the woods behind the house, and was painted a clear green with white trim; the old-fashioned double bed was also painted white, covered with a woven throw. Luke drew the curtains, left his shoes by the wicker chair and hauled his shirt over his head. Then, casually, he put a couple of foil packets on the side table and turned to face Katrin.

She looked like the china doll on her bookshelves, stiff, immovable and wide-eyed. He wanted to sweep her into his arms and cover her with kisses. Instead Luke rested his hands on her shoulders, kneading them lightly, and let his lips wander from her cheekbones to her mouth. With infinite gentleness he dropped the lightest of kisses along its soft curve. "You taste nice," he murmured.

"I don't know what—"

"Hush," Luke said softly, kissing her again, gossamer kisses that made his blood race in his veins. "Everything'll be fine...we have the whole night just for ourselves. And all I want to do is give you pleasure."

"But—"

He closed her mouth with his, stringently reining in his own appetites. This was for Katrin, not for him. With deliberate eroticism he slid his lips down her throat, and felt her shiver in response. Very delicately he traced the arc of her brow and the sweep of bone beneath her eye, letting his fingers slide down her smooth cheek to her lips, so exquisitely warm. With a shock of intimacy he felt the tiny puff of her breathing against his skin; and wondered if he'd be able to maintain his self-control.

Take it slow, Luke. Take it slow.

Suddenly and wholeheartedly, taking him by surprise, Katrin capitulated. With lingering pleasure, she kissed his fingers; then she cupped his face in her hands, kissing him full on the mouth. Like wildfire, the tantalizing pressure of her lips streaked through his body. Her palms moved to his bare chest, stroking it, brushing his nipples, then wrapping themselves around the taut muscles of his shoulders. Her body curved to meet his. And all the while she was nibbling at his lips with a sensual gentleness that set Luke's heart pounding in his chest. "There's no rush," he muttered, and kissed her more deeply, her heated response hardening his groin.

He couldn't afford to lose his restraint. With all the skill he possessed, Luke set about showing her that he wasn't Donald Staines. His tongue dancing with hers, he carefully pulled the pins from her hair, so that it slid in a pale cascade down her back. Burying his fingers in its shiny weight, he kissed her throat, the line of her jaw, then her mouth again, plunging to taste its sweetness.

Her hands were probing the hard planes of his back, sliding down his spine; the press of her breasts against his rib cage set his head spinning. He struggled to slow the pace, when every nerve in his body was longing to throw her on the bed, throw himself on top of her, and bury himself within her. Because she was Katrin. Because he wanted her as he'd never wanted a woman before.

Don't be ridiculous, he told himself sharply. She's just a woman.

Against his lips, Katrin murmured, "I've got too many clothes on."

It had been part of Luke's plan to undress her slowly and deliberately, every move part of his seduction. But he could feel her tugging impatiently at her sweater; when he reached for the hem, his fingers met the warm, silky skin above the waistband of her jeans, and he forgot his plan in the fierce need to see her naked. He pulled the sweater over her head, tossing it on the chair. Her bra was white lace, cupping the sweet curves of her breasts, her skin like cream in the soft light from the hallway.

He almost lost it. He said hoarsely, "You're so beautiful, you take my breath away."

She gave a sudden laugh of delight. "I do?"

He drew her hips to his. "Indisputable evidence," he said; and watched her lips curve in a smile in which shyness and pride were irresistibly mixed.

She was showing her feelings, he realized; and knew he wasn't going to do the same. He didn't operate that way. He kissed her again, determined to control the moves. To control himself as he always did.

She was fumbling with his belt. "Take me to bed,

Luke,'' she said impetuously. ''I'm not nervous anymore, can't you tell?''

Her eyes were a brilliant, depthless blue; her hips were swivelling suggestively against his body, in a way that made a mockery of technique and restraint. Luke reached for the metal button on her jeans, and drew the zipper down. Insensibly her eyes darkened. The pulse at her throat was throbbing against her skin. As he pushed the denim fabric down her hips, she helped him, laughing softly as it caught in her delicate lacy underwear.

He loved her laughter.

Loved it? thought Luke. What the hell kind of statement was that? He didn't know the meaning of the word *love,* and had no intentions of investigating it. So Katrin had a pretty laugh. So what?

''Luke?'' she whispered.

Inwardly cursing himself for losing his focus, Luke eased the denim down her thighs, his fingers pausing to stroke their slender length. Awkwardly she stepped out of her jeans. ''Your turn,'' she said breathlessly.

Standing very still, Luke watched as she fumbled with his zipper, her head bent; the light shone in her hair. Of its own accord, his hand caressed its silken sheen. Like moonlight on water, he thought; and stopped himself from saying the words out loud. He'd never thought of himself as being at all poetic. What was happening to him? Then his trousers dropped to the floor. For a moment outside of control, Luke pulled Katrin against the length of his body, feeling the warm swell of her hips, the concavity of her spine, the push of her breasts to his torso as though he'd never been with a woman before. As though words like *hunger* and *need* were newly coined for this woman and this coupling.

Stow it, he thought dimly, and kissed her again. Then he reached around to undo the clasp of her bra; it joined his trousers on the floor. Like a man in a dream, he cupped

her breasts in his palms, their soft weight arousing in him
a possessiveness he could no more have stifled than he
could have walked out of Katrin's bedroom. He bent his
head, his mouth exploring her breasts' firm slopes, then the
tautness of their rose-pink tips.

She was trembling very lightly. He said urgently, "Are
you all right?"

Her laugh was shaky. "Oh Luke," she said artlessly,
"I've never in my life felt so—so shameless."

Her words went straight through his defenses. She was
saying she trusted him, he thought blankly. Trusted him
enough to free her sexuality.

He mustn't misuse that trust. But equally he mustn't allow it to develop into anything else. With sudden impatience he stripped off his shorts, saying huskily, "Let's go
to bed, Katrin."

Her movements imbued with a seductive grace, she
pulled off the last of her garments, and again he was aware
of the shyness lurking very close to her outer poise. He
lifted her and laid her on the bed, her hair fanned on the
pillows like a sweep of pale satin. For a moment he hovered
over her, resting on his elbows, drinking in her beauty. Her
courage, he thought. Her utter vulnerability. And with a
clench at his heart knew he mustn't misuse these in any
way, either.

He kissed her again, slowly lowering his body to hers,
rubbing the roughness of his body hair to her sweet curves,
always careful to keep his weight from crushing her. Before
he was ready, she pulled him down hard on top of her,
wrapping her thighs around his, murmuring his name in
between fierce little kisses.

Cool it, Luke, cool it. Where's your famous technique?

Stroking her breasts, he lowered his head to lave her
nipples with his tongue, hearing her moan with pleasure.
Gradually he moved lower down her body, exploring with

his hands and his mouth, discovering all her sensitivities. As he cupped the warm mound between her thighs, caressing the petals of her flesh with exquisite control, she cried out, begging him for more.

Only then did Luke take the little foil packet, deal with its contents, and slide into her. Her slick heat enveloped him; they fit as though they were made for each other. Now, he thought. Now. And knew as he watched the storm gather in her face that his timing was perfect. Her inner throbbing caught and magnified his own; he felt himself falling deeper and deeper into the cataclysm, joining her there.

But even then, Luke stifled the raw cry that was crowding his throat.

Resting some of his weight on his elbows, he dropped his head to her shoulder. His heartbeat eventually slowed, his breathing returning to normal. Gently he eased her onto her side and laid down facing her. She was lying still, her eyes closed. "Katrin?" he whispered. "Are you okay?"

She burrowed her face into his chest, as though not yet ready to look at him. "I'm fine," she mumbled, her breath warm on his chest. "What about you?"

"Great," he said.

She suddenly reared her head. "Really? Because you were holding back the whole time. You never really let go, even at the end."

He should have remembered how acute she was. "I wanted to make sure you were all right," he said; and knew it for only a partial reply.

"You didn't want to lose control."

"I hate postmortems," he said curtly.

"You hate it when I get too close to the truth. Too close to you."

For a man who only minutes ago had been convulsed by sexual passion, Luke felt extraordinarily angry. "So who did you prefer, Katrin? Me or Donald?"

"You. Of course. Donald was as self-centered in bed as out."

"I rest my case—I was trying to look after you, and I obviously succeeded."

"Why do I think I've been very cleverly sidetracked—and by a real pro?"

"You're putting the worst possible interpretation on everything I say and do!"

She pushed herself up on one arm. "So tell me about your parents, Luke. Your brothers and sisters and relatives. Where you grew up. Why you react so strongly to the mere mention of anything like a relationship."

"We made a deal. And that kind of talk's not in it."

"So we did," Katrin said. "In fact, I instigated it…silly me." With a brilliant smile that didn't quite reach her eyes, she added, "Since we've only got one night, we shouldn't waste any time…talk's certainly not getting us anywhere."

He was still angry. "For obvious reasons, I have to go to the bathroom."

"I hope you brought enough protection for the whole night," she said provocatively.

Luke stalked out of the room. But before he left the bathroom, he gazed at himself in the mirror. She hadn't liked him holding back; that was obvious. She saw it as a challenge. Well, she was out of luck. If she didn't like him as he was, too bad.

When he walked back in the room, she was lying just as he'd left her. He climbed into bed and lay down beside her. Her cheekbones were shadowed, as shadowed as her collarbone; darkness lay between her breasts. The dip of her waist, the rise of her hip, the smooth length of her thighs: all known to him now. And still desired, he realized with an unnerving jolt. Desired more strongly than before; the past three-quarters of an hour might never have happened.

She wasn't out of his system.

She'd become part of him instead. Invaded him in a way a woman never had before. Wouldn't that be closer to the truth?

The laugh was on him.

# CHAPTER ELEVEN

As LUKE lay there, his mind racing, Katrin reached up, took his face between her palms and began kissing him with a slow sensuality that made his pulses quicken. Her fingertips light as feathers, she brushed his cheekbones, his deep-set eyes and the dark lines of his brows; as though she were blind and seeking an image of him in her mind. Then her lips wandered down the taut cords of his throat. And all the while, her body was pressed to his, moving against him with leisurely seductiveness.

He tried to hold back. Tried to take control. But as she teased his chest hair with one hand, her other hand slid lower. He was more than ready for her; and felt her touch surge through his body, flooding him with a primitive and all-consuming hunger. Her hair slipping like water over his ribs and navel, she moved lower, finding the jut of his hip-bones, his navel, the arrow of hair that led her mouth to the hardness that was need and the ache for consummation.

Luke shuddered with pleasure. She said softly, "You're so silky, so warm," her tongue laving where her fingers had moved. He moaned deep in his throat, trapped by sensation. With the inexorability of fire, pleasure and hunger mounted, feeding on each other, hotter and hotter.

Just when he was sure he couldn't bear it any longer, Katrin slid away from him. She rolled on her back, thighs shamelessly spread, and took his hands in hers. "Make love to me, Luke. As if this were the very first time for both of us… I want to know everything you can teach me."

His heart pounding like a mallet in his chest, Luke said

with an honesty as naked as his body, "I've never wanted a woman as I want you."

She brought his hands to her breasts. "Touch me here...and here."

He plummeted to find her mouth, kissing her with an imperative hunger; then he licked the rise of her breasts, the hardness of her nipples, the long arc of each collarbone. Her hands were roaming his body, loosing in him waves of eroticism that he couldn't suppress and was helpless to resist.

As though the tides had engulfed him, Luke abandoned technique and control and restraint. Instead his own body and Katrin's ardent responses became his only guides in a territory new to him, that he'd never entered before. In a tumult of longing he caught her in his arms, kissing her, his fingers buried in her hair. She met him more than halfway, her generosity inflaming all his senses. Her taste, the delicate scent of her skin, the silken ripples of her hair, how would he ever get enough of them?

Drowning in passion, Luke sought to imprint himself on every inch of her body. Making it his; because she belonged to him. Impetuously he lifted her to straddle him, watching all the changing expressions on her face, so open and unguarded. So alive. So utterly beautiful.

With a seductiveness that nearly drove him out of his mind, Katrin rode him slowly, her knees clasping his hips. When he touched her gently between her thighs, finding that place where she was most sensitive, she threw her head back, her breasts lifted, crying out his name over and over again. He could feel her inner pulsing as though it were his own, a release that triggered his. He rose to meet her, their gazes locked in an intimacy beyond anything he'd ever known. With a deep cry of satiation, he met her climax, and heard that cry echo in his ears.

With a long moan Katrin collapsed on top of him, her hair falling over his face like a shield that would shelter him from the world of normality. Her heart was racing against his chest; she felt boneless, so close to him that Luke wasn't sure where he ended and she began. He wound his arms around her and held on as though all his boundaries had dissolved. As though his very life depended on her.

He said nothing. There was nothing to say.

She slipped her knees farther down the bed, resting her cheek on his shoulder. Her arms were loosely curved to fit his body, her thighs enclosing his. Gradually he became aware that her breathing had slowed and deepened into sleep.

He lay still, eyes wide-open, one hand absently stroking her hair; in the turmoil of emotion that had him in its grip, a sense of rightness was predominant.

She belonged to him.

The words repeated themselves in his head. *Katrin belongs to me.* What was he thinking of? They were a lie, of course. Katrin didn't belong to him. She didn't want to. So how could he account for this deep current of possessiveness, the need to imprint himself on her so that she'd never go elsewhere?

Atavism, he told himself forcibly. The caveman asserting himself over all the constraints of a so-called civilized man. That's all it was.

He'd lost control. Totally. She'd seen to that.

Briefly he closed his eyes, suffused by a longing to simply go to sleep. To wake in her arms and make love again. To spend the day reading in her sunlit kitchen, waiting for her to come home from work; and then to go to bed with her once more. If his world had shifted in the last couple of hours, what would happen in two days? Two weeks?

Very carefully Luke shifted Katrin's sleeping body back onto the mattress. She stirred, her lashes fluttering; then she slipped back into sleep, her cheek buried in the pillow. His heart clenched. Defenseless, passionate, generous, fiery-tempered: what other facets of her personality had he not yet plumbed?

Would never plumb.

Because he was leaving. Now. He wasn't going to risk another of those cataclysmic matings.

He got out of bed with infinite care not to disturb her; and it was then that he saw the second foil packet on the table. He'd forgotten all about it; he'd never done that before.

She could be pregnant.

He wasn't going to follow that thought; the mere possibility was too overwhelming. All his movements clumsy, Luke got dressed in the semidarkness. Without a backward look he left the room, went down the hall and out to the kitchen. The side door creaked as he pulled it open. He froze, waiting for Katrin to call his name, wondering what he'd say if she did. But the house was encased in silence. He stepped outside, snipped the latch, got in his car and backed out of the driveway.

Because he lived in a city, he'd forgotten how completely dark the countryside could be. The vast panoply of stars was starkly lonely; it was a relief to see the lights of the resort through the trees. At the desk, not caring what the clerk thought, he checked out. Then he went upstairs, packed in a matter of minutes and left the room. Five minutes later, on the road that would eventually take him to the airport, Luke drove past Katrin's house in the village. But he saw no lights. No signs of life.

No indication that his own life had turned upside down in that little house on the shore of a vast lake.

He was running away. No question of it.

*    *    *

Two weeks later Luke and Ramon were seated in an oyster bar on Fisherman's Wharf. Through the open window they could see the crowded boardwalk, filled with tourists in bright clothes, with jugglers and musicians; and beyond them, the colorful prows of fishing boats. Everyone was having a good time, Luke thought sourly. Except for him.

Ramon raised his glass of beer. "Cheers, *amigo.* I'm glad you were free at such short notice." As they clinked glasses, he added, "Although you look like a man on death row."

"Thanks a lot," Luke said. When they'd played their regular tennis game last week, he'd been ignominiously defeated. He was sleeping lousily, Katrin haunted his thoughts night and day, and he bitterly regretted his impulsive trip to the resort. Other than that, he was fine.

Ramon said, "I have news for you. About the Staines murder case."

Luke plunked his glass down so hard that beer sloshed onto the table. "News?" he rapped.

"So you are still interested…I thought you might be."

"Give, Ramon."

"We've had a confession. And the DNA matches up. The case is solved, Luke. I know Katrin Staines was legally cleared at the trial…but a lot of people still thought she had something to do with it. Now we can prove she was completely innocent."

Luke sat back in his chair. The mellow strains of a jazz trumpet floated into the restaurant; a breeze ruffled the striped awnings. He pushed his dark glasses further up his forehead. "You're sure? About the confession, I mean?"

"It'll be in all the papers tomorrow morning. I wanted you to hear it from me first."

Luke said awkwardly, "You're a good friend."

"But not so good that you'll tell me what hold this Katrin has over you."

"If I ever figure it out, you'll be the first to know," Luke said with suppressed violence.

"I won't hold my breath," Ramon remarked. "The man who confessed, Edmond Langille, was a business associate of Donald's, who'd had a meeting with Donald earlier on the evening of the murder. Not one of the servants, of course, had seen him enter the house…where are witnesses when you need them? Nor did they see him leave, because he didn't. He overheard the row between Katrin and Donald and took full advantage of it instead."

"So why's he confessing now?"

"He's dying," Ramon said bluntly. "Cancer. Wants his conscience clear before he meets his Maker." Appreciatively Ramon chewed on his garlic bread, then forked a broiled oyster. "Katrin knew Edmond, although not well. So she'll have to come here for questioning."

"Not another trial?" Luke said, horrified.

"No, no. A formality, merely. I'll be phoning her this afternoon to make the arrangements."

Ramon then engrossed himself in his oysters, letting the silence hang. Luke said rapidly, "I went to Manitoba after you told me about her. We made love on the understanding we'd never see each other again."

Ramon said with an indifference that grated on Luke's nerves, "San Francisco's a big city. You don't have to see her… I can't imagine she'll stay long."

"I like my life the way it is!" Luke said violently.

"Then you are a fortunate man," Ramon said with a faint smile. "Eat your oysters before they get cold."

Paying very little attention to an excellent lunch, Luke cleared his plate, talking nonstop about the Democratic convention, the latest African coup and the price of gold. But as he and Ramon parted company on the boardwalk, Ramon said calmly, "Rosita would kill me for interfering—but Katrin's an exceptional woman, Luke. She could be the making of you. If you let her." He grinned. "See you at the courts next Tuesday. Try and have your mind on the game, *sí?*"

He walked away before Luke could reply, a big man easy in his own skin. Luke watched him go.

Katrin would be here in San Francisco. Soon. He'd have to phone her this evening.

He had to. He had no choice.


Luke phoned Katrin at ten-thirty her time. The phone rang six times; he was about to disconnect when she picked up the receiver. "Hello?" she said warily.

"Katrin, it's Luke." Now what was he supposed to say? *How are you?* "I hear you'll be coming to San Francisco."

"How did you know that?" she demanded.

"The police chief who's in command of the case is a good friend of mine. Ramon Torres."

"Just my luck that he'd be your friend."

"Ramon's a good man!"

"I couldn't agree more—even though he's a policeman, he was the one bright spot in the whole investigation," she said without a trace of emotion in her voice.

Silence hummed along the line. Wishing he could see her face, Luke said, "Are you there? Katrin?"

"I can't bear the thought of it all opening up again," she said raggedly. "I just can't bear it."

"But this will totally clear your name."

"I don't care anymore!"

He gripped the receiver tighter. "Are you crying?"

"No! I never cry...well, hardly ever."

"I want you to stay with me," he said.

"I've booked a hotel room."

"The media are going to be out in full force," Luke said, ruthlessly using the only weapon he could think of. "At my place you'll be protected from all that."

"It was over two years ago," Katrin cried, "what possible interest could they have in me now?"

"You're young, blond and beautiful. And you inherited a fortune."

"I gave it all away," she announced with defiant emphasis.

More than once he'd wondered why a rich woman like Katrin would be working as a waitress. Now he knew. He felt laughter rise in his chest. "Who to?"

"Shelters for the homeless. Soup kitchens. Overseas aid. You name it."

"No wonder the media are after you," Luke said. "That's not exactly standard behavior when someone inherits a whole wad of money."

"What was I supposed to do? Stay in a house I loathed, living off the shady dealings of a man I didn't love or respect? I don't think so."

Katrin would never be after his money, thought Luke. Not that he'd ever really thought she would be. "Have you booked your flight? I'll meet you at the airport and we'll go straight to my place."

"Luke," she said in a clipped voice, "I will not sleep with you."

"I haven't asked you to. Give me your flight times."

She made an indecipherable noise expressive of frustration and fury. Then he heard her shuffling papers. She read the information tonelessly, finishing, "I'll see you tomorrow. If you're not at the airport, I'll assume you've changed your mind."

''I won't change my mind. Goodbye, Katrin.'' Very quietly Luke replaced the receiver.

She didn't want to share his bed; she was sticking to the deal they'd made in the kitchen of her house. One night together and no more. All he had to do was stick to it, too.

And why wouldn't he? Hadn't he run away from all the implications of that passionate lovemaking in her little house beside the lake?

# CHAPTER TWELVE

AT THE airport, Luke saw Katrin before she saw him. She was among the many deplaning passengers, searching for him in the crowd at the arrivals area. She was wearing a tailored lime-green suit, the jacket hip-length, fastened all the way to her throat with big gold buttons; the skirt was narrow-fitting, skimming her knees. Her hair was loose, straight, smooth and shiny. On her head she'd perched a lime-green straw hat, tilted at an audacious angle. She looked both sophisticated and unapproachable.

Not like the naked woman who'd twined herself around him just two weeks ago.

As Luke moved forward, Katrin caught sight of him. Briefly she faltered. But the other passengers carried her with them; seconds later, she was standing in front of him. Luke kissed her lightly on both cheeks. "You look very elegant."

"I'm a wreck."

"Then you're doing a wonderful job of hiding it. Let's get your luggage."

Her eyes kept flicking over the crowds; she was fiddling with the strap of her shoulder bag. Normally she wasn't a restless woman. As Luke took her by the arm, he discovered her muscles were as unyielding as a chunk of wood. He led the way to the carousel, where her one suitcase soon arrived. He picked it up. "I'm in the parking lot...let's go."

But as they emerged onto the sidewalk and the heat of a California afternoon, a crowd of reporters who had been waiting outdoors rushed toward them, mobbing them. A camera was thrust in Katrin's face, the bulb flashing with blinding rapidity. A barrage of questions was flung at her, microphones assaulting her on all sides. "Mrs. Staines, how does it feel to be back in San Francisco? What do you think about this latest development in the murder case? Did you ever suspect Edmond Langille was the murderer? Sir, your name, please?"

Luke said curtly, "Hang on, Katrin." Using her suitcase to shield her, his other arm tight around her shoulders, he pushed through the crowd with brute strength. But his strong-arm tactics only prolonged the interrogation; the reporters pursued them into the parking lot, their ceaseless questions shredding his self-control. "Is this man your lover, Mrs. Staines? Will you remarry now that you're proved innocent? Would you ever move back to San Francisco?"

His car was in one of the first rows. Luke dropped Katrin's case, unlocked the passenger door and pushed her down onto the seat, slamming the door in one man's face. He dumped her case in the trunk and went around to his side of the car. But before he got in, he said furiously, "What Mrs. Staines does with her life is none of your goddamned business—why don't you just leave her alone? You're a flock of vultures, and yes, you can quote me on that."

A flashbulb popped in his face. Ignoring it, he got in the car, put it in reverse, and accelerated backward. To his considerable satisfaction the reporters scattered like startled hens. He said tightly, "My God, I'm naive... I was expecting a couple of local journalists, but nothing like that. I don't know how they tracked you down. It sure wasn't anything I said."

He swung out of the lot, his anger still very close to the

surface. Aware that Katrin had yet to say a word, he glanced over at her. Her head was bent, her hands clenched in her lap. Even as he watched, a tear plopped onto the back of her left hand.

Swiftly Luke checked his rearview mirror to make sure none of the reporters was pursuing them. Then he pulled over into a business complex grouped with palm trees, and parked in the shade. "Katrin," he said urgently, "don't cry. They're not worth it."

Her knuckles tightened until the skin was white. Another tear splashed on her hand. As Luke put his arm around her and pulled her to his chest, her hat fell to the floor. He cradled her head to his shoulder, wishing with all his heart that he could protect her from the next couple of days.

But he couldn't.

He didn't like feeling so helpless. So inept.

Despite the heat, she was shivering; her tears soaked through his cotton shirt. He stroked her hair, murmuring her name, trying his best to comfort her. Then he heard her mutter, "I have to blow my nose."

He reached into the back of his car, grabbed the box of tissues and pulled out several, passing them to her. She blew her nose and wiped her tearstained cheeks. Her makeup was no longer impeccable; the tip of her nose was pink. Filled with a ridiculous tenderness, Luke said roughly, "I should have driven over the whole crew of them. Cameras and all."

With a shaky laugh, she said, "You'd have been put on trial for murder. It's not worth it, trust me."

That she could joke when she was so clearly upset brought on another of those irrational surges of tenderness. "I couldn't even protect you from them," Luke said in frustration.

Katrin looked right at him. "You did your best, and a

very impressive display it was. But the odds were something like twenty-five to one, Luke—give yourself a break.''

"Yeah…'' Very gently he reached over and dabbed at a tear on her jawline. "You never cry. So you said.''

"Those reporters brought it all back,'' she said unevenly. "On and on it went, day after day, until I thought I'd have hysterics, or else collapse in a puddle on the floor… I never did cry in front of them, though.''

"It's okay to cry in front of me,'' Luke said clumsily.

She shot him an unreadable glance, sat up straighter and said with attempted lightness, "Fancy car.''

He'd said something wrong, although he had no idea what. But two could play that game. As he turned back on the road, Luke said, "I always wanted a silver sportscar that could go from zero to sixty in less than five seconds. Is your hat okay?''

She bent to pick it up, then rolled the window partway down, leaned back in her seat and closed her eyes. She murmured, "Wake me when we get there.''

Luke took the 101 and gunned the engine. He needed a respite; there'd been altogether too much emotion in the last half hour. But before he was quite ready for it, he was turning into his driveway in Pacific Heights. Katrin stirred, opening her eyes. "This is your house?''

He nodded. "The owner before me didn't like Georgian brick. So he tore down the original house and built this instead.''

"Minimalist,'' she said politely.

"Hideous,'' said Luke.

"Deconstruction's all the rage.''

"Tear it down, you mean?'' He laughed, delighting in her mischievous smile. "I'm about ready to sell it and move outside the city. Or maybe to Presidio Heights, I've seen a couple of places I like there. Let's go in.''

After he'd unlocked the front door, Katrin entered ahead of him, preceding him into the living room with its sparse, modern furniture. ''The view is wonderful,'' she said spontaneously.

He could see all the way from the Golden Gate Bridge to Fisherman's Wharf; the island of Alcatraz loomed above the cold, choppy waters of the bay, where sailboats bobbed like white-painted toys. ''Can I get you a drink?''

''I need to clean up,'' she said.

He took her past the dining room and the library up a short flight of stairs to the guest wing. Her bedroom also had a wide view of the bay, and came with its own balcony. ''My room's upstairs,'' he said briefly. ''You'll be entirely private here.''

She slid her feet out of her Italian pumps. ''I might have a nap,'' she said evasively, ''I didn't sleep well last night, and I'll need my wits about me tomorrow. Will you call me whenever you want dinner?''

''I went to the deli, got a bunch of stuff we can reheat in the microwave.'' His smile felt stiff. ''I'm no cook.''

''That'll be fine… I just need to be alone for a while.''

Her body language was easily read: keep your distance. Luke nodded coolly, closed her door and walked back to the living room. He was the one who'd run away from her so he wouldn't make love to her again; but right now he'd have given his eyeteeth to have been in bed with her.

Go figure.

Cursing himself under his breath, he changed into shorts and a tank top in his room and spent an hour in the fully equipped gym on the upper floor. Then he heard Katrin moving around downstairs. He ran down in his bare feet;

she'd changed into white cotton pants and a pink shirt. "Ready to eat?" he asked.

Her lashes flickered. "Whenever you are."

"You don't have to be so polite!"

"How else are we supposed to deal with this?"

"We slept together, Katrin—or are you forgetting that?"

"I slept. You left."

He flinched. "Okay, okay…come on through to the kitchen."

"I wish you'd put some clothes on first," she said irritably.

"I'm wearing clothes."

In a deadly quiet voice she said, "Why did you leave in the middle of the night, Luke?"

"Why did you say on the phone that we wouldn't make love again?"

"I don't see why I have to answer that."

"Fine. That can work both ways."

She glared at him. "I have yet to see a single photo in this house. Or anything personal. It's like a house in a magazine, perfect and soulless. Don't you have any photos of your parents?"

"Obviously not," he said shortly, and went on the attack. "Are you pregnant, Katrin? We didn't use anything that second time."

"No. I'm not."

His chest tight with a mixture of emotions he couldn't possibly have sorted out, although relief and a sharp regret were certainly among them, Luke marched into the kitchen. Which did indeed look perfect and soulless. "Let's eat… I thought we'd go out on the balcony."

He reached into the refrigerator. "The salads can go on plates from the cupboard over the sink. I'll heat up the chicken and the garlic bread."

The kitchen was large. But as he took out a platter for the chicken, he bumped into Katrin as she turned to ask him something. The platter landed on the counter. He put his arms around her and kissed her with a blatant and smoldering sensuality that, after the briefest of hesitations, she more than matched. His body on fire with need, he found her breast under her pink shirt, its warmth and weight so well remembered, so greatly desired.

She yanked her head free and struck at his hand. "Don't, Luke! We can't do this."

"Why not? We both want to," he said with infallible logic.

"We agreed we wouldn't."

"Agreements can be renegotiated."

"I can't take this anymore," she said incoherently, "it's all too much!"

Remembering with compunction the reason she was here, Luke said slowly, "You're right on the edge, aren't you?"

"You got that right. Don't you see? I made the biggest mistake of my life when I married Donald. Who was a very rich man. And now here I am back in the same city involved with another rich man."

"I don't do shady deals," Luke grated. "And I'm not asking you to marry me."

"How true…you're not, are you?" she said in a peculiar voice. "I'll be here three days…so are you suggesting we have three successive one-night stands? Is that it?"

"That sounds so damn crude!"

"I call it like I see it."

Her cheeks were now as pink as her shirt; but there was real desperation in her blue eyes. Luke said carefully, "Look, you've got a heavy-duty day ahead of you tomorrow, Katrin. Why don't we call a truce? At least until you're done with the police and the fancy lawyers.''

"And then we'll pick up where we left off?'' she snorted.

"Why not?'' He grinned at her. "It was a very nice kiss.''

"I could think of several words to describe that kiss. Nice isn't one of them.''

"Oh? Do tell.''

Hands on her hips, she glowered at him. "You're one heck of an infuriating man, Luke MacRae...do you have a middle name, by the way?''

"Where I come from, they didn't go in for middle names,'' Luke muttered; then could have bitten off his tongue.

"And if I were to ask you where that was, you'd shut up tighter than the proverbial clam.''

He raked his fingers through his sweat-damp hair. "Supper. On the balcony. Isn't that what we came out here for?''

She grabbed a white dish towel from the rack, waving it in front of him. "And the truce—don't forget the truce.''

He suddenly started to laugh. "You won't let me.''

Her lips curved in an answering smile. "You're getting the picture. What kind of chicken did you buy?''

Fifteen minutes later they were seated on teak chairs amidst the tangle of vines and flowering shrubs on the balcony; the bay and the distant hills were topped by a pearl-gray evening sky. Luke filled Katrin's wineglass with a California Chardonnay. "To better days,'' he said.

"I'll drink to that.'' She tore off a chunk of hot garlic bread, licked her fingers and said with a sigh, "I feel much better. Let's talk about movies and Paris and whether you're afraid of snakes.''

"It's spiders that do me in,'' he said solemnly, and obligingly asked her what movies she'd seen lately, buried as she was in Askja. One thing led to another, until Luke found himself telling her stories about some of his jaunts into mines ranging from the Arctic to the tropics. Her questions were intelligent, her interest genuine: encouraged, he talked far longer than was his custom, revealing more of himself than he'd intended. Peeling her a ripe peach, he said, "You're a good listener."

"I've learned more about you in the last hour than since we met." She licked peach juice from her fingers. "With the exception of when we were in bed."

His knife skidded dangerously close to the ball of his thumb. "And what did you learn about me there?"

"How closely you guard yourself and your secrets," Katrin said. "How passionate you can be, when you allow those barriers to drop."

"Did I have a choice?" Luke heard himself ask; then added in true fury, "I thought we'd set up a truce."

"Why did you leave in the middle of the night?" she said for the second time, a dangerous glint in her eye.

"You're as bad as those reporters!"

"No, I'm not—because I care about the answer," she retorted. "Don't you see? You give me a glimpse of the real man, and then you run like crazy in the opposite direction...why, Luke?"

He pushed back his chair, his shoulders rigid. "I'm going to put some coffee on...can I get you more wine?"

"You're doing it again!"

"You have a choice here, Katrin," he said, each word dropping like a stone. "Take me as I am. Or back off."

"That's not a choice. It's an ultimatum. And you know it."

"It's all you're being offered."

"No coffee. No wine," she said, her eyes almost black

in the dusk. "I'm going to bed. I'll see you in the morning."

But as she marched around a tall potted cactus, Luke took her by the waist, pulled her toward him and kissed her with an explosive mixture of desire and fury. Before she could respond, he pushed her away. "Sleep well," he said. "I'll drive you to the police station in the morning."

"No, you won't—I'll get a cab."

"You will not."

"I hate domineering men!"

"I'm just being a good host," he said smoothly. "Good night, Katrin."

She whirled, slid open the glass doors and vanished inside the house. Luke drained his wineglass, gazing out over the brilliant lights of the city and the slick, dark waters of the bay. Whether he went to bed with Katrin or not, he was getting in deeper merely by being within ten feet of her.

Why had he invited her here? This house, even though he no longer liked it, was still his sanctuary, where he could drop his public persona and simply be himself. Be as private as he liked. Why hadn't he listened to Ramon? *San Francisco's a big city,* the burly policeman had said... *you don't have to see her.*

The mood he was in, the reporters had better keep their distance tomorrow.

When Luke picked Katrin up at the front entrance of the police station late the following afternoon, the reporters were clustered around the side door. She got in quickly, and Luke drove away. She was wearing her lime-green suit without the hat, her hair in a loose knot. She said faintly, "Ramon let the word slip I'd be going out the side door. And they fell for it."

Luke eased into the flow of traffic. "How did it go?"

"I'm finished. I can go home."

His palms were suddenly cold on the wheel. He wasn't ready for her to leave. Not yet. "There's a big charity ball tonight at one of the hotels on Nob Hill, I've had the tickets for a couple of weeks. I think we should go."

She sat up straight. "Are you out of your mind? The last thing I want to do is go out in public."

"Ashamed of me, Katrin?"

"Don't be obtuse! After the spread in today's papers, you think I should go to a function full of people I met years ago, with a man the media are insinuating is my lover?"

The newspapers had certainly gone to town; the photo of his furious face as he'd tried to shield a beautiful woman in a wide-brimmed hat had made the front pages. No one at his office had mentioned it, they'd known better; but all day there'd been a tendency for silence to fall as soon as he entered a room. Luke said forcibly, "You've done nothing wrong, nothing to be ashamed of. Why should you leave here under a cloud? Blazon it out, that's the only way to go."

"You're nuts."

"We're going to Union Square to buy you an evening gown. You can fly home tomorrow."

"You're also autocratic, overbearing and tyrannical!"

"I'm a very good dancer as well," he said, stopping for a red light and smiling at her. "Do you like to dance?"

She scowled at him. "I love to. Add conceited."

"We can trade insults while the band's taking its breaks."

"Have I just been coerced into doing something that I know I shouldn't?"

He swung around a corner, then sneaked another glance at her. "Yep."

Her eyes narrowed. "What's in this for you, Luke? A new twist? Something to relieve the tedium of your life?"

He said flatly, "I can't answer that. Because I don't know what to say."

"Well, that's honest at least."

"Do we have to analyze everything we do?"

"If I'm analyzing, it's called self-protection," Katrin said vigorously. "I'm not sure you're aware of the effect you have just by entering a room. Every woman between puberty and senility stares at you as if you're the best thing since sliced bread. Regrettably, I have to include myself among them."

Heat crept up his neck. "Shove it, Katrin."

"I'm telling the truth! You're the sexiest man I've ever laid eyes on."

Wishing he could gun the car, but forced to crawl at five miles an hour because of the traffic, Luke muttered, "You're exaggerating and you know it."

"I am not. Anyway, to get back to this charity ball—I can't afford an evening gown. I'm saving to go to law school."

"It's a present. From me." He took a deep breath, quelled the panic in his gut, and added, "To say I'm sorry I left in the middle of the night."

To his dismay the light at the next intersection turned orange. He pulled up behind an SUV. Katrin said quietly, "For the third time, Luke, why did you leave?"

"Because I was afraid to stay."

*"Afraid?"*

"That's what I said." For Pete's sake, he thought, fuming, why couldn't the light change?

"Afraid of me?"

"Afraid of what you do to me," he said shortly.

In a small voice she said, "I thought you didn't like making love to me, and that's why you left."

His jaw dropped. "Didn't *like* it? Are you serious?"

The driver behind him blasted on the horn. The light was green; Luke pressed hard on the accelerator. Katrin said crossly, "What else was I supposed to think? I figured I was—despite my marriage, or perhaps because of it—too inexperienced for you. Too gauche. Too unsophisticated."

She couldn't have been further from the truth. "I ran away because I hate losing control," he said harshly.

Her fingers slowly relaxed in her lap. "So I've noticed."

"You notice too much," Luke announced. "I don't know what it is about you, but I've told you more in the last month than I've ever told Ramon, whom I've known for years."

"It's my big blue eyes," she said pertly.

He pulled into a parking garage north of the square, his mouth set. "You're going to buy a gorgeous dress and anything else you need to go with it. Money is no object and don't argue."

"No, sir," she said in a perfect imitation of her waitressing voice.

Luke started to laugh, his ill humor dissolving. "I'm beginning to think I led a very boring life until you came along."

They left the car and walked south, the clang of cable car bells accompanying them. At the edge of the square with its palm trees, clipped hedges and massed flowerbeds, Luke asked, "Want to start at Saks?"

Her cheeks pink, Katrin said, "I don't want you to see the dress until this evening."

He grinned at her. "In that case I'll find a bar, and you can come and get me when you're ready."

He had time to slowly drink a glass of Chablis and read

the entire newspaper before Katrin reappeared. She said breathlessly, "I've run up rather large bills at three different stores."

"Good," said Luke; and half an hour later, several boxes in the trunk of the car, was driving toward Pacific Heights. They had a snack in the kitchen to tide them over until the dinner at the hotel, then Katrin disappeared to get dressed. Luke went upstairs, showered and shaved, and got into his tuxedo. He didn't have a clue what was going on, although he was quite sure if he had any sense he wouldn't be taking Katrin to a charity ball where he'd meet just about everyone he knew; and discovered that he didn't care.

He felt alive. Disturbingly and wholeheartedly alive.

Which implied, of course, that he'd been going through the motions for a very long time.

## CHAPTER THIRTEEN

LUKE was waiting in the living room when he heard Katrin on the stairs of the guest wing. He walked through to the hallway; and when he saw her, stopped dead. Her dress, sleeveless and form-fitting, was made of black fishnet adorned with intricate patterns of multicolored feathers: it was an outrageous dress, that she wore with panache. Her sandals were stiletto-heeled, her makeup dramatic, her hair a smooth sweep of gold. He said in a cracked voice, "Katrin..."

She stopped two steps above him. "Do you like it?"

"You look magnificent."

She blushed. "It's the dress. Very expensive."

"It's the woman wearing the dress," he said. "You also look very sexy."

Her flush deepened. "I could say the same of you."

"A penguin compared to a bird of paradise?"

Her laughter, as always, entranced him. "Actually," she said, "they're dyed rooster feathers, I checked just in case they'd used endangered birds." She descended the last two steps. "And I don't feel at all sexy. I feel, if you want the truth, extremely nervous."

"You don't need to be nervous," Luke said. He held out his arm; his voice roughened. "I'm with you every step of the way, and I'll look after you to the best of my ability."

Had he ever felt such a tumult of raw sexual longing and possessiveness? But that wasn't all that was new. His instinctive need to protect her, to support her in any way he could, was something he'd never experienced with any other woman. As she tucked her arm in his, he rested the

135

fingers of his free hand on hers, their warmth searing him with desire.

She said unsteadily, "When you look at me like that, I melt."

"Like ice cream on a sunny day?" he said, his heart pounding under his pleated white shirt.

She glanced down at her pastiche of feathers. "Mint, cherry and blueberry mist."

"If I kiss you," Luke said deliberately, "I'll get scarlet lipstick all over me."

"You could kiss my cheek."

Instead, his face intent, Luke leaned over and slid his mouth down her throat, her delicate perfume tantalizing his nostrils. She quivered in response, her blue eyes brilliant as jewels. "We'll be late for dinner," she whispered.

He stepped back, his gaze trained on her vividly expressive features. "That was the aperitif."

"I can hardly wait for the main course."

What did she mean—that when they got home tonight, she wanted to make love to him? "Not to mention dessert," he said. Impulsively, he raised her hand to his lips, kissing her fingers with lingering pleasure. When he looked up, he could have sworn there were tears in her eyes. "Katrin?" he said in quick concern.

"It's nothing...so often you take me by surprise." Her smile as brilliant as her eyes, she added, "Let's go. We'll take them by storm."

Which, Luke thought midway through the evening, was exactly what they'd done. Friends and associates of his had made a point of introducing themselves to Katrin with genuine pleasure; while old friends of hers were clearly happy to see her again. The others, gossips and rivals, he didn't care about. Within half an hour of arriving in the elegant ballroom, Katrin had relaxed. Her poise, her dignity and friendliness, weren't new to him; but to see her in his own setting among his compatriots had a sense of rightness about it that both pleased and alarmed him.

He was getting in deeper with every passing minute; and couldn't, for the life of him, have pulled back. The signals between him and Katrin were unmistakable; he knew in his bones that the evening would end with her in his bed.

Where she belonged.

They were dancing a samba at two in the morning when she said, out of the blue, "Thank you, Luke."

Her hips were swaying, all her movements so graceful that he was on fire with wanting her. "For what?"

"For suggesting we do this." She gave him a sly grin. "Or should I say, for insisting we do this...and for taking such good care of me all evening."

He led her through some intricate footwork. "Not exactly difficult."

"I mean it," she said with sudden intensity.

He said huskily, "I think we should go home."

She looked at him through her lashes. "Because my feet hurt?"

"Because my tie's choking me."

"If you take off my shoes, I'll take off your tie."

"Best offer I've had all evening."

"I should hope so," said Katrin.

They left the ballroom amidst a chorus of goodbyes, and drove back to Pacific Heights in a silence charged with the unspoken knowledge of what they were about to do. Once in the house, Luke picked Katrin up in his arms, carried her upstairs to his room, and then, looking down at her, said, "In the movies, I'd fling you on the bed and rip the dress from your body. But, quite frankly, I don't have a clue how to get you out of all those feathers."

She chuckled. "If you put me down on the floor, I'm sure you can find the zipper that's very cleverly hidden among the black zigzags."

Instead Luke put her down on the edge of the bed, then knelt in front of her, removing her elegant sandals one by one. As she wriggled her toes in relief, he smoothed her arches in his hands, rubbing her heels and stroking her ankles with a slow, sensual pleasure. Then he felt her very lightly caressing his hair. As he glanced up, her beauty struck him anew, piercing him to the core. He said jaggedly, "I'm the luckiest man in San Francisco right now. Hell, in the whole wide world."

Her response was to lean forward and find his mouth with hers, kissing him until his whole body was nothing but raw need. With awkward haste they undressed each other, the feathered dress crumpling on the carpet in a froth of color. Then Katrin's naked body was beneath his, and Luke forgot everything but a craving to give her the most intense pleasure he was capable of. As she opened to him with an ardent generosity that touched him to the heart, he was freed of any constraint; they climaxed all too soon, their cries of satiation mingling in the darkness.

Luke lay still, his breathing harsh in his ears. He was, he realized, most passionately himself at the exact moment that he lost himself within her.

What did that mean?

He said unevenly, "Kind of a rush job."

"We have all night, Luke."

There was the faintest shadow of a question in her words. He said roughly, "All night. All week. All month...don't go back tomorrow, Katrin. Stay."

"All right," she said.

With an incredulous laugh, Luke said, "Just like that?"

"You like what we do together in bed—don't you?"

"Nah...I'm only putting up with it so I won't hurt your feelings." Then he reared up on his elbow, stroking her hair back from her forehead. "Give me five minutes and

I'll show you how much I like it. I can't get enough of you, Katrin, you're in my blood and my bones.''

"And you in mine," she said in a low voice. "Make love to me, Luke. As I've never been made love to before…"

"My pleasure," he said huskily, and set out to do just that.

The days and nights passed, one by one. During the days, Luke worked as hard as he'd ever worked; even though he whistled as he ran up the flights of stairs to his office, and smiled more at his staff, his focus was absolute, his efficiency unimpaired. At night, he made love to Katrin; and woke sometimes in the night to find her asleep beside him, her soft breathing so familiar, so much a part of him.

He kept these two compartments of his life completely separate. He didn't invite Katrin up to his office or to have lunch with any of his staff; he didn't bring work home from the office. This arrangement worked fine for him. Sex with Katrin—living with Katrin—might be a form of divine madness. But the rest of his life was totally under control. Just as it should be.

When they'd been together almost two weeks, he was driving up the street toward his house after work when he screeched to a halt. The front garden, attractively landscaped with cacti and ornamental grasses, had been taken over by a flock of large, supremely ugly, pink plastic flamingos. In the middle of them a large white sign said, Happy Birthday, Luke.

He stared at them, torn between laughter and something akin to panic. He never made a deal of his birthday. His father, as far as he could tell, had never really wanted him; certainly his mother hadn't. So why celebrate a day that was completely meaningless?

Somehow Katrin had found out that today was his birthday.

He didn't like her knowing even that smallest of secrets.

Luke parked in the driveway and walked up to the front door. Each flamingo sported a white satin bow around its neck, and had long black lashes painted over demurely downcast eyes. Where in heaven's name had she found anything so tacky?

He unlocked the front door. She came out of the kitchen, wearing loose cotton pants and an apple green shirt, her hair in a long braid down her back. "Happy birthday," she said jauntily.

"I hope you're only renting those ornithological disasters."

She pouted. "You don't like them?"

He grinned; how could he help it? "You're lowering the tone of the neighborhood."

"The neighborhood's too stuffy by far. Be glad I didn't choose purple pandas."

"I never told you when my birthday was."

"Your driver's licence fell out of your wallet one day. I saw the date when I picked it up. Come into the kitchen."

The kitchen ceiling was aquiver with helium balloons. A birthday cake, one side sagging slightly, was sitting on the counter; it bristled with candles. Katrin reached in the refrigerator, took out a bottle of Dom Pérignon, and expertly blew the cork. She poured two glasses, passing one to Luke. "To celebrate the fact that you were born," she said.

The bubbles prickled his nose. "Did you make the cake?"

"I did. I'm no pro when it comes to cakes. But first we're going out for dinner. My treat. The dress code's casual."

Half an hour later, Luke saw why. She took him to Chinatown; arm in arm, they strolled the busy streets, past tea houses, flashing neon signs, roofs shaped like pagodas, and tiny grocery stores crammed with Chinese vegetables. In the narrow alleys, wind chimes vied with the clatter of mah-jongg tiles, the air pungent with joss sticks. The restaurant Katrin had chosen was small and intimate; the pot stickers and Cantonese-style bass were the best Luke had ever eaten.

Afterward, they went home and had cake; then Katrin, without much difficulty, seduced him. As she drifted off to sleep in his arms, she murmured, "Did you enjoy your birthday?"

"I did," Luke said, and discovered to his surprise that this was true. "When do the flamingos fly south?"

"Tomorrow morning at nine o'clock."

"Good," he said, and in a surge of tenderness kissed her cheek. "Good night, darling Katrin," he whispered.

But she was asleep.

Early in the morning two days later, Katrin and Luke were sitting on the balcony drinking coffee and reading the papers. She passed him another slice of toast and said casually, "I'm coming downtown later on today, can I drop into your office to say hello? I'd like to see where you work."

Luke glanced up from the headlines. "I don't think that's such a good idea."

"No?"

Her blue eyes were looking straight at him. Refusing to back down, Luke said, "I like to keep business just that—business. Nothing to do with what goes on here, in the house. I've always kept the two separate, this is nothing to do with you personally."

She bit her lip. "Work is a big part of your life. It pays for everything we do. I'd like to know more about it."

"I've told you about some of my latest deals."

"I'd like to meet your staff. Joe and Lindy and the rest."

"No, Katrin," Luke said, restlessly shuffling the newspaper. "You met some of my friends at the charity ball, that's enough."

Small flags of temper stained her cheeks. "You told me once you've never been married. Have you ever been in love?"

"No."

"Have you ever wanted children?"

"No."

"Have you ever lived with someone? Other than me."

"No."

"What's so special about me, Luke?"

He could feel his own temper rising. "Do we have to dissect what's going on? Why can't we just let it be?"

"I'll tell you why. Because you're virtually a stranger to me. Sure, I know your body as I know my own, and you've freed my sexuality for the first time in my life. Both those things are hugely important and utterly wonderful. But other than that, you're an unknown quantity. There isn't a single personal photograph in this house, I know nothing about your past, where you come from, what made you the way you are. It's as though the past doesn't exist for you."

"It's irrelevant. What happens here and now is what's important."

"I want to know more about you!"

"Then you're out of luck."

"You know a great deal about me. I've talked to you about my parents, my disastrous marriage, the trial. Why can't you reciprocate?" She suddenly paled. "Did you do something terrible? Is that what it is?"

"Stop it, Katrin!" he exploded. "I'm not a criminal, if that's what you're implying."

"Then tell me!"

"You want all of me, don't you?" he said bitterly. "You can't be satisfied with what you've got."

"I want the whole man. Not just the lover."

He pushed back his chair, flinging the paper on the table. "I've got to go, or I'll be late for work."

She stood up too, her slim body in its silk robe limned by the early sun. "You're going to Dallas the day after tomorrow, on business. Take me with you... I can easily amuse myself in the daytime."

"It's only for four days. There's plenty here for you to amuse yourself with."

"But I want to be with you."

"No," he said in a hard voice, pulled the glass door open and ran upstairs to finish dressing. What was the matter with her? Their life together was perfect. Why did she have to go messing around with it? Spoiling it?

But by late afternoon, when it was time for him to head home, Luke was aware of an uneasy mixture of guilt and compunction. He hadn't changed his mind about Dallas. But he could have phrased his refusal rather more diplomatically. And wasn't the incredible physical closeness between him and Katrin far more significant than a disagreement about something as silly as a business trip? On impulse he stopped off at Union Square, choosing after some thought an Italian gold filigree bracelet and matching earrings. He had them boxed and wrapped, then drove home.

Katrin was in the kitchen. She was an erratic cook, rarely satisfied to leave a recipe as it was; tonight's shrimp salad, however, looked entirely successful. He said casually, "I bought you a present."

She put down the paring knife. Staring at the elegantly wrapped package in his hand, she said in a strained voice, "Please, Luke, will you take me to Dallas?"

"I already said no. Aren't you going to open this?"

"I don't want presents. I want you. All of you."

"I'm getting tired of saying no."

"Then try yes for a change."

"Yes, you're being unreasonable and demanding. Yes, you're ruining what we've got by hankering after more."

"Are you saying I'm greedy?" Katrin snapped.

"I'd be willing to bet that what we share upstairs in the bedroom is fifty times better than most couples on this block. But are you satisfied? No, you're not. If I give you the moon, you'll want the stars. If I give you the stars, you'll want the whole universe."

Her voice rose. "That's not true. Just because I want to know more about you doesn't make me into some kind of insatiable monster."

Luke tossed the box on the counter. "I really hate coming home from work and having a fight before I even have the chance to take my tie off."

"Would you rather I pretend everything's wonderful when it's not? When I'm unhappy?"

Unhappy. Hastily Luke buried this word deep in his psyche. "I'd rather you stopped being a romantic dreamer. This is real life, Katrin. Real life has limits and boundaries. I'm not some sort of hero you can shape to fit your own ends."

"Are all men alike?" she flashed. "Donald wanted a cipher for a wife. Someone who kept the house running smoothly, who could act as a hostess for his friends. Someone to warm his bed when he remembered to get into it. And like a fool, I fell for it. Don't get me wrong, Luke— in most ways you're totally different from Donald. But you want me to fit a certain mold, too. Be your mistress but not your wife. Share your body but not your soul." Her eyes were as adamant as sapphires. "You've got the wrong woman."

"I'm beginning to think I have," he said.

She drew in her breath sharply, as though he'd physically hit her. "I'm going for a walk," she muttered, grabbed the spare key from the ring by the door and ran from the kitchen.

Luke didn't run after her. Discovering he'd been gripping the edge of the counter so hard his fingertips were white, he made a huge effort to relax. He'd been so careful all his life to choose women who wanted nothing more of him than he was willing to give. But with Katrin, he'd blown it.

She wanted all of him.

There was no way she would get it.

Luke was just starting to worry when he heard Katrin unlock the front door. He came out of the den, where he'd been watching some mindless TV, more relieved to see her than he was going to admit to himself or her. Hadn't he been wondering if she'd taken the first flight north?

He said noncommittally, "Nice walk?"

She stopped several feet away from him. "Have you changed your mind? About Dallas, I mean?"

"You should know me better than that."

"Then I'll sleep in the guest room tonight."

"Using your body as a bargaining chip?"

"That's a cheap shot!"

"I'm not retracting it."

"I feel a million miles away from you," Katrin said with desperate intensity. "How can I share your bed?"

"Our bed."

"That's the only place that's really ours. Everything else is yours."

"So we're back to square one," Luke said harshly.

"I guess we are." Standing tall, she said, "Good night, Luke."

The words burst from him. "Katrin, don't do this!"

"I don't know what else to do. How else to handle it."

Before she could walk past him, he seized her by the

wrist; her sweater was damp from the fog that had swathed the city all day. With a distant part of his brain, he saw drops like dew on her hair, glittering as brilliantly as diamonds.

"Don't!" she cried, and tried to pull away.

As quickly as he'd grabbed her, Luke let go. As if he were four years old again, back in the old kitchen in Teal Lake, he remembered his father wrapping his fingers around his mother's wrist, then shoving her hard against the wall, pinning her there with his big body. He, Luke, shouldn't have been so critical of his mother because she'd left a violent, drunken man. What he still found hard to forgive was that she'd abandoned her small son; and had never once been in touch with him since.

"Luke, don't look like that," Katrin whispered. "What's wrong?"

He stepped back, wiping his hands down the sides of his trousers. "I'm not going to beg you to share my bed, we've gone too far for that," he said curtly. "Good night, Katrin."

She made the smallest of gestures toward him. But he turned away, going back into the den as though whatever was on TV was more important than she was. Through the canned laughter of a sitcom, he heard her footsteps retreat toward the guest wing, then the quiet closing of the adjoining door.

Luke flicked the power off, staring at the blank screen as if it could give him some answers.

# CHAPTER FOURTEEN

LUKE got up very early the next morning and left the house almost immediately. He didn't want to see Katrin. He was as bereft of answers in the morning as he had been the night before; and just as angry.

He worked out at the gym adjoining the tennis court, showered, and had breakfast at a little diner he knew. Then he went to the office and threw himself into his newest project with a driven energy that had all his staff on tiptoes. After ordering a sandwich at his desk for lunch, he worked until nearly six. The last thing he did before leaving the office was to make sure all his arrangements for Dallas were in place. One passenger. Traveling alone.

Katrin was in the kitchen when Luke got home. As he leaned over to kiss her, she turned her head so that he kissed her cheek rather than her lips. He said evenly, "Want to go out for supper?"

"I made a meat loaf, except I tried marinated tofu instead of beef," she said in a staccato voice. "It tastes a bit weird."

"But very good for us."

She bit her lip. "Luke, I'll make a deal with you. I won't mention Dallas again if you'll promise me four days of your time when you get back. We'll go somewhere of my choice, and you won't ask any questions until we get there."

He put his briefcase on the counter. "You're still angry."

"Will you do it?"

"Playing games with me?"

147

"No more than you are with me."

He loosened his tie and dropped his jacket over a chair. "I don't think I am. And I don't like being manipulated."

"I don't like being excluded."

His voice hardened. "I'm not going to change, Katrin. Not for you or for anyone."

"Four days, Luke. That's all I'm asking."

Even as it infuriated him, he was reluctantly admiring her spirit. She had it all worked out. He was getting four days without her in Dallas. She'd get four days with him heaven knows where. But wasn't that better than the stalemate of the last twenty-four hours? He'd slept lousily last night, his bed a wasteland without her.

"I'll tell you one thing, living with you isn't dull," he said irritably. "I agree."

"Thank you," she said, and reached for the spice rack.

The jeweler's box, fully wrapped, was still lying on the counter. "Are you ever going to open that present?"

"The present I want, you're not prepared to give," she said edgily. "And money can't buy it. So what am I supposed to do—make do with substitutes?"

"You're the only woman I've known who'd turn down a Tiffany's box!"

"Adversity's good for the character," she retorted. "Or at least, that's what I keep telling myself. And sure, I'm curious to know what's in it—I'm only human."

"I didn't buy you something to make up for not taking you to Dallas," Luke said, his words falling over one another. "I bought it because waking up in the night and finding you there beside me makes me happier than I've ever been in my life."

Dammit, he'd done it again. Said more than he'd ever meant to say, just because a woman with big blue eyes was pushing him beyond his limits.

Those same blue eyes were now filmed with tears. "It does?" Katrin said jaggedly.

"Surely I don't have to tell you that?"

"It would be really nice if reading your mind was one of my talents," she said. "But it isn't."

Luke didn't want her reading his mind; he had to keep some parts of himself inviolate. "I didn't sleep more than five consecutive minutes last night."

"Neither did I." Giving him a small smile, Katrin reached for the jeweler's box. As she lifted the delicate bracelet from the box, her face lit with delight. "It's beautiful, Luke, thank you. Will you do it up for me?"

He fumbled with the tiny clasp, her scent filling his nostrils. When he kissed the pulse in her wrist, it raced beneath his lips; they were very late eating the marinated tofu. Which did indeed taste rather weird.

Luke went to Dallas on his own, missed Katrin unrelentingly, and flew home late on Friday. He didn't like missing her, reaching for her in the night, wanting to share a joke with her or a conversation. No matter how earth-shattering it was, sex was just sex. He'd better not forget it.

When he unlocked the front door, it was past eleven. A note was on the kitchen table. "Gone to bed...see you there?"

Luke ran up the stairs two at a time, hoping she wasn't asleep. He opened the bedroom door, stopped in his tracks and started to laugh, a laugh that came all the way from his belly.

"You don't laugh often enough." Katrin said, "Welcome home, Luke."

She was lying in a seductive pose on black satin sheets, wearing a sheer white nightgown that left nothing to his imagination. Red roses were strewn on the bed, while there were enough candles burning in the room to start a major fire. Marlene Dietrich was singing something sultry on the stereo; strings of tiny white lights glittered like stars all over the ceiling.

Katrin said innocently, "Did I go overboard enough? You'll notice there are no flamingos."

"Perhaps you should have included a fire extinguisher."

"The kind of fire I'm interested in can't be put out so easily," she rejoined, tossing her hair back with a gesture worthy of Dietrich.

Her nipples were pushing at the filmy white nylon, which clung to her hips and thighs. Luke said huskily, "I could help you light the fire."

"I was hoping you'd offer."

He dropped his clothes on the carpet and, naked, walked over to the bed. "As you see, I won't take much persuading."

She blushed in a very un-Dietrichlike way. "None at all, by the looks of you."

He buried his face in the softness of her breasts, her creamy skin and ardent embrace wondrously familiar. He could have told her he'd missed her; he didn't. "I hope the roses don't have thorns," he murmured; and said nothing else for quite a while.

Early the next morning Katrin and Luke boarded the first leg of a flight to Winnipeg, capital city of Manitoba. So, thought Luke, they were going back to Askja. He had no objections whatsoever; they could swim, sail and hike, and he might even get around to a little fishing.

Four days with Katrin in the village where she grew up would be just fine.

After they'd landed in Winnipeg, Katrin picked up a rental vehicle that turned out to be a four-wheel-drive wagon. She headed toward the perimeter highway that circled the city. Luke was tired; Dallas had been strenuous and he hadn't slept much the night before. "Would you mind if I have a snooze?" he asked. "I could drive after that."

"Sure," she said.

She didn't look entirely relaxed. Perhaps, he thought wryly, she was going to show him more of her past in Askja, and expected him to reciprocate. He hoped not. He'd much rather make love than war. He settled back in the seat, closed his eyes and drifted off to sleep.

He had no idea how much time had passed when he woke up. Stretching, he glanced at the clock on the dash. "Good grief, did I sleep that long? You must have worn me out last night, Katrin...we should be nearly there."

He looked around in growing puzzlement. The landscape looked both unfamiliar, yet frighteningly familiar. He said slowly, "This isn't the way to Askja."

"We're not going to Askja."

"We're in Ontario."

"Yes. We crossed the border a little while ago."

"What's up, Katrin?" Luke said tightly.

"You'll see. You agreed not to ask any questions, remember?"

He had. Relax, Luke, he told himself. Katrin doesn't know about Teal Lake. She's taking you to a resort on Lake of the Woods, that's all. He said, "Would you like me to drive?"

"No, I'm fine. If you're hungry, there are some chocolate bars and sandwiches in my pack."

He munched on a sandwich, subliminally aware that she was gripping the wheel much too tightly for someone on a perfectly innocent vacation. What was up? Why was she so tense?

He found out ten minutes later when they came to the green and white sign for Teal Lake. At the last minute

Katrin slowed, flicked on her left-hand signal and took the turnoff. Luke said sharply, "Where are we going?"

Her knuckles were now white as bone. "Teal Lake," she said. "Where else?"

"Katrin," he said in a deadly quiet voice, "turn around."

"No, Luke."

"I don't want to go anywhere near Teal Lake!"

"I'm sure you don't."

He could have grabbed the wheel. But if they both ended up in the ditch, that would solve nothing. "For the last time, turn around."

"You promised me four days of your time, no questions asked."

"I also said I loathe being manipulated," he said icily. "How did you find out about Teal Lake?"

"I had lunch with Ramon the day before you left for Dallas. He told me."

Mixed with rage was now the sharp pain of betrayal. "What did he tell you?"

"Only that the place meant something to you. Nothing more. He can be as closemouthed as you." She added with a small smile, obviously trying to lighten the atmosphere, "Although it made a change for me to ask him the questions."

The wagon was bouncing over the ruts in the dirt road. Which would, Luke knew, get worse before they got better. No wonder she'd hired a four-wheel drive. "You had this all planned, didn't you? Clever little Katrin."

A muscle twitched in her jaw. "How long will it take us to get there?"

"Oh," he said, "you'll find out." Then he leaned back in the seat and closed his eyes again. He was damned if he was going to count every tree and chunk of granite between here and their destination. Let her deal with the potholes, the culverts and washboard slopes. This was, after all, her idea.

Had he ever been so angry in his whole life?

It'd be a lifetime before he made Katrin—or any other woman—another blind promise like the one he'd made so innocently in the kitchen. He'd trusted Katrin; and she, like Ramon, had betrayed him.

He wasn't sure which was worse: anger or pain.

Time passed. The wagon lurched and bounced. Neither he nor Katrin said a word until she slowed, then turned again, this time to the right. "We're here," she said, parked the vehicle and pulled on the handbrake. Then she got out of the wagon.

Luke sat up and looked around. She'd parked at the beginning of the town. It was deserted now; the mine had closed many years ago, the inhabitants transported to other mining towns along the shield. He had two choices. He could sit here until she tired of wandering among the tumbledown buildings. Or he could join her and have the fight he was spoiling for.

He should join her anyway; this was bear country.

Luke jumped to the ground. It was late afternoon, under a clear sky. Somewhere in the woods a white-throated sparrow sang its pure, single notes, while a thrush was piping from the tall pines. The mosquitoes descended on him almost immediately. He pulled down his shirt sleeves and buttoned his collar. "So what's the plan, Katrin?" he grated. "Because I'm sure you have one."

"Let's just walk around," she said.

Her spine was like a ramrod under her cotton shirt, and she stumbled over a couple of rocks as she passed the first shack. Luke remembered it all too well. Jim Morton had lived there with his wife and half a dozen kids; the eldest boy had made Luke's life a misery until Luke had grown big enough to turn on him one day and knock him to the ground.

He, Luke, had been small for his age in those days. He'd suddenly shot up when he turned thirteen; a couple of years later, he'd lost all fear of his father.

The roof of the old country store was sagging. Like Katrin's cake, thought Luke, and heard her say, "How long since the place closed down?"

"You mean you didn't do your research?" he said nastily.

"I was hoping you'd tell me."

"You don't know me very well if you think you're going to get a guided tour."

They passed the little church, the paint peeling from its shingles, and three more houses. The windows were boarded up; desolation and abandonment hung like a miasma over the whole settlement. Gradually and inexorably grasses and shrubs were encroaching on the houses. Swallowing them, thought Luke, and wished he were anywhere else in the world but here.

They were approaching the tar-paper shack where he'd lived with his parents, and then with his father once his mother had left. His nerves had tightened to an unbearable pitch. Trying to distract himself from memories that were mobbing him like a flock of crows, he said flatly, "Why did you bring me here?"

"I thought it might open you up. Make you tell me about yourself, your parents, your past."

"Think you're pretty smart, don't you?"

She stopped right in front of his old house. "I didn't know what else to do! I can't live with someone who won't tell me the first thing about himself. You're like a medieval castle, Luke—walls ten feet thick and no windows."

"Yeah?" he said in an ugly voice, emotion seething in his chest. As though a dam had burst inside him, the words came pouring out, unstoppable, carrying everything in their path. "While we're on the subject of windows," he rasped, "why don't you take a look at the place right in front of you. That's where I grew up. You see that broken pane in the kitchen window? My dad put his fist through it one night. He was aiming at my head. But he was dead-drunk and I ducked and so he missed me. He whomped me with his belt for that...is that the kind of thing you want to know?"

Katrin paled. "Where was your mother? Couldn't she have protected you?"

"My mother took off with the local mechanic the summer I turned five. Her morals were what you might call loose...who knows if my dad really was my dad? Certainly they never bothered to get married. I was glad when she left because it meant no more fights in the middle of the night, no more broken crockery and bruises on my mother's face. How in hell could she protect me, even if she'd wanted to—she was shorter than you and my dad was a big man."

"She could have taken you with her."

"She didn't want me. To give my dad his due, he did provide me with some kind of home. At least he didn't run away like my mum. Although we were dirt poor because he drank everything he earned."

"But he used to beat you," Katrin whispered.

Her face, a frozen mask of horror, only served to make Luke angrier. "I learned very young to stay out in the woods all night if he'd been into the booze, and I was always quicker on my feet than him. But sometimes he caught me, yeah. So are you getting the picture? Can you see why I'm not rushing you to the altar, or fathering a dozen kids? I never want to have children!"

"That's why you've made so much money...so you'll

never be poor again," she said in a dazed voice. "Where's your father now, Luke?"

"When I turned fifteen, he took his belt off once too often. I flattened him against the wall and told him I'd beat the tar out of him if he ever tried that again. The next morning I left. Went north. I lied about my age, worked the mines and started saving money."

"Did you ever come back here?"

"Never. I got word two years later that he'd died of a heart attack…there was no reason to come back."

"So you never made peace with him."

Luke's throat tightened; to his horror he felt tears sting his eyes. With a tiny sound of compassion, Katrin stepped closer and tried to put her arms around him. He struck her away. "I've always regretted that I never came back here, or tried to meet my dad on a more even footing. Not everyone saddled with a rebellious kid who might not even be his own flesh and blood would have hung in like my dad did. But I never told him that. And now it's too late. Years too late."

He, Luke, could have ended up in an orphanage; and rough though his upbringing had been, Luke knew in his bones that an orphanage would have stifled him. His fists clenched at his sides, he went on, "There was more to my dad than the booze and his belt. His whole life he worked to get unions into the mines. Every mine I own is unionized, and the safety regulations are strictly adhered to or I close the place down…it's the least I can do for him."

"It's a fine legacy," Katrin said unsteadily.

"Maybe he loved my mum, despite her infidelities. Maybe that's why he drank. Or maybe it was because of his own childhood—he came over here from the slums of Glasgow, God knows what his upbringing was like. There's so much I never asked him. And now I can't."

Katrin was gazing at the little house as though it might

tell her all its secrets. "Wasn't there anyone here who loved you? Someone you could run to when you were in trouble?"

"Me? Run for help? Not likely," Luke said ironically. "You asked me once what my middle name was. How about independence?"

"You have two middle names," Katrin said with a flare of her normal spirit. "The second one's pride."

She'd got that right. "You think I was going to tell the whole village what my life was like? How terrified I was sometimes? How lonely I felt, how unloved?" He gave a derisive laugh. "There are worse things than the occasional night in the woods."

"You've never told anyone any of this."

"Imagine that."

"Not everyone's like your parents!"

"Right," he said sarcastically, raking his fingers through his hair. "Have you seen enough? Or do we have to walk the whole goddamned street?"

"I've seen enough."

"Good. Then let's get out of here."

Katrin dragged her eyes away from the rotting wooden gutters, where flaps of tar paper hung from the roof. In a low voice she said, "I brought you here for another reason."

"I think you've done enough damage for one day."

"I didn't mean to hurt you! I needed to know more about you, to try and understand you. To get behind all those barriers you hide behind."

"Why do you need to do that?" he exploded. "What business is it of yours?"

She drew in a ragged breath. "Haven't you guessed?" she said. "I'm in love with you, Luke."

# CHAPTER FIFTEEN

INTO the silence came the whitethroat's clear lament, piercingly sweet. Luke said with careful restraint, "Would you mind repeating that?"

"You heard," Katrin said with a touch of desperation. "I love you. I've been in love with you for weeks, that's why I was so devastated when you left in the middle of the night after we first made love. That's why I want more of you than you're giving me. Don't get me wrong, I love how we are in bed together, it's truly wonderful. But it's not enough. I can't build a relationship on sex, Luke. There has to be more than that."

His heart felt like a chunk of ice. The lake used to freeze solid every winter, he remembered absently, that's when he'd learned how to skate. He said flatly, "You've ruined everything."

"Don't say that!"

"I don't know how to love. And I don't want to learn. Not with you. Not with anyone. It's too late."

She said with passionate conviction, "It's never too late to learn how to love someone. Never."

"Then sooner or later you'll learn to love someone else, won't you?" he blazed. "Because I'm not available. Will you get that through your head?"

"I don't want someone else. I want you."

"Then you're a fool," Luke grated, too angry to care what he said. "I've had enough of this. As far as I'm concerned, you've forfeited your other three days—I want to go straight back to the airport. You can come back to San Francisco with me or not, as you please. If you do, I'll be faithful to you and I'll put you through law school. But I won't fall in love with you and I won't marry you.''

''And you won't take me on business trips, don't forget that,'' she flared. ''Let's go—we can't get to the airport soon enough for me.''

She marched ahead of him down the dirt road, her hips swinging in her cotton trousers, one hand slapping at a mosquito on the back of her neck. Luke took off after her, swung her around, planted a furious kiss on her parted lips, and snarled, ''I'm doing the driving. I've had enough surprises for one day.''

''You can do what you damn well please!''

Her eyes were as turbulent as an ocean storm; she looked so beautiful that he had to bite back the one question he refused to ask. Whether she was coming back to San Francisco with him or not.

If she was in love with him, it would be better if she didn't. He said furiously, ''I'll tell you one thing—you don't look like you're in love with me. You look like you hate my guts.''

''How would you know what love looks like?''

How indeed? ''Give me the keys to the wagon,'' he ordered. She hauled them out of her pocket, dropped them on his palm without touching him, and kept on walking.

He didn't want to look at the houses, or the pale beauty of the evening sky. He certainly didn't want to look at Katrin. Never so glad in his life to get behind the wheel of a vehicle, Luke snapped his seat belt and took off in a spurt of gravel.

Two hours later, during which neither he nor Katrin had said a single word to each other, they arrived at the airport. Katrin said with icy precision, ''You can stop at the arrivals area. I'm staying here.''

In his heart Luke had known that would be her decision. But not for the richest gold mine in the world would he tell her how it stabbed him to the core, cutting through anger as though it were water. "Fine," he said.

He skirted the brick buildings, pulling up outside the international entrance. Flicking the button for the trunk, so he could get out his bag, he left the engine running. "Goodbye, Katrin," he said.

What else could he add? That said it all.

She blurted, "If you change your mind, will you get in touch with me?"

His jaw tightened. "Don't hold your breath."

"In the long run, you're the loser here."

"That's only your opinion," he said and got out of the wagon. He took his duffel bag from the trunk, slammed it shut and walked through the glass doors without a second look. Only when he got to the counter did he glance back. The wagon was gone.

Katrin was gone. Katrin, who was in love with him.

When Luke got home the next day, he went through his house from top to bottom, getting rid of every trace of Katrin's presence. Her clothes, including the feathered dress, he packed in a box to send to her, along with her cosmetics, and a couple of books she'd bought. His face set, he took the black satin sheets off the bed, tossing them in the box, too. He hung fresh towels in the bathroom, putting the ones she'd used into the washer. Finally he cleaned out the food she'd left in the refrigerator, and threw the drooping red roses and the candle stubs into the garbage as well.

If only he could exorcise her from his head as easily.

He kept expecting her to come running down the stairs, smiling at him with that warmth that he now knew sprang from loving him. If only she hadn't been so stupid as to fall in love. If only they could have gone on as they were…

Swearing under his breath, Luke taped up the box and

addressed it to her in Askja. He hadn't put a note inside. What was there to say?

They'd both said too much. Words that couldn't be taken back.

It was a relief to leave the box at the post office the next morning on his way to work; and even more of a relief to go back to the office, where immediately he was submerged in the innumerable details of his various projects. If any of his staff wondered why he'd come back from vacation early, one look at his face would have discouraged them from asking.

He looked awful.

It was a case of too much emotion and a sleepless night. He'd get over it.

But a week later Luke looked worse, with his eyes dark-shadowed and new lines around his mouth. Nor had his sleep patterns improved. No matter how much he told himself it was only sexual deprivation, he was still haunted by dreams: erotic dreams and dreams of loss that figured a woman with blond hair smooth as a river. Equally bad were nightmares about his father, suffused with the same leaden and unredeemable regret.

In the bright sun or beneath the white clouds of a San Francisco September day, Luke could persuade himself these were only dreams; but at night he couldn't as easily shake them off.

He hadn't gotten in touch with Ramon, still bothered by a sense of betrayal. When Ramon phoned him at work exactly eight days after his return, and suggested lunch, Luke agreed with an inner reluctance he did his best to conceal. They met in their favorite Thai restaurant, ordering curried *mat saman* and beer. Ramon raised his glass. "I've been meaning to call you for several days, Luke. But a new case took over and there's been no time." He took a long gulp. "I need to say this to you face-to-face—I told Katrin nothing but the name Teal Lake and the fact that you and I had had boyhoods that were far from ideal.''

"You sure get right to the point.''

"You're my friend.'' Ramon shrugged. "And life is short. Too short for misunderstandings. A couple of weeks ago she phoned me at work and asked if we could meet for lunch. It was then that she asked me if I knew anything about your childhood. I could have told her nothing. I weighed that against the way your tennis has gone downhill, and decided to tell her the absolute minimum. But by the look of you, I shouldn't have.''

"We went to Teal Lake,'' Luke said. "She and I. It was a disaster. I haven't seen her since, nor will I.''

Ramon raised his brow. "I repeat…life is short, too short for misunderstandings.''

"She says she's in love with me. I can't handle that. So I backed off. That's not what I'd call a misunderstanding.''

The waiter put spring rolls and peanut sauce in front of them. Thoughtfully Ramon began to eat. "The price of gold and precious metals is down. Is that why you look like a whipped cur?''

"What other reason?''

"Rosita wants you to come to the house tonight,'' Ramon added casually. "She's making tamales.''

Three or four times Luke had eaten Rosita's fiery and delicious Mexican food. "You know I can't turn that invitation down.''

"Good. Six o'clock? You know the way.'' Ramon then began to discuss an interesting new development in lie detection. To Luke's relief, Teal Lake wasn't mentioned again.

Promptly at six, Luke presented himself at Ramon and Rosita's Victorian house on the western edge of the Mission District, a vibrantly Hispanic area of the city. He'd always enjoyed his visits here, entering the alien world of a close-knit family, then returning to his house afterward with secret pleasure that it was so quiet and peaceful. Rosita opened the door with a welcoming smile. "Come in, Luke."

She was tall, her jet-black hair a tumble of curls around a face as beautiful and full of character in its own way as Katrin's was. As he passed her a bottle of red wine from his cellars, she said, "*Gracias*... we're eating right away, the children have to go to bed early as it's a school night."

She led him into the kitchen, with its terra-cotta tiles. Copper pans and bunched herbs hung from the beamed ceiling. The oak table in the alcove was set with Mexican woven mats; the shutters were closed, giving an artificial dimness. Felipe, who was seven, was lighting tall white tapers with an air of intense concentration; Constancia, a year younger, was arranging some rather tattered daisies as a centerpiece. Maria, aged three, ran over to Luke, grabbed him around the knees, and crowed, "Lift me, lift me."

They'd played this game before, although the last time was probably three months ago. Touched that she'd remembered, Luke swung her chubby little body high over his head, almost to the oak beams. Then he swooped her down again. She shrieked with delight. "More, more!"

Her weight, her gleeful chortle and unselfconscious delight filled Luke with a sudden, devastating poignancy. He'd always closed himself off from the possibility of having children of his own; it wasn't in the cards. But tonight, Katrin's absence was like an open wound and he was achingly aware of another lack: that no child of his would ever run to him, trustingly, like Maria.

His child and Katrin's?

"Do it again!" Maria shrieked.

With a start, Luke came back to the present. Was he seriously contemplating fatherhood? Which, in his books, would require marriage as the prerequisite. He gave his head a stunned shake, quite unaware that Ramon was watching him from the corner of the room, looking rather pleased with himself.

After one last swoop through the air, Luke put Maria down on the tiled floor. Shy Constancia favored Luke with her grave smile. Felipe, whose present ambition was to be a racing driver, asked about his sports car. Ramon, in a T-shirt and jeans, poured the wine, and Rosita brought the food to the table.

The untidy, laughter-filled kitchen was like a haven, thought Luke. Katrin would like the Torres family. He pushed this insight away as Felipe said grace in Spanish and they all began to eat, the candles illuminating the circle of faces. Luke ate too much, the wine slipping down easily; afterward, he and Ramon cleaned up the dishes while Rosita got the children ready for bed. As he always did, Luke read all three children a story, then said good night to them.

As he softly closed Felipe's door, Luke was visited again by that disturbing sense of poignancy. He'd always assumed that because of his upbringing, he'd make a lousy father. After all, what kind of a model had he had? But maybe he'd underestimated himself. Maybe he'd be okay.

A daughter or a son of his own. Would they be dark-haired like himself? Or blond and blue-eyed like Katrin?

*I never want children.* That's what he'd told her. Children or marriage or commitment. And so he'd driven her away.

He needed three hard sets of tennis. That's what he needed. Kids and marriage and love…what did he know about all that?

Rosita left for a class she was taking at the art school; Ramon poured glasses of tequila and the two men watched part of a basketball game on TV. Luke could see Ramon was tired; about nine, he stood up. "I'm off. Thanks so much, Ramon."

Ramon stood up, too. "A word, Luke," he said with an odd formality, "before you go. Over the years, we have never talked about the things that happened to us as little boys. Young like Felipe. But this evening I need to speak about it."

"Not on my account, you don't."

"Yes," Ramon said, "on your account. Our friendship is too important for me to stay silent."

Luke tugged at the neck of his sweater. "I don't need any lectures, Ramon, no matter how well-meant. I'm doing fine."

Ramon said curtly, "Shut up, *amigo,* and listen."

Ramon had never used that tone of voice to Luke before; not for the first time, Luke understood how the other man had risen from a rookie on the beat to his present position. He, Luke, could have responded in kind—he was no slouch in that department himself—but he realized he was curious to hear what Ramon had to say. "Okay," he said, "I'll shut up."

"At Felipe's age," Ramon began, "I was just one more street kid in Mexico City. Scavenging for food, staying one step ahead of the law." For a moment he was silent, his dark eyes lost in the past. Then he picked up the thread again. "I had *machismo.* I knew how to steal and shoplift, how to wire cars and pick locks…and I never got caught. Just as well, or I wouldn't have made it into the police force. I am a good policeman. I know the other side, you see." Ramon grinned. "When I was eighteen, I met Rosita. I wanted her, *Dios,* how I wanted her. But she told me I had to go straight, get a job…and then, maybe, she would let me into her bed."

Forgetting his ill-temper, Luke said intuitively, "I bet you ran away as if the devil was at your heels."

Ramon chuckled. "For ten months, I stayed away. But she was my fate, Luke, my destiny. So I got a job at the fish market, I went to night school, and the rest is history."

"Are you trying to tell me Katrin's my fate?" Luke said quizzically.

"I'm telling you she's a remarkable woman. I saw her under the worst of circumstances, so I know. And you are a good man. Don't run away from her as I did from Rosita. Marry her, have children, fill that empty house on the hill with love…if I can do it, so can you. And now I'm going to end this so solemn sermon, and I will never mention my childhood again."

He clapped Luke on the shoulder, and said good night. Luke drove home. On his way upstairs he went into the kitchen to put a couple of tamales Rosita had given him into the refrigerator. The kitchen was clean, sterile, and silent as the grave. Is that what he wanted for the rest of his life? To be half alive?

He walked upstairs, in no hurry to get to his empty bedroom. He and Ramon had been friends for many years; for the first time ever, Luke found himself envying Ramon the laughter, intimacy and tangible love that had filled every corner of the old Victorian house. Ramon would never make a fortune, as Luke had. But maybe Ramon had something far more precious, that money couldn't buy. A wife who adored him. Children who loved him.

And Ramon in turn adored Rosita, loved his children, would protect them with his last breath.

Just as Luke had wanted to protect Katrin.

He sank down on the bed, gazing at the patch of carpet where Katrin's feathered dress had fallen in a crumpled heap. He couldn't live with her. He couldn't live without her.

Classic.

What was he going to do?

He could pick up the phone. Speak to her. Tell her he missed her. That he was no longer self-sufficient. That his whole life was out of whack and only she could fix it.

This was nothing to do with love. But maybe it was a start.

# CHAPTER SIXTEEN

BEFORE he could change his mind, Luke reached for the telephone, absently noticing that the red message signal was flashing. It wouldn't be Katrin; she was too proud to get in touch with him after he'd made it so abundantly clear he didn't want anything to do with her unless it was on his terms. He dialed her number quickly, waiting for her to answer, his heart racing.

It rang four times. Then her voice, calm and impersonal, told him he could leave a message at the sound of the beep and she'd get back to him as soon as possible.

She wasn't home.

He had no idea where she was. But surely she hadn't left Askja permanently; the phone would be disconnected if she had.

He put the receiver down without leaving a message. Aware of a crushing disappointment, he rested his head in his hands. What had he expected? That the moment he phoned her, she'd be there waiting for him?

How arrogant was that?

Desperate for something to do, Luke entered the password to his voice mail. A woman's voice started speaking. "This is Anna Bendickt, from Askja...we met briefly at Margret's tearoom, I'm Lara and Tomas's mother... I have some bad news. Katrin is very ill...she doesn't know I'm phoning you. She's in hospital in Winnipeg with pneumonia, she had an accident in her daysailer. If you want more information, you can phone me." She then gave the name of the hospital, and her own phone number. Her voice, Luke noticed, wasn't overly friendly. But why would it be?

After the second attempt, he managed to put the receiver back in its cradle. His hands were shaking as if he had a tremor. Katrin was ill. So ill that Anna, who must thoroughly dislike him for the way he'd treated Katrin, had been impelled to call him.

He had to see Katrin. Luke gripped his knees hard, trying to still his trembling fingers. If he'd needed proof that she meant something to him, something of deep significance, he now had it. But was the terror he was feeling a measure of love?

He didn't know what love was.

What if he lost Katrin before he had the chance to tell her how important she was to him? To apologize for being such a stubborn fool?

What if he was too late?

Think, Luke. Think.

His company jet, which had been in east Africa when he and Katrin had flown to Manitoba, was now here, at the airport. Swiftly he phoned the pilot and made the necessary arrangements. Then he phoned the hospital, and after a series of delays, spoke to the floor supervisor for respiratory diseases. "My name's Luke MacRae," he said, "I'm calling from San Francisco. I'm a good friend of Katrin Sigurdson's, I only just found out she's ill."

"Her condition is quite serious, Mr. MacRae...to put it bluntly, she's not putting up much of a fight." The supervisor gave a few details, then added, "If you can do anything to improve matters, I'd suggest you come very soon."

"I will," Luke said hoarsely. "I'll get there as quickly as I can. Thank you."

Nothing his father had ever done had induced in him such dread as he was feeling now. He threw a few clothes into an overnight bag, left a message at the office, and ran downstairs to the garage. His whole body was focussed on one thing and one thing only: to see Katrin. To instill in her the will to fight.

She loved him. He'd turned her away. Was that why she lacked the will to live?

Was love that powerful?

It was still dark when Luke got to the hospital. The taxi dropped him at the front door. He hurried inside, was given directions to the floor he needed and took the elevator. It moved with agonizing slowness.

Once the jet had taken off from the Winnipeg airport, Luke had spoken to Anna. Katrin, so Anna had said, had overturned the daysailer, fallen into the cold waters of the lake, and within a few days had succumbed to a bronchial infection that turned into full-blown pneumonia. Anna herself had been at the hospital, but had had to return home because her elderly mother had come down with the flu. At the end of the conversation, Luke had said awkwardly, "Thank you for letting me know, Anna."

"I'm glad you'll be with her," Anna said stiffly. "If— when she regains consciousness, give her my love."

"When. Not if," Luke said forcibly. "And, yes, I will."

He'd also phoned the hospital, to be told Katrin was no better and no worse.

The elevator doors slid open with a metallic sigh. Luke marched to the desk, and was directed to Katrin's room. A nurse was sitting quietly by the bed. But Luke's eyes went straight to the woman in the bed.

Beneath a crisp white coverlet, Katrin was lying very still, except for the labored exhalations of her breathing. Intravenous tubes were delivering saline and antibiotics through her left arm. Her cheeks were flushed, and when he reached out his hand and rested it on her forehead, it was burningly hot. Her hair was damp with sweat.

Luke pulled up a chair and sat down. He clasped her

hand in his, gently stroking her palm; it had been a private signal of theirs, an acknowledgment of the physical closeness they'd so often shared.

Pain clenched his heart. Forgetting the nurse's presence almost immediately, he focused his whole being on Katrin, bringing all his willpower to bear on her. Very softly he said, "Katrin, it's Luke. I'm here, with you. I should never have left you, I'm more sorry than I can say for doing that to you. But I'm here, right now, and I'm not going away until your fever's gone and you're over the worst. You're going to get better, Katrin, of course you are…your whole life is ahead of you."

He talked on and on, telling her about his evening with Ramon and Rosita, describing what Ramon had said; and finding in the darkness the courage to express how he valued this friendship between two strong-minded men. He told her about Felipe, Constancia and Maria; he described Rosita's fiery temperament and equally inflammatory enchiladas. And from there, he started to talk more fully about his childhood years with all their loneliness and fear.

But there had been more to Teal Lake than unhappiness, and Luke told her about that, too. The eagles that had arrived every September; the moose and deer in the woods, the shy black bears, and the mountain lion he had once sighted on a granite outcrop. Wild blueberries and raspberries, spruce gum, drinking from the clear streams of the backwoods, he described them all.

The nurses changed shifts. Someone brought him some very strong tea and a sugared doughnut. His cell phone rang twice, both times from the office with news of two crises, one in central Africa, the other in Malaysia. And still Luke talked.

Katrin was moving restlessly in the bed now, her cheeks hectically flushed. A doctor arrived, made noncommittal noises, and left. Intuitively Luke knew the medical staff was doing all that could be done; it was up to Katrin now.

It was up to him.

He got up from the chair for a few minutes, splashed cold water on his face in the bathroom, and stretched. Then he sat down again, taking both her hands in his, resting his cheek against her smooth skin. "Katrin," he whispered, "you must get well. I need you."

For the second time since he'd met her, tears stung his eyes. "I need you," he repeated. And then Luke heard himself say the words he'd never believed he'd say to any woman. "I love you, Katrin."

The words replayed in his mind, such simple words with such enormous portent. Then his heart leaped in his chest. Had her fingers moved ever so slightly? Or had he imagined it? Imagined it because he so desperately needed a sign of hope, a signal that at some level she was hearing him?

He raised his head, saying more strongly, "Katrin, I love you. I'm sorry it's taken me this long to figure it out, more sorry than I can say. But it's true…I love you. I want you, I need you, you must get well so we can be together."

In his pocket, his cell phone rang. He shut it off impatiently, all his attention on the woman lying in the bed. The woman he loved with all his heart.

Briefly he dropped his forehead to her hands again, his whole body suffused with this new knowledge, so inescapable, so full of the unknown. What would it mean to him? How could he possibly guess? She had to get better, so he could find out what it was like to love a woman. A woman who loved him back.

Perhaps, he thought humbly, he was about to embark on the greatest adventure of his life.

Again Luke focussed every ounce of his energy on Katrin and her struggle for life, willing her to feel his presence through the fever that claimed her. The seconds turned to minutes, to an hour. Then the doctor returned, asked Luke to leave the room, and within a few minutes came back out. "Well," he said, "I don't know what you did, but she's over the hump…the fever's broken. She should regain consciousness within the next few hours. Good work."

He ambled off, an older man who looked as though, like Luke, he'd been up all night. Leaning against the wall, Luke watched him go. Katrin was going to recover. That's what he'd said. She was going to be all right.

Luke sagged against the pale green paint, aware of a deep exhaustion in every fiber of his body. He'd never wanted anything—money, power, prestige—as much as he wanted Katrin to get well. Nor ever would.

He'd crossed a watershed in the last few hours. And there was no going back.

Pushing himself away from the wall, he went back in the room. The nurse smiled at him. "I'll be leaving now that she's over the worst." She patted him on the sleeve. "Very good news."

"Yes," Luke said blankly, "it is. Thanks for everything you've done."

"I think you did more than I did," said the nurse, and left the room.

Luke sank down on the chair, not sure he had the energy to stand up. Katrin looked different, he gradually realized. Her cheeks were a softer pink, her breathing less labored. The doctor was right: she was going to recover.

For a long time Luke simply sat there, allowing simple gratitude to work its way through his tired mind. Eventually he reached in his pocket for the mints he kept there, knowing he should go to the cafeteria and eat something more substantial, yet reluctant to leave her. His hand bumped against his cell phone. When he turned it back on, it started to flash imperiously.

The crises, he learned as he listened to the messages from two of his senior assistants, had worsened. There was a strike in the mine in central Africa, and much worse, a serious accident in his new mine in Malaysia. Several miners were trapped, some feared dead.

Ever since the mining accident in Teal Lake that had killed eleven men the summer Luke was six, he'd had a dread of such occurrences; and, as an adult, a lasting sense of responsibility toward them. He should be there, he thought, on site. Making sure that everything that humanly could be done was being done.

But that meant he'd have to leave Katrin before she regained consciousness. Leave her without telling her to her face that he loved her.

He walked out of the room again, spoke to both his assistants, and then to the pilot at the Winnipeg airport. He delegated the strike, but he had to go to Malaysia himself. He'd always put the safety and well-being of his miners before profits, a stance that had sometimes gotten him in trouble with his stockholders. He couldn't change that now. Honor was a very old-fashioned concept. But his honor was at stake here.

He could explain to Katrin. Surely, when she heard about the underground explosion and the trapped miners, she'd understand.

Quickly he scribbled a note to her, explaining what was going on. But then his pen stopped, digging into the paper. He could sign it *love, Luke*. Or he could just sign it *Luke*.

*Luke,* he wrote, and tore the paper from the pad. He wanted to say that word to her first, rather than write it. It was too basic to be scrawled on a scrap of paper and left at her bedside.

Back in the room, he put the note prominently on the

stand that held her personal effects; he'd tell the nurses it was there, to make sure she got it. Then he leaned over, kissed Katrin's blessedly cool cheek and said softly, "I'll be back. I love you, Katrin. More than I can say."

An hour later he was on his way to Malaysia.

The next day, from halfway around the world, Luke managed to speak to Katrin. She sounded very tired; she also sounded more distant than the miles between them warranted. He said clumsily, "Did you get my note?"

"Yes, I did."

"It's a waiting game here, Katrin. They're tunneling through solid rock to get to the trapped men, I don't feel I can leave until we know more."

"Of course not."

"You do understand?"

"Oh, yes," she said, an indecipherable note in her voice.

"How are you feeling?"

"I'm as weak as a newborn kitten. Otherwise fine. They're saying I can go home tomorrow."

"Already?"

"They need the bed for someone sicker than me."

"Katrin, I—" Luke broke off. The words that had come so easily to his lips when she was lying there unconscious were now lodged somewhere in his larynx. Stuck like a fishbone.

*I love you.* Why couldn't he say it? What kind of a man was he? It wasn't that he no longer felt it, that wasn't the issue. He longed to be with her, to touch her, hold her, pour out everything that was in his heart.

That was it. He needed to be face-to-face with her in order to say those three small, so important words. "Will Anna be able to look in on you when you're back home?" he asked.

"I'm sure she will. Her mother's feeling better already."

"I wish to God I was there," he exploded.

The line crackled. Katrin said nothing. Cursing himself for being so inept, Luke retreated to familiar territory, describing the situation at the pithead more fully. Then he said with sudden urgency, "I've got to go, the foreman's signaling. Bye, Katrin, I'll call you tomorrow."

"I could be in transit tomorrow," she said with that same daunting politeness. "Goodbye, Luke."

The connection was broken. Luke shoved the phone in his pocket. Everything would be all right once he saw her.

He'd waited thirty-four years to say I love you. Another week wasn't going to make any difference.

# CHAPTER SEVENTEEN

JUST over a week later Luke was on his way back to Winnipeg. They'd been able to rescue all but five of the miners. He'd stayed for the funerals, and to ensure that everything possible would be done for the families of the dead men. He hadn't talked to Katrin for the last three days; she hadn't been home and hadn't responded to any of his messages.

He was desperate to see her.

Why hadn't she gotten in touch with him?

He showered on the jet, changed into clean clothes and decided that the bush gear he'd been wearing for what felt like the whole time should probably be incinerated. He then shaved, avoiding the ugly gash in his cheek that he'd gotten at the mine face. After he'd eaten, he tried very hard to catch up on some sleep; but he was too wired to sleep. Until he was holding Katrin in his arms, he couldn't relax or sleep. It was that simple.

Or that complicated.

The flight seemed to take forever. But finally, after three stopovers for refueling and customs, Luke was running down the steps toward the car waiting for him on the tarmac. He got in, consulted the map briefly, and headed north out of the city. He'd tried to reach Anna, when he'd been unsuccessful in talking to Katrin, but with no better luck.

He could be on a wild-goose chase. Maybe Katrin was no longer in Askja.

He should have told her on the phone that he loved her, should have forgotten all his scruples about being face-to-face with her. As far as she knew, he was still totally averse to falling in love, or to commitment of any kind.

He'd been a stupid jerk.

If she wasn't in Askja, he thought grimly, he'd follow her to the ends of the earth. Because that, so he was learning, was what love was all about.

When Luke reached the little village, he went first to Katrin's house. But when he banged on the side door and then rang the front doorbell, there was no response. Her car wasn't parked in the driveway or in the run-down garage. Anxiety thrumming along his nerves, he drove to the resort. Katrin's car wasn't in the staff parking lot, either. He then traveled the length of the village to Anna's house.

Anna was out in the garden, wearing a jacket against the cool knife of wind from the lake. Luke got out of the car and walked toward her. She watched him, unsmiling, her garden gloves caked with dirt. "Anna," he said, "I know I've been behaving like a prize idiot. But if I can, I've come here to make amends. Katrin's car's gone. Do you know where she is?"

"She's gone camping."

"Where? Do you know?"

"After today, are you going to get in your car and drive away again?" Anna demanded. "Leaving her alone?"

"I want to marry her," Luke said.

Of course he did. That's why he'd come all this way.

"Oh." Anna's smile was quick and generous. "Well, then. She's gone north of here. If you have a map, I can show you."

She stripped off her muddy gloves, and traced the route Luke should take. "I didn't want her to go. The nights are cold, and she's still not quite back to normal. But you know Katrin, she can be very stubborn."

"Like me," Luke said wryly, folding the map so he could see the relevant section of the lakeshore. He then added with awkward sincerity, "Thank you, Anna. If Katrin will have me, I swear I'll do my best to make her happy."

"Start by persuading her to give up this camping foolishness. Or," Anna's smile was demure, "find a way of keeping her warm."

Abruptly realizing that he liked Anna very much, Luke laughed. "I'll see what I can do. Wish me luck."

He then got in his car and drove north. The highway followed the shoreline, the lake sometimes hidden by trees, at other times stretching to the horizon with the dull gleam of pewter. It was going to be dark by the time he got there; he only hoped he could locate Katrin's campsite.

He finally arrived at the little provincial park whose name Anna had given him. There was a map of all the campsites at the kiosk; but because it was late in the season, the kiosk was empty. A hand-printed sign asked him to choose his own campsite and pay in the morning.

Luke took a copy of the map and started driving along the narrow dirt road. Most of the sites were empty, although there were a few trailers lined up to one side. He followed the curve of the road, passed several empty sites, then saw Katrin's car parked at the most secluded end of the campground. He parked in the next site, got out and locked his car. Doing up his jacket, he started down the little slope that led to the lake.

He halted briefly. Tucked in a small hollow, sheltered from the wind, was a green dome tent. He called Katrin's name softly, not wanting to scare her, and walked up to it. It was then that he saw, down by the lakeshore, the flicker of flames. His shoes slipping on the pine needles, he walked closer, stopping so that he was partly hidden by the trunk of a tall pine.

Overhead the needled boughs of the pine and the golden leaves of poplars rustled secretively. Waves lapped on the stones. From deeper in the forest an owl hooted, rhythmically and repetitively. Then the hair rose on the back of Luke's neck. Far across the lake a wolf howled, the prolonged and infinitely lonely voice of the wilderness.

Katrin was sitting on a boulder by the fire, her back to the lake. She was feeding twigs to the flames. She looked very unhappy. But more than unhappy, Luke decided slowly. The slump of her shoulders, the downward curve of her lips spoke of defeat.

Defeated? His strong and courageous Katrin?

Even as he watched, she stood up, turning to face the water. She was wearing a dark red fleece jacket, hiking boots on her feet, her hair in a thick braid down her back. She leaned against the trunk of a poplar, then suddenly bowed her head as though she were crying.

She never cried.

He couldn't stand seeing her like this, so isolated and unhappy. Luke shuffled his feet in the underbrush, dislodging some rocks that skittered down the slope, and called out her name.

She whirled, staring upward beyond the circle of flame into the darkness. Swiping at her cheeks, she said sharply, "Who's there?"

"It's me. Luke," he said, and loped down the slope toward her. "I'm sorry, I didn't mean to frighten you."

"I'm not frightened," she said, standing very straight. "How did you find me here?"

"Anna told me where you were."

"Some friend she is," Katrin said bitterly. "Why don't you turn right around and go back where you came from, Luke MacRae? After all, that's what you do best."

"I know you must think that. But—"

"I can't bear you wandering in and out of my life like this!" she flared. "You were at the hospital, I know you were. But did you hang around long enough to talk to me once I'd regained consciousness? Oh no, you took off again. Because someone called you from work. After all, compared to a Malaysian mine, who am I? You know where your priorities are, and they sure don't have my name on them. It's not good enough, Luke, I won't put myself through this over and over again. I won't, do you hear me?''

''That's all changed—''

He might just as well not have spoken. Her words tumbling over one another, she went on, ''You don't know how often I've regretted telling you I loved you. I've made some big mistakes in my life, Donald being one of them. But saying I'd fallen for you was even stupider than marrying Donald—it was a licence for you to walk all over me.''

Stung, Luke said, ''I've never walked all over you!''

''Great-aunt Gudrun brought me up to believe in honesty. Well, Great-aunt Gudrun was wrong. There are times when saying what's on your mind is a shortcut to disaster.''

Luke clenched his fists at his side. ''Have you changed your mind?'' he croaked. ''Don't you love me anymore?''

''That's none of your business!''

Desperate to know the answer, Luke stepped out of the shadows and into the open, his face illumined by the orange glow of the flames. In a shocked voice Katrin said, ''What happened to your face?''

He put a hand up to the scrape on his cheek; the bruise underlying it was now an ugly purple-yellow. ''It's nothing.''

''What happened? Tell me.''

''I went down in the mine with the rescue team,'' Luke said impatiently. ''I always do. There was a minor rockslide, that's when I got hit. But we all got out with no trouble, and the next day they were able to break through and rescue the miners who were still alive.''

''You could have been killed,'' she whispered.

"Well, I wasn't." Now that he'd started, he seemed unable to stop. "When I was six, there was an accident in the mine at Teal Lake, before it was unionized or there were proper safety measures. I've never forgotten it—my dad's drinking got worse after that, and why not? So I feel responsible if ever there are accidents in the mines that I own. A few of the guys at the conferences laugh at me for that. But they're laughing at the wrong man."

"In so many ways, Teal Lake has made you what you are," Katrin said slowly. "For better and for worse."

"I went to the hospital the minute I heard you were ill," Luke said violently. "I stayed the rest of the night and into the next day, until your fever broke and the doctors said you were going to be okay. I got the message about the mine explosion shortly after I got to the hospital. But I ignored it, Katrin. Until you were out of danger, I put you first. You're the only woman I've ever done that for."

"I knew you were there," she said. "Don't ask me how I knew, when I wasn't even conscious. But I knew. When I came to and you were gone... I was so bitterly disappointed, it was terrible. Oh, Luke, I know I blew it taking you to Teal Lake. But what else was I to do? How else could I have broken through to you?"

"I don't know what else you could have done."

Her smile was wobbly. "That's a huge admission."

"Yeah...but I'd never told anyone about all the stuff that went on there. About my mother, my father and his drinking, my loneliness and isolation. Afterward, I felt naked. Stripped. Flayed. I couldn't bear to be around you. So I took off faster than a bat out of hell. And for that I'm sorry."

"And then you took off again, from the hospital. You can't keep doing this to me."

The strain in her voice hurt him deep inside, in a place he'd always kept separate. "But I've changed," he said roughly. "I've realized something. Something that's been staring me in the face for days. For weeks." Hadn't he come here just to tell her these three small words? And now that the moment had arrived, Luke found it unexpectedly easy. "I love you," he said. "Katrin, I love you."

The owl hooted again, closer this time. Katrin thrust her hands in her pockets. "You said you didn't know how to love anyone. And you weren't interested in learning."

"I said a lot that day at Teal Lake that I regret."

"I won't settle for being on the sidelines of your life. Someone you turn on and off, as it suits you. I want the whole man."

His nails digging into his palms, Luke asked the crucial question. "Do you still love me? Or have I destroyed that, too? Because I'm the one who's responsible for you ending up in hospital."

"You weren't responsible for me falling into the lake," she said roundly. "There was a freak storm, no one predicted it. But at the hospital... I was just so tired, I didn't have the energy to fight. Yet once you arrived, I somehow knew you were there, holding my hand, talking to me. So you saved my life, Luke. That's what you did."

"I talked more that night than the rest of my life put together. I told you everything I could think of about Teal Lake. Then I talked about Ramon and his wife and kids. At the end, I even told you I loved you." His voice roughened. "But when we talked on the phone the next day—I couldn't get the words out. I knew I had to be face-to-face with you. Because they're the three most important words in the world."

She bit her lip. "For me they are."

"Katrin, I have to know—do you still love me?"

Her eyes were dark pools, black as the night. A waft of smoke blew across her face, as at her feet a pile of twigs collapsed in a crackle of orange and red. She said quietly,

"Love can't be destroyed so easily…yes, I love you, Luke. I always will."

He let out his breath in a long sigh. "I don't know the first thing about love," he said. "But I can learn. You could teach me. Because there's one more thing I haven't said. The most important of all. I want you to marry me, Katrin. Be my wife."

"You *do?*"

"I want the whole deal," Luke said, his eyes intent on her face. "A proper wedding, you always by my side. Living with me, traveling with me, being with me. Day and night."

"Oh, Luke," she said unsteadily, "when you do something, you do it wholeheartedly."

He closed the distance between them, putting his arms around her waist and pulling her to the length of his body. "Marry me? Because I love you more than I can say."

Her smile glimmered amidst the sheen of tears in her eyes. "One condition," she said.

He grinned. "Conditions, huh? I've already told you you're more important that fifty mines."

"Your house," she said. "You've got to sell it—I don't want to live in a concrete box."

He threw back his head and laughed. "We'll live wherever you like, my darling."

"You've never called me that before," she said shakily.

"Dearest, darling and most adorable Katrin, I love you," Luke said. "The house'll be on the market quicker than you spilled brandy on Guy Wharton."

Her smile suddenly vanished; unconsciously she drew back. "There's something else, Luke," she said. "Something far more important than a house. You said at Teal Lake that you didn't want children. Donald never wanted me to have a baby, either. But I want children. I always have."

He laced his fingers behind her back. "Maria, Ramon's youngest, took a shine to me as soon as she was old enough to smile. The last—"

"I can't imagine why," Katrin said.

"Stop interrupting. The last time I was there, I was lifting her high in the air and she was laughing fit to beat the band, and something shifted inside me. I realized I wanted to have children. But not just any children. Your children, Katrin. That if I never did that, I'd be a poor man for the rest of my days."

"If we have a little girl," Katrin said, her smile dazzling, "we could call her Maria."

"There's one slight hitch," Luke replied. "Here we are planning the kids' names, and you haven't actually said in so many words that you'll marry me."

"Serious oversight." She took his face in her palms, her features suffused with such tenderness that Luke felt his throat close. "Yes, Luke, I'll marry you. Because I love you with all my heart."

"I swear I'll never shut myself off from you again. Or leave you the way I did in Teal Lake."

"I believe you."

It was a vow, he thought, every bit as serious as the vows of marriage. Needing to lighten the atmosphere, he said, "I think we should dump some water on this fire, then go up to the tent and make love. Maybe I won't really believe any of this is real until I hold you in my arms. Besides, it's making love that makes babies, dearest Katrin. Or so I've been told."

"Great-aunt Gudrun said it was. And I never knew her to lie."

"Although if you've only got one sleeping bag, making love might be difficult."

She grabbed the pot of water that was sitting in the bushes, and threw its contents on the fire. The coals hissed, sending up a small cloud of ashes and smoke. "I also have two extra blankets. We can spread those under us, and use the sleeping bag on top."

"That's what I like. A resourceful woman."

"I aim to please," she said.

She led the way up the slope to the tent, where she crouched to unlace her hiking boots. Luke took off his shoes, crawling inside the tent behind her. She spread the blankets out while he unzippered her down bag. "It's cold," he said, tossing his jacket to one side and hauling off his shirt.

She gazed at his bare chest. "You mean I've got to take off all my clothes? I'm not sure Great-aunt Gudrun told me about that."

"Your courage is another quality I admire," Luke teased. "And I promise I'll keep you warm."

"I'll hold you to that," she said darkly, and pulled the fleece jacket over her head. Luke leaned forward, his fingers brushing her breasts as he unbuttoned her shirt. He wanted her so badly that he ached with need; as his eyes adjusted to the darkness, he saw the matching intensity in her face.

He stripped off the rest of his clothes, and drew her under the covers, her breasts soft and yielding against his chest. "Make love to me, Katrin," he said huskily. "Warm me, body and soul."

So she did. And afterward, as they lay naked in each other's arms, Luke knew himself to be the richest man in the world.

# HER TYCOON
# PROTECTOR

BY
AMANDA BROWNING

**Amanda Browning** still lives in the Essex house where she was born. The third of four children – her sister being her twin – she enjoyed the rough and tumble of life with two brothers as much as she did reading books. Writing came naturally as an outlet for her fertile imagination. The love of books led her to a career in libraries and being single allowed her to take a leap into writing for a living. Success is still something of a wonder, but allows her to indulge in hobbies as varied as embroidery and bird-watching.

# CHAPTER ONE

SHELBY GREER paced angrily across the carpet. She looked wildly dramatic in her electric-blue suit, with her shoulder-length auburn hair bouncing at every long-legged stride. She had been blessed with a classically oval face and fine features that would be considered beautiful by any standards, but right now her ice-green eyes, with their thick long lashes, were flashing sparks. She was fuming. A volatile volcano just waiting to explode. Abruptly she turned to face the man who stood before the elegant Adam fireplace.

'No! Absolutely not! There's no way I'm going to have my world turned upside down—not in a million years. I'm not giving up my independence on the basis of a threat that might not be real,' she declared vehemently in response to his proposal.

'Now, Shelby, be reasonable,' her father pleaded with her. 'If you won't come and stay here where I can look after you, then you have to have a bodyguard.'

'No, I most certainly do not!' Shelby disagreed instantly. 'I'm perfectly capable of looking after myself. If you think for one second that I would allow a complete stranger to enter my home and invade my privacy, you're crazy.' The mere thought of it made her shudder with distaste.

'If it's crazy to care what happens to you, then I'm guilty as charged,' her father shot back. 'Threats have been made against you, Shelby. I have to take them seriously. Why won't you?'

'Because it's all so utterly ridiculous! The man's a crank, out for what he can get. Why should I allow him to upset

5

my life? No, I'm sorry, Dad, but to keep trying to change my mind is a complete and utter waste of time,' she declared adamantly, though she secretly admitted to a few butterflies in her stomach when he had first told her. 'Trust me on this. Nothing is going to happen.'

'So you keep telling me,' Oscar Greer responded calmly to his only daughter's outburst. He had, after all, known what to expect. She was headstrong and independent and, on occasions such as these, over-confident that she knew best.

Shelby flung up her hands despairingly. 'Then why aren't you listening to me?' She loved her father dearly, and knew he had only her best interests at heart, but this was going too far. 'I don't need a nursemaid, Dad!'

'I'm glad to hear it,' her father returned dryly. 'At twenty-eight, you should be able to wash, dress and feed yourself.'

That piece of whimsy earned him another exasperated look. 'You know what I mean. This is so unnecessary.'

'Really? I had no idea you could look into the future?'

Shelby turned away in frustration. There was no getting through to him. He wasn't going to budge an inch. There were times when she could twist him round her little finger, but this was not one of them. He loved her, but he would only twist when he wanted to. This time he intended to have his way. Well, she was as determined as he was. She was not about to give in this time.

Sighing heavily, she walked to the window and looked out at the rain-lashed gardens of her father's Hampstead home. She had grown up here, an only child but never a lonely one. Her father was London's most successful media magnate, but he had always had time for his daughter. The bond was a close one. He needed her compliance for his own peace of mind. Normally she would gladly have given it to him, but this was different. She couldn't alter her life because of a threat she didn't believe existed, however much she loved her father. All she could try to do was make him see things from her point of view.

'Let's go over it again. What exactly did the message say?' she asked in a more reasonable tone as she turned to her parent.

Oscar Greer's expression became grim. 'The gist of it was that one of our papers had printed something this individual didn't like, and he intended to take some form of revenge. He used the phrase, 'The sins of the father shall pass down to the daughter.' Which the police consider a direct threat to you. Which is why you are going to have a bodyguard, like it or not. You're all I have and I'm not prepared to risk losing you.'

That, of course, tweaked her heartstrings, and with a faint groan she hurried over to give him a hug. 'You aren't going to lose me,' she reassured him fiercely. 'But I'm still not going to have a bodyguard!' she added hastily, so he wouldn't think she had given in.

Her father grimaced as he hugged her back. 'My God, but you're stubborn. The police wanted to lock you away somewhere safe for the duration, but I knew I'd never get you to agree to that either!' he told her as he released her.

Shelby's lips curved in an unseen smile of relief as she crossed to the tray of drinks on the antique sideboard, helping herself to a small brandy. She needed it, for she had never had to fight so strongly with her father before. It wasn't comfortable. Now that she had won, she began to relax.

'You were right about that. I have commitments. I can't just up sticks and disappear.'

She was that most fashion conscious of modern individuals—an interior designer. Her mother had been an artist, and it was from her that Shelby had inherited her eye for colour and texture. After a false start, she had studied art and design at college and then had gone on to start her own business. There had been small jobs to begin with, but word of mouth had soon spread about the quality of her work. One thing had led to another, until now she was so busy she had taken on a small staff of helpers. She was fully aware that there were people who thought that, as her father's heir, she led a cushioned existence and only played at her work. They were wrong. Her business was her own baby from start to finish and she took it very seriously indeed. Her books were full and she even had a waiting list.

With a wry shake of her head, she curled up in a corner of the couch. 'Lord, I can't believe you actually expected me to agree to have a minder!' Funnily enough, she had been told once that she needed a minder, but she shied away from the memory. It had been totally embarrassing for her. He, of course, had found it vastly amusing. 'You've had threats before. Why are you taking this one so seriously?'

'I prefer not to take chances with your life, my girl,' Oscar pronounced, glancing at his watch, then checking that against the mantel clock. Rocking back on his heels, he slipped his hand into his jacket pocket and studied his polished shoes.

'Are you expecting someone?' she asked, fascinated by these unexpected signs of unease in him.

He cleared his throat. 'Since you ask, the chap I've arranged to watch your back is arriving tonight.'

Shelby's eyes widened in shock. 'You already arranged it? Before asking me?' So much for winning! She should have guessed he would do something like this.

'I knew you wouldn't agree, so I made the decision for you,' her father confirmed with a nod of his head. 'I decided the best option was to present you with a *fait accompli.*'

She was on her feet in an instant. 'You had no right to do that, Dad. I know you're concerned, but this is my life we're talking about. Well, I hope you and he have an enjoyable evening, because you'll be spending it without me. I'm leaving!' She moved to make good her threat, but had only taken one short step towards her handbag when her father spoke.

'Stay right where you are, Shelby. You're going nowhere,' he commanded in a voice she hadn't heard in years. It brought her up short, blinking in surprise.

'You can't force me to have a bodyguard!' she protested in disbelief, which made Oscar Greer smile grimly.

'I can, and I am.'

'This is absurd!' Shelby exclaimed, but she sat down again just as the front doorbell rang loudly. She twisted round so she could watch the lounge door from over the back of the couch. 'Is this him? Well, I don't care how nice he is; I'm not going to have anything to do with him,' she added for good measure, listening to the housekeeper opening the front door, and the sound of voices joined in friendly conversation. Then footsteps headed towards the closed door and she held her breath.

The man who entered was in his mid-thirties, black-haired, blue-eyed and handsome as sin. Wearing a brown leather bomber jacket over blue shirt and jeans, he was indeed the sexiest thing on two legs she had seen in many a long day. Broad-shouldered to boot. He was tall and had the sort of long legs and lean hips that she found particularly attractive. He also had the kind of chest a girl could snuggle up on and drift into dreams that would make an angel blush. She didn't have to ask if he was also charming and witty. She knew. He was, after all, Gray Compton, her father's troubleshooter and the man she had been in love with for simply aeons.

For one intense moment Shelby's world stood still. Lord,

but her heart was pleased to see him. Life had been a desert since the last time they had met. Not that he would know it, she reminded herself as time ticked on again. She had her pride, after all.

They had been friends once, when she was younger. He had been the closest thing to a brother she would ever have. They had teased and taunted each other, much as all brothers and sisters did, and it might have stayed that way if fate had not intervened. Quite out of the blue, and when she had least expected it, she had fallen in love with him. Naturally, having done something so rash, and knowing he still only saw her as a sister, she had had to camouflage her feelings for her own protection.

She had often teased Gray about the women in his life, but had found herself in the unenviable position of wanting to be one. The only one. To her despair, he had never seen her that way. Jealousy had raised its ugly head. To combat it she had taken to dating like it was going out of fashion, though rarely dating the same man for long, to hide the fact there was only one man she really wanted. For his part, Gray had observed her behaviour with undisguised amusement.

Their relationship had stayed pretty much the same, although he had now started teasing her about the men in her life too. She had hidden her unhappiness well and, save for one minor blip when she had succumbed to a moment of recklessness, she had lived with the situation. So it might have gone on, but then something had happened which had made her hate him. She couldn't forget it, nor forgive it, no matter how much she loved him—and, for her sins, she did still love him.

So now, whenever they met, they engaged in a constant war of words. It was the perfect shield, and Shelby doubted if anyone but herself knew how she really felt. Right now, though, she wished she had had some warning he was coming to dinner tonight, in order to get her defences in place.

Gray Compton allowed his gaze to meet that of a bemused Shelby. 'Hi, there, Red. Long time no see.'

Shelby winced at the nickname she had been given as a child because of her hair. Of course, Gray would insist on using it still, just to irritate her. She smiled thinly. 'Well, well, if it isn't Dad's blue-eyed boy. What are you doing here, Gray? Coming to see what trouble you can cause?'

For once he didn't come back with a mocking rejoinder. 'My job, sweetheart. Just my job,' he told her briefly, making her frown.

Having grown used to their bickering over recent years, Oscar Greer ignored it and crossed the room, hand held out. 'Gray, my boy. Thank you for coming.'

The younger man smiled warmly and shook his hand. 'You knew I would, Oscar.' He had been sorting out a problem in Japan when he had received Oscar's call for help. 'I jumped on the first plane out.'

'How was the trip?'

'Tiring, but I'm used to it.'

Light dawned for Shelby, and her heart sank. Her eyes hastily sought her father's, hoping to have her fears allayed. 'Dad, please tell me this isn't the man you've roped in to look after me!' she pleaded in horror, more appalled than she could ever reveal. If there was one person she didn't want to spend any intimate time with, Gray was that man. Mostly because the only person she wanted was the self-same man!

Gray walked further into the room, his expression one of grim amusement at her response. 'I didn't think you'd be thrilled, but think about it, Red. Who else would be doing a spot of troubleshooting for the boss?'

Their eyes locked. The challenge given and received. Both understood the message. Whether the work was clean or dirty, Gray was the man for the job. Especially where she was concerned.

'When it comes to sorting out trouble, you are the best in the business, Gray,' her father complimented, seemingly unaware of the undercurrents swirling around the room. 'I would willingly pay you double your salary for what you're doing for us.'

The younger man shook his head. 'You know that's not necessary, Oscar. I'm only too happy to help you and my old sparring partner, Red, here. In fact, I wouldn't want it any other way.'

Oh, she knew how he threw himself into his work all right, Shelby acknowledged bitterly. She swung her feet to the floor and stood up for a second time. 'OK, that's it. I'm not having him. If I wanted anyone, which I don't, I most certainly wouldn't have him. He'll make my life a misery.' She refused point-blank, earning herself a mocking look from Gray for her pains.

'Then you'll just have to be miserable,' her father declared sternly. 'I chose Gray to be your bodyguard, so let that be an end to it. Now, can I get you something to drink, Gray? Whisky was always your favourite tipple.'

'Better make it a small one, with plenty of water. I'm driving.'

'But, Dad!' Shelby tried to protest as he crossed to the other side of the room, only to find he wasn't listening. 'What did I do to deserve this?' she muttered, then caught Gray's eye and the mockery there. 'Don't say a word!'

'And you looked so grown up too,' he derided with a shake of his head. 'Now I get closer I can see you're still the same old Shelby, always thinking more about yourself than anyone else.'

She was outraged at the claim. 'How can you say that?'

'Easily. I grew up with you, remember. You always brought your trials and tribulations to your father. I lost count of the number of times I was there when you came to bemoan the fate of your latest romance,' he responded sardonically, reminding her of hazy summer days when life was simpler, before she had fallen in love with him and discovered she would have to keep it a secret from everyone for the sake of her pride and her heart.

'Where else was I supposed to go? I never had a mother to confide in,' Shelby reminded him. Her mother had died when she was little more than a baby, leaving her father to take on both roles, which he had done magnificently so far as she was concerned.

'Hmm, your mother might have altered your dating habits. Has anyone told you that you go through men like a hot knife through butter?' he asked her, and she sent him a scathing look.

'You're a fine one to talk. Watching the turnover of women in your life makes me dizzy!' she returned swiftly, knowing that the difference between them was that she dated to hide the fact her heart was already hooked. As smokescreens went, it was pretty damn good. He never saw through it, and that was the whole point of the exercise.

'You can't think so badly of me when you're attracted to me yourself. Let's not forget you even made a play for me once.'

Her heart twisted at the painful reminder, but she managed to hide behind a curl of her lip. 'Yes, well, I was less discriminating when I was young.' She had been twenty and heartsick and, bolstered by liquid courage, she had made her only attempt to seduce him. Her failure had bruised her pride, but her feelings hadn't changed. Then, of course, there was that other time... 'Your actions later had nothing so reasonable to commend them. Merely a slavish devotion to duty,' she returned scornfully.

A nerve ticked in Gray's jaw as he shook his head wryly.

'You certainly know how to hold a grudge, don't you, Red?'

Shelby smiled at him frostily. 'Did you think I wouldn't? You were a first-class rat, and that's the way I shall always think of you,' she hissed back. Oh, what a whopper of a lie that was.

'All because I did nothing?'

'It isn't what you did or didn't do, it was why you did it. My God, you made me think you wanted me, when all you were doing was following orders. It was crass and unworthy of you, Gray. How could you have stooped so low, even for my father? Don't expect me to ever forgive you.' Shelby declared bitingly, her green eyes icy with scorn.

Gray's eyes glittered. 'You know, Red, you have to be one of the few redheads I know who actually live up to their billing. Makes a man wonder.'

It was a leading remark, and she knew she shouldn't go there, but she just couldn't help herself. It was always like that with Gray.

'Makes you wonder what?' she asked, and his wicked grin was fair warning that she wouldn't like what he was about to say.

'If you're as passionate in bed as out of it,' Gray responded, with the kind of glint in his eye that made her heart turn over.

She looked at him haughtily. 'Too late. You had your chance and you blew it. Trust me, Gray, that is the one thing you will never, ever find out now.' As she would never find out what it would be like to be made love to by him. But that was a mental path better not travelled.

He tutted. 'You're just put out because I discovered you were attracted to me,' he riposted, taking her breath away at his gall.

Sadly, she couldn't deny it. She had given herself away in the unexpected joy of what she had believed the moment was. 'All that does is make me human, even if my taste is doubtful. What does it say of you, when you merely pretended to want me?' she countered thickly.

'Who said it was all pretence? You're an attractive woman, despite your faults,' Gray argued, momentarily knocking Shelby off balance, but she rallied swiftly.

'*I* do. I was there, remember? You turned the heat on and off as easily as flicking a switch! It was disgusting. You didn't want me. You were just doing your job. I hope your conscience doesn't let you sleep nights.'

Something flickered in and out of his eyes before she could catch it, and his jaw set. 'If my conscience bothers me, it wouldn't be because of you. Anyway, I'm curious. What irks you more, Red? That I might have pretended to want you, or that I stopped before things went too far?'

Oh, that took the biscuit. She felt like scratching his eyes out. 'You have no idea how glad I am you stopped. I would never have felt clean again if you hadn't. No wonder my father likes you so much. Your commitment to your work is unparalleled. But I don't like you, and if you imagine for one second I'm going to sit still for this—' she began, only to end on a gasp as his hand snaked out and fastened on her wrist.

Gray's lips remained curved in a smile in case Oscar should turn and see them, but his eyes were coldly angry. 'Listen to me, you're going to do exactly what's expected of you. I have a great deal of respect and affection for your father, and I won't have you worrying him so much he ends up in hospital. For some reason that escapes me, he loves you, and if you have any feelings for him at all you'll put his mind at rest. Do you hear me?' he hissed through gritted teeth.

She stared at him, throat tight with emotion. 'Despite what you think, I love my father very much!' she exclaimed, cut to the quick that he could think her so selfish.

Yet, even as she thought it, she knew she *had* been behaving selfishly. Her father was seriously worried, and all she could think about was not wanting to have her life disrupted! She was ashamed of herself.

'Then do the right thing for once in your life,' he growled in a powerful undertone.

Shelby quivered with emotion, eyes flashing stormily. Oh, how she hated that it was Gray who made her see sense. 'I hate you!'

He smiled mockingly. 'I know. Hell, isn't it? Hating me and yet wanting me?'

Her stomach lurched at the arrogance in his tone. 'I don't want you,' she denied through gritted teeth, but he merely laughed softly.

'I could prove otherwise, but at the moment we have more pressing things to sort out. So, what's it to be?'

As if there was a choice. Shelby loved her father, and would never do anything to hurt him. OK, she didn't take the threat seriously, but all she really needed to know was that he did. That was what she had to think about. 'All right, I'll agree to the bodyguard. Now let me go!'

Having secured her agreement, he released her hand, trailing his fingers over her palm as he did so. The small action made her catch her breath and he smiled knowingly as he straightened up. 'Wise choice. Like it or not, you're stuck with me now,' he added and, much to her chagrin, laughed softly. 'So, tell me, what have you been doing with yourself lately? Still running amok through the local male population?'

Before she could come back with a pithy retort, her father returned with their drinks. 'Here you are, Gray.' He handed over a glass of golden liquid, which the younger man took but didn't immediately touch. 'What are you two talking about? Old times?'

Blue eyes glinted roguishly. 'Actually, I was just asking

Shelby about her love life,' Gray remarked goadingly, and Shelby's heart sank. Her father strongly disapproved of her dating habits.

Oscar Greer snorted. 'Love life? I wouldn't call it that! She's like a butterfly, flitting from man to man, never stopping long enough to find out if there could be a relationship. Whatever she's looking for, she'll never find it going on the way she does.'

'Dad!' Shelby exclaimed in protest, although there was far too much truth in what her father had said. Of course she didn't linger, but there was a reason for that. She wouldn't give false hope to any man. She had already found what she was looking for, and it was a closed door. So she wasn't so much searching as marking time. Catching Gray's mocking glance, she rushed to change the subject. 'Gray doesn't want to hear about my love life.'

Gray quirked an eyebrow at her. 'If you want to keep secrets, try being more circumspect. I learn all I need to from the gossip columns.'

Colour stormed into her cheeks, for those columns were a constant source of misery for her. Unfortunately it was the price of fame. 'You shouldn't believe all you read.' They made her out to be some sort of maneater, which she most certainly wasn't. Far from it, in fact.

'You're just as bad, Gray. You have no staying power either,' Oscar told his right-hand man, and Shelby laughed.

'You tell him, Dad. It's shocking the way he goes on,' she sniped whilst blue eyes threatened retribution.

Her father tsked, though there was a reluctant gleam of humour in the twitch of his lips. 'Sometimes I want to knock both your heads together. When are you going to settle down? The way you're going on, you're both going to end up with nobody.'

Her throat closed over at her father's obvious concern. 'I'll settle down one day, Dad. When I find the right man.'

'He could be under your nose and you wouldn't see him!'

Shelby bit her lip at the unwitting accuracy of his words. Except she had seen him. How could she tell her father the man she wanted hadn't wanted her? 'I'll have my eyes tested, I promise,' she said, attempting to tease him out of his mood. She succeeded, for Oscar Greer patted her hand and smiled at her.

'I'm nagging, I know, but it's a father's prerogative to worry about his daughter.'

'Speaking of which,' Gray inserted swiftly, 'Shelby has something she wants to tell you,' he declared, shooting her a pointed look.

Having been put on the spot, Shelby cleared her throat and looked at her father. 'I've, er, been talking to Gray, and we…that is, *I* realise I've been behaving stupidly. So…' She took a deep breath and dived in. 'I'll agree to the bodyguard,' she ended on a rush. Glancing at Gray, she set her jaw. 'Happy now?'

Fortunately her father chose not to question the how of it, but sent her a broad smile of relief. 'Thank you, darling. That's a weight off my mind. I didn't know how I was going to get through this if you kept on refusing to see sense.'

Which made her feel even more guilty than she had been. 'Yes, well, Gray made me see things more clearly,' she enlarged uncomfortably, and Oscar looked past her to the younger man.

'Thank you, Gray.'

'My pleasure.'

'We should sit down and talk about tactics,' her father said, urging them towards the comfortable chairs and couches ranged around the fireplace. Shelby took a seat at the other end of the couch from Gray and waited to hear her fate.

'It goes without saying that we put ourselves entirely in your hands,' Oscar told the younger man the moment they were all seated.

Shelby immediately saw a flaw. 'Hang on a second. I know I've agreed in principle, but I'd like to know what qualifies Gray for the job before I hand myself over to him on a plate.'

One eyebrow quirked lazily. 'Don't you trust me, Red? I'm hurt. I thought you knew better.'

She knew what he was referring to, and it was just like him to throw that in her face. Of course, he had no idea of the real blow he had dealt her, for she had licked her wounds in private, and still did. Her palm itched to slap him, but all she did was send him a narrow look. 'I was wondering what qualifications you could possibly have for this job,' she shot back. It was, after all, a reasonable question.

'I wear many hats, Red. Amongst other things, I am a security expert. If you want my credentials, all I can tell you is that I learnt my trade in the forces.'

'You were in the army?' That came as a total surprise. She immediately had visions of him doing the daring sort of things she had seen done in numerous Hollywood movies.

He shrugged lightly. 'You know how it is with boys; we never get over playing with our toy soldiers.'

'I never saw you playing with soldiers,' Shelby pointed out. 'And what you're talking about is hi-tech stuff. That's not just ordinary soldiering. It sounds more…covert.' The notion intrigued her. 'What sort of things did you do?'

Gray suddenly looked amused. 'As they say in all the best movies, I could tell you but then I'd have to kill you,' he said with a wry grin.

Her father laughed. 'Suffice it to say he is eminently qualified for the job, Shelby.'

In her heart of hearts she knew it. Gray had always been the kind of man who did well at whatever he chose to take on. It was time to give in as gracefully as possible. 'OK, OK, point taken. So what happens next?'

All laughter vanished as Gray's expression grew serious. 'We become joined at the hip, for however long it takes.'

That sounded awfully intimate—something that didn't sit well with her at all. She frowned at him. 'I understood you would be watching me from a distance.'

To her dismay he shook his head. 'Then you understood wrongly. If I'm to be of any use, then I have to be on hand twenty-four-seven.'

Shelby had a sinking feeling in the pit of her stomach. 'By 'on hand' you mean…?'

Gray's smile reappeared, laden with mockery. 'Just what you think I mean, Red. I'll be moving into your spare room for the duration.'

At that point Shelby closed her eyes. It was her worst nightmare. She could handle her feelings for Gray at a distance, but having him in her own home would mean that after this was all over he would be imprinted in her rooms. She would be able to imagine him there, and her sanctuary would no longer exist. Yet what could she do? Creating a scene was out of the question now that she had agreed to have the bodyguard. She was doomed.

Or was she? There was, of course, one other possibility. Perhaps she was just dreaming all this, and when she woke it would all fade away. When she really opened her eyes, Gray would be gone and her life would be back to normal again.

Her despairing thoughts were interrupted by the ringing of the telephone and she opened her eyes to see her father crossing the room to answer it. Gray, meanwhile, sat watching her from the opposite end of the couch. It wasn't a dream. It was for real.

'Sorry to disappoint you, but I'm still here,' he told her, clearly knowing exactly what she had been thinking.

Deeply rattled, Shelby crossed one silk-clad leg over the other and crossed her arms to match. 'You're enjoying this, aren't you?' she challenged with a basilisk glare.

Gray didn't laugh. 'I see nothing amusing in protecting you from being seriously hurt...or worse.'

Shelby tapped out a tattoo on her arm with her fingers. 'You can't possibly take it all seriously.'

That, if anything, made him look grimmer. 'Better that than to do nothing and live with the consequences. I've been down that road, and I'll tell you this for nothing—it isn't going to happen again!'

Shelby's lips parted on a tiny gasp of surprise. This was an unexpected revelation. 'What do you mean? What happened?'

Now his mouth twisted into a bitter smile as he shook his head. 'You don't want to know. The important thing is that I'm going to be doing everything in my power to prevent anything like it happening to you!'

She pressed a hand to a suddenly queasy stomach. His message got through loud and clear. 'Why? I mean, what do you care what happens to me?'

'I care because your father is a good man.'

'It's...all for him, then?' For a fleeting moment she had harboured the idea that he might just care about her a little. Her heart suffered another bruise as she realised she ought to have known better.

Gray's eyes looked piercingly into hers for an instant. 'Did you think it would be for you?'

Shelby swallowed her hurt and shrugged. 'Of course not. I know better than that.'

'I'm glad to hear it. After all, why should I care anything for a woman who has done all the things you have?' Gray observed sardonically.

Which, as it happened, was very much what she thought too. She had done nothing to endear herself to him. Why would he fall in love with her, or care anything about her? She had no answer, only wished that, despite everything, he could somehow do both. Flying pigs, though, were in short supply these days. So she rallied her spirit and responded swiftly.

'Leave my past out of this, Gray!' she commanded sharply, making him shake his head again.

'I can see why you would want to. It's not very flattering.'

No, it wasn't, but she had worked hard to live it down. A fact he chose to overlook. 'I'm trying to put all that behind me,' she insisted, and he gave her a measuring look.

'Well, now. Let's hope you live long enough to do it. Which brings us back to why I'm here.'

Before Shelby could say anything more, her father rejoined them.

'Sorry about that. Now, where were we?' he asked as he made himself comfortable in his chair once more.

'I'd just told Shelby that I would be moving into her spare room.'

Oscar shot her a quick glance. 'How did she take it?'

Gray's lips twitched. 'About as well as we expected.'

Shelby rolled her eyes. 'Will you please stop talking about me as if I'm not here?' she commanded in exasperation. 'I have the right to make the important decisions about my life.'

'That's good, because you've already made the most important one. You agreed with your father's decision to ask for my help,' Gray put in swiftly. 'And, as I told you, I'm not going to let anything happen to you, Red,' he added in the quietly confident way of his that had the uncanny knack of calming the nerves in her stomach immediately.

She stared at him hard, trying to penetrate those devilish blue eyes. 'That's a promise, is it?'

'Cross my heart,' he retorted, making the gesture to confirm it.

However much she trusted him when it came to his work, Shelby wasn't going to appear to be won over too quickly. 'Do you really have to move in to do it? Couldn't you… oh, I don't know…surveille—is that a word?—the house from a plain vehicle or something?' she suggested rather wildly in a last-ditch attempt to retrieve her privacy.

Not surprisingly, Gray's brows had risen as she meandered on and by the end he was frowning. 'You've been watching far too many movies. Trust me, I know what's needed.'

'And you need to be in my home.' It was a flat statement rather than a question. Gray answered it anyway.

'Following your every step like Peter Pan's shadow.'

That was hardly designed to improve her mood, and she knew it was a deliberate goad. She was going to have to resign herself to his being there for some time, and the worst of it was that she was still convinced the whole thing was a waste of time. However, her father feared the worst, and she wasn't about to add to his worries. She could do this for him.

'How long will it take you to get your things together?' Shelby enquired with a heavy heart.

'I have everything I need in the boot of my car, so I'll be ready to leave whenever you are,' he informed her, and her hope that he would delay his arrival until the next day was dashed.

Her father was all smiles. 'You'll be staying to dinner, I hope, now that everything's decided?'

Gray looked to Shelby, one eyebrow raised questioningly. 'Unless Shelby wants to go home now?'

Had she been going alone she would have decided to

leave, but as that was impossible she decided to drag out the moment as long as she could.

'Oh, I'll be having dinner here,' she responded, making a show of settling herself comfortably for a long stay. 'I never miss the chance of eating one of Mrs Grundy's meals.'

Oscar Greer rubbed his hands together. 'You're in for a treat, my boy,' he declared as he stood up yet again. 'I'll just go and tell Mrs G to set another place. I won't be long.'

Silence fell as he left the room, and, as if to balance that out Shelby became intensely aware of Gray's physical presence. From the corner of her eye she could see his hand resting on his knee, and her heart twisted. It recalled the precise moment when she had fallen in love with him. He had offered her a hand to help her out of a taxi, and the touch had been like magic. Exactly as they said it felt in the movies, only for real. She had known then that Gray was special. What the movies hadn't said was that it didn't have to be mutual. From his behaviour, Gray had clearly felt nothing, whilst she had suffered an emotional sea change. She had been eighteen then and, ten years later, her feelings hadn't changed one iota. He was still that special someone and she was still lonely.

'So,' Gray said conversationally, drawing her out of her reverie and making her glance his way. 'Here we are. Together again.'

Shelby laughed harshly and looked at him askance. 'I'd hardly call us together. We just happen to be in the same room.'

A reply that had his blue eyes gleaming with devilment. 'I recall a time when a situation like this was just what you wanted,' he went on, spreading his hands to take in the fact that there were just the two of them.

As was his wont, he was deliberately trying to embarrass her, but she didn't embarrass so easily. 'Well, you were dating every woman within a ten-mile radius. Good Lord, they were falling over themselves to be next in line, so I thought I might as well see what all the fuss was about. I got over it.'

He acknowledged that with a tip of his head, and added, 'Cold shower helped, did it? I told you it would.'

Shelby ground her teeth together irritably. 'I just knew you wouldn't be able to resist saying I told you so.'

Her response drew a laugh. 'I would have hated to disappoint you. At least now you know I'm every bit as bad as all the nasty things you called me.'

Shelby started to open her mouth to deny doing any such thing, but he gave her such a look that she thought better of it. 'I hope your ears burned,' she said instead, and his smile reappeared.

'Stung for days afterwards.'

'Good. I'm delighted to hear it. Of course, it was less than you deserved,' she told him haughtily and he pulled a pained face.

'Hmm, I wince at the idea of what you would consider just payment,' Gray declared with a sharp intake of breath, and Shelby laughed this time.

'You're right to be afraid. As far as I'm concerned, there is no statute of limitations on your particular crime,' she informed him with a challenging look.

Gray eyed her thoughtfully, and there was no way she could read what was going on in his fertile mind. 'Looks like I'm in for an interesting assignment, doesn't it?' he said at last, and there was something in the way he said it that sent alarm signals through her system. She couldn't say why, but all of a sudden there was something... dangerous in the air.

Shelby's eyes narrowed suspiciously. 'What are you planning?'

His smile was as innocent as the day was long. 'Why,

just to keep you out of harm's way. What did you think I would do?'

She didn't trust him, especially when he looked so innocent. 'Just remember you're here on sufferance. If it was left up to me, we wouldn't be going through this.'

'Don't worry, I understand perfectly. You're putting your father's mind at rest, and you're accepting my presence under duress,' he summarised for her. 'Correct?'

'Why is it that the instant you start being reasonable, I start to get nervous?'

He grinned broadly. 'Maybe it's something to do with not wanting to be beholden to me for anything. Rest easy, this is for your Dad, not you.'

'Fine. That's fine,' she muttered, silently praying that the whole ridiculous situation would be over soon.

At that fortuitous moment Oscar Greer returned to the room, looking much more cheerful than he had for days. She knew it was Gray's presence which had brought that about, and it confirmed to her that she was doing the right thing. If it would put her father's mind at rest, she would bite the bullet. After all, it wouldn't be for long. She was utterly sure of that.

Why, she was willing to bet that by this time next week Gray Compton would have packed his bags and disappeared from whence he came. Then her life would get back to normal. By that she meant—*Gray Free*. Which wasn't the way she wanted it, but it was how it was doomed to be.

# CHAPTER TWO

SHELBY drew her car to a halt at yet another red light, and her eyes automatically trained in on the pair of headlights she could see in the rear view mirror. Gray was following her home, matching every turn she made. It had been tempting to draw out the journey by going out of her way, but it also occurred to her that Gray was just the sort of person who would have checked out her route home beforehand. Any deviation she made would be cause for comment, and therefore making her seem childish in the extreme. So she had taken her usual route, constantly aware of those never wavering headlights.

Sitting there in the dark, fingers tapping out a nervy tattoo on the steering-wheel, she imagined she could feel Gray's eyes boring into the back of her head. Not for the first time, she wondered what he was thinking. Did he, for instance, ever think back to the events of that long ago evening, when all her hopes and dreams had come crashing down around her ears?

Of course, it would never have happened if she hadn't been feeling sorry for herself. She had been acting as hostess for one of her father's dinner parties, and had been let down by the man who she was then dating. By coincidence, Gray had turned up without a partner too, which had somehow made her feel that this was her chance. She had been eating her heart out over him for two years, and had still had hopes that a miracle would happen. Sometimes, though, miracles needed a helping hand, and she had decided to make a bold venture. Late on in the evening, when the party had split into groups, she had seen Gray wander out on to the patio. When a quick glance told her that everyone else was accounted for, she had followed him...

A sharp blast from a car horn made Shelby jump violently, pulling her out of her daydream, and she realised she had been sitting there whilst the lights had changed to green. She ground the gears getting the car into first and grimaced at the thought of the smile Gray would be wearing when he heard it. Something similar to the one he had worn when he had held her away from him after she had attempted to kiss him that night. But she was getting ahead of herself.

When she had joined him in the relative privacy of the patio, he had turned to face her, resting one hip against the low wall of the parapet.

'Lost your way, Red?' he asked her lightly and she shrugged, though she was feeling far from relaxed. 'You don't usually seek me out these days.'

She shook her head as she slowly walked towards him, trembling hands linked loosely behind her back. 'Things change.'

His lips twitched and one eyebrow quirked rakishly. 'In what way?'

'As we're the only ones without partners, I thought we could be company for each other,' she told him, reaching out to brush off a non-existent piece of debris from the front of his dinner jacket.

'Did you now?' he responded suavely and, gathering her resolve, Shelby took a small step towards him, closing the gap, placed both hands on his chest and looked up at him seductively.

'Um-hm. It's too good an opportunity to miss. Here we are, just you, me and the night. It's perfect for getting to know one another better,' she insisted in a sultry voice that carried a tremor of anticipation. She tried to caress his cheek, but he foiled her plan, holding her wrist in a light yet unremitting grip.

'How much have you had to drink, Shelby?'

She sighed, smiling. 'Just enough to blunt the edges. Come on, Gray, relax, let yourself go a little,' she urged him, her eyes locked on the lips she longed to kiss.

She didn't see his eyes narrow. 'And do what…seduce you?'

'Sounds like a plan,' she agreed, and would have put her arm around his neck only he abruptly pushed her away.

'What the hell do you think you're doing, little girl?' he demanded mockingly, finally bursting the delicious bubble she had been floating in.

'Little girl?' she gasped, cut to the quick. 'I'm twenty years old. That makes me a woman, not a girl!'

'You're playing out of your league, Red. Just because your boyfriend stood you up doesn't mean you can practice your seduction skills on me.'

That got through like nothing else, and her hopes and dreams dissolved around her. Yet, smarting though she was, she realised he had at least left her the means to save face. Swallowing hard, she covered her retreat with style. 'I should have known you wouldn't want me, but you can't blame a girl for trying!' she retorted ruefully, stepping away from him.

He shook his head. 'You're going to give your father grey hairs before his time. A fact you might want to re-member. Seducing the boss's daughter is a non-starter.'

The remark rubbed salt into the wound, but she battled on bravely. 'Is that all that stopped you? Listen, we wouldn't have to tell him.'

'Sorry, Red, but I'd know. Besides, you're too young for me. If I was looking to be seduced tonight, it would be by a woman who knows what she's doing,' he added for good measure, making her feel worse.

At the same time she was relieved that he was falling for her ploy. He would never know how deep the wounds went, or how much blood he had drawn. 'For a man who's known for his charm, that wasn't very subtle, Gray. But there's no harm done. I won't bother you again.' So saying, she returned to the house.

Rejoining the other guests, she stayed there, not looking up when Gray came back in, although she was aware of him with every nerve in her body. She held it all together until everyone had gone. Then she retreated to her room and sobbed into her pillow.

Only when the tears of despair and mortification had dried up had she been grateful that her feelings for him had remained secret. She had pulled off a feat of acting that was worthy of an award. Amazingly, her love for him hadn't withered under the blow. It had been too strong for that.

It still was, Shelby conceded as she stopped briefly at a junction, then turned right. The headlights followed her. She hadn't seen Gray for a while after that. She had braced herself for days for that inevitable first meeting, only to be told by her father that he had gone abroad again. When he had returned, she had had her protective armour in place. She had battled with him just as she always had, and that one small incident had faded into history.

In fact, it was only at moments such as these that she thought of it at all, she mused as she drove through a one-way system. Of course, there had been that second, more devastating meeting between them later, but she tried not to think of that. Bad enough to go through it once, why choose to relive it in glorious Technicolor? Better to concentrate on her driving.

A short while later she turned down the ramp of the underground car park belonging to the modern block of apartments in which she lived. Using her remote control, she opened the security gates and drove through. Parking in her reserved spot, she climbed out and indicated that Gray should park beside her. The spot belonged to a neighbour who was working abroad for the next few months. Shelby collected her bag and set the car alarm.

Gray, meanwhile, had alighted from his four-by-four and was rummaging around in the back. Having retrieved what he wanted, he walked round to join her. 'Tell me, do you always take the same route home?'

'From Dad's? Yes, of course. I've found it's the quickest,' Shelby confirmed, then frowned when he looked concerned.

'Forget the quickest. From tomorrow you start varying your routes. Especially places you go to frequently. Nothing will help this creep more than your own habits,' he informed her bluntly, then looked around him. 'How do we get in?'

'The lifts are over here.' She pointed off to her right and was surprised when Gray slipped a hand under her elbow and urged her along. 'Hey...'

'This isn't personal. I'm not holding you because I want to.'

'I know that,' she shot back scornfully. 'You're under orders again.'

He shot her a narrow look. 'We'll never get beyond that, will we?'

'Not in this life or the next,' she confirmed scathingly and he made a grunting sound in his throat.

'Let's hope the next life doesn't come along sooner than you expect!' Gray returned dryly.

Shelby looked at him in shock. 'Surely this nut case wouldn't try to kill me?' she asked in some alarm.

To her dismay he didn't play that down with a laugh. 'Don't worry. I'm here to make sure he never gets the chance.'

She frowned as her confidence took a knock. 'But this is just a scam!'

Gray's smile was tight. 'Let's hope you're right, but in the meantime I'm taking no chances. I never like to see mistakes repeated.'

'Mistakes?' She knew instantly he was referring to that security situation which had gone wrong. 'What happened?'

'Let's just say someone died, and it wasn't pretty. Now, I've imagined seeing you in all sorts of situations, but never lifeless at my feet. I'd prefer to keep it that way,' Gray returned dryly, not about to be drawn.

Shelby found the remark at once surprising and intriguing. It was rather comforting to know he didn't want to see her harmed, but what were these other ways he had pictured her? Her mind reeled but could find no answer. By which time they had reached the lift.

'OK, if you have gates on the garage, can I assume there's a doorman inside the lobby?' Gray wanted to know as he jabbed the call button.

She was glad she could confirm that much at least. 'Twenty-four hour cover, taken in shifts. It was one of the reasons I took this apartment,' she added pointedly. He might think she wasn't security conscious, but in this day and age it was silly not to be.

He looked at her, one eyebrow raised quizzically. 'Glad to hear you've got some sense then, Red. I was beginning to wonder.'

Shelby shot him a sideways glare. 'Did you have to work hard at getting so rude, or did it come naturally?' she gibed, but could have saved herself the effort for it was like water off a duck's back.

'Naturally, of course,' he confirmed mockingly. The lift arrived and they stepped inside. 'Which floor?'

'The top.' As she had known she wouldn't have a garden, she had settled for a view.

The doors closed and they began the nearly silent ascent. Gray's lips twitched. 'How do you resist calling it the penthouse? I would have thought it would add to your mystique.'

She rolled her eyes heavenwards. 'I'm sure it hasn't escaped your notice that there are only six floors, Gray. To call the top the penthouse would make me look ridiculous.'

He didn't allow her to get away with that. 'So, what do you call it?'

Shelby frowned and shifted from foot to foot uncomfortably. She didn't want to tell him, for she knew in her bones he would laugh and call it pretentious. 'Who says I call it anything?'

'Because I know the way you think. To your father it's the top right apartment, but to the clients you want to impress you'd call it something much more upmarket,' Gray eyed her consideringly. 'It would have to be something arty. Something like...*pied-à-terre*.'

Her eyes narrowed suspiciously as he hit the nail squarely on the head. 'You knew. Dad told you!' she exclaimed, unwilling to believe he would think of it himself.

As ever, he found her vastly entertaining, and laughed. 'Not a bit of it. I had a lucky guess. But you've disappointed me, Red. I didn't imagine you would be so predictable.'

For an instant Shelby would dearly have loved to give him a predictable thump on his big head! Fortunately for him, she wasn't given to physical violence. 'My clients like it. That's all that counts.'

'Aren't you afraid for your immortal soul?' he asked dryly and, goaded, Shelby snapped.

'I'll hit you in a minute!'

Gray laughed even more heartily. 'Now that sounds more

like the Shelby I know. You never used to go in for all this pretentious nonsense.'

'True, but then I wasn't trying to earn a living,' she told him caustically, wondering how she was ever going to get through the next few days with her sanity intact.

The lift arrived at the top and deposited them on to the landing. There were three doors leading off the small area. Two were clearly to apartments, the other was the fire escape. Gray examined it carefully, then nodded, satisfied.

'Who lives opposite and below you?' he wanted to know next, and Shelby quickly got herself together.

'Opposite are a married couple in their thirties. They both have high-powered jobs. I don't see much of them. Tim lives below me, but he's abroad for the next few months. You're parking in his space. Why?'

Gray didn't look too happy with what she told him. 'That leaves you pretty much isolated up here. Let's go inside so I can have a quick look around.'

Shelby reached into her bag for her keys, feeling ever so slightly on edge. She had felt perfectly safe up until he started shaking his head at what he saw. OK, she still didn't believe anything was going to happen, but he was certainly putting the wind up her. Opening the door to apartment 6A, she would have walked in, except that Gray quickly caught her arm and held her back.

'I'll go first, to be on the safe side.'

Jittery or not, so far as Shelby was concerned that was going too far. 'Oh, come on. There's nobody in there,' she protested, and drew a cool look from her companion.

'You'd better start thinking defensively, or you're asking for trouble,' Gray advised sternly and walked past her, dropping his bag just inside the hallway before switching on the light.

No doubt to have both hands free to deal with whatever came his way. Shelby thought irritably. Trust him to talk about her being pretentious, when he was acting like some comic book hero.

She stepped inside, closing the door behind her, and when she turned round again all thought of intruders—real or imagined—vanished. Shelby found she had an unobstructed view of Gray striding away from her and, quick as a flash, her mouth went dry as a wave of heat swept over her. The cause of this rush of longing was totally unaware that, with his leather bomber jacket resting on his hips, she had the perfect view of his long legs and extremely sexy physique. His walk had an animal quality about it, and it made her decidedly weak at the knees.

Oh, boy, she thought as he disappeared into her lounge, and groaned helplessly. She couldn't recall ever being turned on so quickly, and he hadn't even touched her. Yet she had known for years that Gray had that certain something which no other man had. Just being near him was enough to set her pulse racing. Out of necessity she had become adept at hiding her reaction, but the situation she found herself in was far beyond the norm. She was going to have to be on her guard not to let anything slip.

Shelby was bracing herself to walk forward when Gray reappeared in the hallway as if he had been magicked there. Whereupon Shelby was struck by another pulse of awareness. She hadn't felt it so keenly at her father's house, but now they were alone in her apartment it was another matter. The instinctual female side of her was vitally aware of the pure maleness of him. He exuded a particularly potent brand of sexuality that struck a chord, and her whole body thrummed in reply. She pulled a face as she acknowledged that functioning naturally might be a problem.

Gray's expression, however, was stony. 'I told you to stay outside.'

Shelby tensed immediately, not caring for his tone. 'I

heard you, but this is my home and you can't order me around in it.'

Unimpressed, he took a step closer. 'I give the orders here, and you will do what I say when I say. Is that clear?'

Anger surged inside her, and Shelby instinctively took a step back. 'You can't browbeat me. I'm not scared of you, Gray Compton!' she raged, and his lip curled.

'Trust you to get things backwards. It's the man out there you should be afraid of and, until you get that through your thick head, I'm going to be doing my best to keep you safe in spite of yourself!' he growled back and stooped to pick up his bag.

When he straightened up they were virtually nose to nose. Quick as a flash, Shelby found her heart was suddenly going at a gallop, and almost groaned. Get a grip, you idiot, she thought, taking herself firmly to task. You don't want him to see how strongly you're still attracted to him.

Meeting his gaze, she noted there was a glint in his eye which she didn't like the look of. 'By the way, if you're still hungry, try looking in the kitchen. I'm not on the menu tonight,' he drawled mockingly, and her heart lurched as she realised she hadn't acted swiftly enough. He had seen far too much.

'I wouldn't want you even if you were,' she denied at once, only to find herself being observed in sardonic amusement.

'That's not the message your eyes were sending out a minute ago. You still want me.'

The very fact that she knew it was true meant she had no option but to fight a rearguard action. 'Why would I do anything so puerile?'

He shrugged. 'Probably because I'm the one who got away. That's not supposed to happen. You have to put the record straight.'

Appalled that he could think she would have to have him

solely to salve her pride, Shelby hastened to deny it.
'You're out of your mind!'

His lips twitched, revealing his hidden amusement.
'Shame. I was toying with the idea of maybe letting you
catch me this time,' he said as he turned away. 'Do you
have a security system?'

Stunned into silence by his offhand remark, Shelby followed him as he retraced his steps, switching on more lights
as he went. 'What do you mean, you might let me catch
you?' she charged, finding her voice at last.

'It was just a thought. I'd have to decide whether the
joys of sharing a bed with you would be worth all the
aggravation of dealing with you out of it before I made up
my mind,' he enlarged mockingly.

That was a red rag of the largest kind. Of all the…! She
was beside herself. How dared he assume she'd simply fall
into his arms. 'Oh, you would, would you? Well, let me
tell you something, Gray. It isn't up to you. If I caught you
I'd throw you right back! Do you know why?'

He tipped his head as he looked at her. 'I'm sure you're
about to tell me.'

'Because, after what you did, I could never trust you
again. You lied to me, and you used me,' she declared
fervently, feeling the pain of betrayal even as she spoke,
and he smiled grimly.

'I regretted having to do it, but it was necessary,' he
countered tersely and she laughed harshly.

'Is that an apology?'

Blue eyes searched hers. 'Would it make a difference if
it was?' he asked and her chin went up.

'No,' she said with cutting finality, and saw a muscle
tense in his jaw for a moment before he sighed heavily.

'You speak with absolute certainty, yet it doesn't appear
to have stopped you wanting me,' he reminded her, bringing a faint wash of colour to her cheeks.

As he knew already, there was no point in denying it. 'Obviously not, but I'm not about to give in to temptation. However attractively packaged.'

That had him shaking his head. 'So it's a case of looking but not touching, is it?' he asked mockingly. 'Think you can keep to the rules?'

A cruel smile curved her lips. 'Oh, yes. All I have to do is think back to that night, and there's no problem. So dream on. I'm not for sale at any price!'

Gray smiled back. 'Everyone has their price, Red. I'll just have to find yours. If I decide I want to take the matter further, that is. For the moment just try and keep your mind on the matter at hand. You can dream about me later. Now, let's get back to the security system. Do you have one?'

It irked her no end that he had to have the last word. But there was no real harm done. So what if he knew she was still physically attracted to him despite everything that had happened? It wasn't the end of the world. He didn't know she loved him, and that was how it had to stay. Taking a steadying breath, she concentrated her mind on what he had asked her.

'Security system? Yes, there is one, but I never use it. The man on the desk is supposed to stop unwanted guests,' she told him, and Gray stared at her incredulously.

'Mercy, but you're not safe to be let out without a keeper! Do you have any sense of self-preservation? Uninvited guests don't arrive by the front door. From tomorrow you start using it,' he decided for her.

She didn't see the point, but no doubt he'd be reporting to her father and he'd blow his top, which wasn't what she wanted, so Shelby took a deep breath and nodded. 'All right, but I wish to goodness you'd stop barking orders at me. Don't you know you catch more flies with honey?'

'Your point being?'

'You could try asking me instead of telling me. After

all, I'm only doing this for Dad, not because I take it seriously.'

Gray folded his arms and observed her thoughtfully. 'I can't make up my mind if you're being wilfully stupid or you really are that naive. What will make you take it seriously?'

'Nothing you could possibly say. The value of your word has been seriously devalued by your actions,' she told him with a belligerent lift of her chin.

Anger and something else she couldn't name flashed in his eyes and he gritted his teeth. 'OK, Red, I've said it before and this is the last time I'll repeat it. After that, all bets are off. This is what we do. We compromise. Until this proves to be the damp squib you insist it is, we play the game my way. Agreed?'

'And if I don't?'

His smile was grim. 'You won't be leaving this apartment any time soon. It's up to you.'

Knowing he would do it too, Shelby eyed him scathingly. 'So, you'd add kidnapping to the list of your crimes, would you? It doesn't surprise me. I know the lengths you'll go to for Dad.'

Blue eyes flashed dangerously. 'You know nothing, Red. Maybe I have a vested interest in keeping you alive.'

She shrugged indifferently. 'Course you do. You want to keep your job!'

Gray muttered something dire under his breath. 'If you want to find out how far you can push me, sweetheart, keep this up,' he threatened darkly and, having got the result she wanted, Shelby subsided.

'I had no idea you were so touchy,' she murmured, dropping down on to the nearest couch. 'Well, this wasn't how I planned to spend the evening.'

'Sorry if I'm cramping your style, but it brings me to my next point,' Gray responded as he walked to the windows and closed the curtains. Turning to face her, he folded his arms across his chest. 'I was going to suggest you tell your current boyfriend not to come calling for the duration. You can do without for a few days, can't you?' he enquired with less than subtle irony, and Shelby tensed instantly.

She couldn't believe what she had just heard. Was he really asking what she thought he was? 'What exactly can I do without?' she demanded to know in a voice icy enough to do serious damage to brass monkeys.

He had the nerve to quirk an eyebrow at her. 'I was referring to male company in general. Look at it this way. A couple of days abstinence could do wonders for your love life.'

Shelby closed her eyes and counted to ten. 'For your information, there's nothing wrong with my love life,' she told him through gritted teeth and he grinned.

'I'm happy for you. Truly,' he returned sardonically, and she very nearly threw something at him. 'So, can you put the boyfriend off?'

She stared him squarely in the eye. 'You know, two can play at this game. How's your love life, Gray? Can *you* do without female company for a few days?'

His response was to wince dramatically. 'Ouch, I think I hit a sore spot. Something tells me you're between men right now.'

She shot to her feet in righteous wrath. 'And you're dicing with death!'

Gray rocked back on his heels, blue eyes gleaming mockingly. 'It never takes long to get that volatile temper of yours to ignite, does it?' he said, and Shelby balled her hands into fists at her sides.

'Not where you're concerned, no,' she agreed snappily. 'I think you delight in doing it.'

'You've discovered my secret,' he confirmed lazily. 'It

always fascinated me to see what happened when I lit the blue touch-paper.'

This time she raised an eyebrow at him. 'Maybe you should remember the warning advises you to retire immediately.'

'Oh, I've fantasised about that many a night,' he revealed huskily, holding her gaze, and a wave of heat surged through her. Suddenly the air between them was charged with electricity and her wayward senses couldn't help responding. This was how it had been that other time, when she had fallen for his charming brand of lies. He had made her believe he was really interested in her and, because she had wanted it to be true, she had plunged headlong. Now, as then, she could no more be indifferent to him than she could stop breathing. Yet she wasn't about to fall under his spell, no matter how much she still wanted him, for she was wise to the games he played. With Gray, nothing was as it seemed.

'I don't wish to know that!' she said with a shudder.

'Have you never fantasised about me?' he went on, amusement dancing in his eyes.

'I might have once, but now it would give me bad dreams!' she declared, and he smiled wryly.

'God forbid that dreams of me should give you nightmares!' Gray exclaimed mockingly, walking over to the sideboard and leaning against it. 'I must be losing my touch.'

'Not really. I know what you're capable of. There's no length you wouldn't go to.'

'To keep you from harm I'd even walk through fire,' he confirmed, and her heart contracted, for she knew it was his loyalty to her father that drove him, not any finer feeling for herself.

'I doubt even Dad would expect that of you,' she retorted scornfully. 'So you're saved.'

'Actually, Red, I expect it of myself,' he countered a tad sharply, then pushed himself to his feet, shoving his hands into the pockets of his trousers. 'Getting back to where we were, I was serious about putting off the boyfriend. Can you do that?' He was all business again, and that tiny moment of exasperation was forgotten.

Shelby wished she didn't have to answer. She could see his point. A boyfriend entering into the equation could make things awkward. It was just that her answer was going to make him even more obnoxious. Not that she had a choice.

Squaring her shoulders, she admitted the truth. 'Actually, I'm not seeing anyone just now.'

Which response brought a flash of amusement. 'That must have been hard to say,' he commiserated. 'That's one problem solved.'

She could have let it go at that but she didn't. 'How about you? Can you forgo a few days of slavish devotion?'

His smile took on a rakish edge. 'Just so happens, sweetheart, that I'm in the same boat you are. Nobody to miss me. Nobody to share those special little moments with.'

Shelby's heart was pleased to hear it, which just proved how besotted she was. Aloud, she made a scoffing noise. 'My heart bleeds for you.'

'Careful, Red. Your claws are showing,' he retorted. 'Well, now we've settled the major issues, perhaps you'll show me to my room? By the way, I like the décor. Did you do it yourself?'

Shelby was torn between wanting to black his eye for him and feeling a sense of pride that he liked her work. She had spent a lot of time on it. The main room had a sitting area and separate dining area. She had decorated each differently, yet so that they complemented each other. 'Every last brushstroke. Are you surprised?'

One eyebrow quirked. 'That you could do something

useful with your life? Not at all. I always knew you had it in you,' he answered dryly and she ground her teeth.

'How come every compliment you utter ends up as an insult?' she asked aggrievedly.

He sent her a lopsided grin. 'Takes practice, Red. Plenty of practice.'

Shelby sniffed. 'Well, you can stop practising. Trust me on this. You're good enough already,' she told him with heavy irony. If he got any better, he'd probably reduce her to tears. Glancing his way, she found him watching her and her brows rose.

'My room?' he prompted, and she berated herself for allowing him to divert her into forgetting what she was doing.

Without a word, she led the way down the short hallway which gave access to the bedrooms and bathroom.

'Bathroom,' she declared as she passed the first door. 'This is the guest bedroom,' she added, opening the next door along and switching on the light. 'You should be comfortable in there.'

'I'm sure I shall,' he agreed, walking past her to drop his bag on the bed and glance around. 'Very restful. Which room is yours?'

'The one across the hall,' she revealed reluctantly. 'The third bedroom is now my office.' She indicated the door at the end with a nod of her head.

'I'll have a better look around in the morning. There is just one other thing, though. Do you possess a dressing gown you can wear?'

Shelby frowned faintly. 'Yes. Why?'

'Good. It will spare my blushes if we should bump into each other on the way to the bathroom,' he retorted with a glint in his eye.

She caught her breath at that. 'I have my own bathroom,' she pointed out quickly, then had a mental vision of bumping into him in the morning whilst they were both in their night-clothes. Assuming he wore pyjamas. Automatically she looked at him doubtfully, whereupon Gray shook his head.

'Not since I was a small boy,' he responded, looking as if he was having trouble holding back a grin.

Her chin dropped. 'But you can't walk about here…' She waved her hands as words failed her.

'Buck naked?' he supplied for her, and the grin began to tweak the corner of his mouth. 'Don't worry. I thought it would be best not to put temptation in your way, so I brought plenty of boxer shorts with me.'

She underwent a moment of relief before the rest of what he had said struck home. Of all the nerve! 'What do you mean, put temptation in my way? There isn't anything the least bit tempting about you!' Which was a lie.

'That's reassuring. I wouldn't want you to take advantage of the situation and pounce on me,' Gray retorted mockingly, and Shelby had never felt more like hitting him.

'I do not pounce on men,' she informed him, stressing each word.

His response to that was to shake his head. 'That's a shame. You might enjoy it!'

He was running rings around her, and Shelby felt like a floundering fish caught on the end of his line. 'So help me, Gray. If you don't shut up, I'll…' Annoyingly, nothing came to mind and she was left staring at him helplessly.

'You'll what? Slap me? Kiss me?' he suggested, and that last had her stomach turning over and her heart doing a diving flip-flop.

'Why would I want to kiss you?' she demanded to know. 'You're not my type!' she added, and both of them knew it was a downright lie. 'Oh, I knew this was a mistake. I should never have agreed to this ridiculous plan.'

Gray shook his head. 'Too late to back out now, Red.

You gave your word and I'm holding you to it. I respect your father too much to leave him in the lurch. He's had to worry too much about you over the years as it is. If I can take some of it off his shoulders now, I will. So get used to the idea. I'm here to stay for the foreseeable future.' With which reminder he closed the bedroom door in her face.

Shelby was left gaping at the wood impotently. She was tempted to hammer on the door and make him explain what he had just said. But, before she could do so, a tweak of conscience stayed her hand. She didn't have to ask him. She knew she was responsible for more than one of her father's grey hairs.

Retreating into her bedroom, she closed the door gently then rested back against it, chewing her lip. It wasn't comfortable remembering the crazy things she had done. Gray's indifference to her had had a backlash. She had needed to prove to herself that she was attractive. So what if he didn't know she was alive, there were plenty more fish in the sea. She had gone out to catch all she could—and had been very successful at it. Of course, she had thrown a lot back. After all, catching them had been the point. Pretty soon she had known that she could have any man she wanted. All she had to do was crook her finger.

Wincing, Shelby straightened up and shook her head in disbelief at her own behaviour. She had gone off the rails with a vengeance. She had wielded her power like a weapon, elated by the notion that she was invincible. The world was her oyster. So she had partied and played for all she was worth, and ignored every sensible word her father had said in his attempts to bring her to her senses. That hadn't happened until Gray had taken a hand.

She hadn't known that was what he was doing. Her father had had to go away to Europe on business for a month, leaving her alone. Gray had taken to calling in to see how she was doing, and had gradually showed her a side of himself that he had previously reserved for the women in his life. Oh, he had been so good at it. His wicked flirting had drawn her like a moth to a flame. He had charmed her with incredible ease, because her heart was aching for him. So when he had eventually invited her to dinner there had been no thought of saying no. It had been perfect, even down to his goodnight kiss.

Soon they had been having lunch together too, as well as dinner every night. She had been in seventh heaven. His kisses had melted her bones, and made her want so much more, but Gray had told her he didn't want to rush things. Of course, by then she had believed that he really cared for her, and it had been like a dream come true. They had been the happiest few weeks of her life. She had had every hope of them leading to something more as time had gone.

Then her father had returned, and the first thing he had wanted to know was if she was still seeing Nick Colby, a young man he had heartily disapproved of. Shelby had actually forgotten all about him. Hadn't seen him at all since Gray had started calling. So, of course she had told her father that she wasn't.

Her father had swept her into a bear hug and smiled down at her. 'That's wonderful, darling. Gray must have said something right,' he remarked and, seeing her confused expression, went on to explain. 'I asked him to have a word with you whilst I was away. He said he would see what he could do. That young man is worth his weight in gold,' he added cheerfully, and went on to talk about other things.

Shelby scarcely heard him. She was dying inside. Whilst her heart cracked wide open, she acknowledged that Gray certainly had done something. He had lied and connived, pretending to feel something for her when he didn't—all so that she would stop seeing the man her father didn't care for! She had never felt so betrayed. The pain was almost unbearable. The only thing which salved her pride was the knowledge that Gray didn't know the full extent of her feelings for him. He knew she wanted him, but that was all.

So when she went in search of him at his office she was able to face him without falling apart. He looked surprised when she walked in, then his smile of welcome faded under the icy glare she sent him.

'What's up?' Gray asked cautiously, and she laughed harshly.

'The game,' she returned smartly. Unable to sit, she paced backwards and forwards in front of the desk. 'Dad's back. He was awfully pleased when he heard I was no longer seeing Nick. Seems to me you're in for a bonus!' she added, rounding on him, so angry she could scream.

Gray's face had frozen into an expressionless mask. 'Take it easy, Shelby. Things aren't quite what they seem,' he started to say, but she jumped on that immediately.

'You mean he didn't ask you to find a way to make me stop seeing Nick?' she demanded, and the question started a muscle flexing in his jaw.

'Yes, he asked me,' Gray confirmed, and the hurt of it reached the very depths of her.

Her green eyes withered him. 'My God, I despise you. I thought you had some integrity, but then you do this. How far would you have gone, Gray? Would you have slept with me, just to make sure?'

Gray came around the desk to her, but when he would have placed his hands on her shoulders she backed away. He drew in a deep breath. 'I can explain, if you'll let me,' he told her, but she had heard enough.

'What can you say that I would believe? It's all lies. Everything you've said and done has been lies. I wouldn't trust you to tell me what time of day it was.'

She had walked out then, before the emotions she was feeling overtook her. The pain had gone deep but she had cried in private, putting on a brave face for the world. She had been such a fool, believing his lies, but it wouldn't happen again. Yet for all she hated him for what he had done, stopping loving him wasn't so easy.

One good thing had come out of it, though. She had made important decisions to change her life. Much to her father's relief, she had stopped partying, finished college and put that part of her life behind her for good.

As for Gray, she could neither forgive nor forget. Nor stop wanting him, if tonight was anything to go by.

Telling herself she was a hopeless case, Shelby sighed and kicked off her shoes. Her shoulders and neck ached with the tension the last few hours had induced, but she had a cure for that. Stripping off her clothes, she padded into the *en suite* bathroom to shower, standing under the warm spray until most of the tightness had gone. Then she dried herself and slipped into a thigh-length strappy silk nightie. About to head to the kitchen for a drink, she remembered just in time that she was not alone, and slipped into the silk robe she kept hanging on the bathroom door.

Locking up as she went, she finally made it to the kitchen and made herself a cup of herb tea. Then she headed back towards her bedroom, coming to an abrupt halt in the middle of the lounge when she saw Gray prowling around. He had stripped off his coat and was wearing a sleeveless black vest that showed off his muscular arms and chest. As she had only ever seen him fully clothed before tonight, Shelby found her eyes riveted to the powerful chest and broad shoulders and her stomach twisted as her senses responded to the sensual male lure.

Gray had stopped also, and now stood with hands braced on his hips as he studied her in his turn. 'Nice robe,' he told her after a second or two. 'Doesn't hide much, but I guess you know that already.'

Actually, Shelby hadn't known anything of the sort and her nerves skittered rather deliciously at his words. However, she did drop a hand to her waist, checking that the belt was still securely tied. Then she stood her ground. No man was going to make her run for cover like a blushing schoolgirl.

'Did you expect me to be wearing one of those neck to toe winceyette ones my granny used to have?'

A wolfish twitch of the lips came and went. 'Not any more,' he declared wickedly. 'This is a much better idea. You always did have a body to die for, Red,' Gray observed reminiscently, and her blood started to pulse thickly through her veins.

She hid her response behind a challengingly raised eyebrow. 'Strange, I don't remember you struggling to keep your hands off it.' Quite the contrary. When he had kissed her, he had been careful not to go too far. At the time, she had been touched by this sign of caring. Later, she had realised it was due to the fact that he didn't really want a physical relationship with her.

Gray shrugged a shoulder. 'The situation was an awkward one for me. It didn't mean I wasn't attracted to you. No red-blooded male could fail to want you, and I'm as red-blooded as the next man. However, I had to be cautious.'

Shelby laughed dryly. 'I know. If you went too far you could have lost your job. That was a narrow line you were treading, trying to keep both of us sweet!' she returned with derision.

This time he smiled wryly. 'You'll never know how many cold showers I had over you.'

She wasn't foolish enough to believe that. 'Sure, and you probably had a lot of sleepless nights, too.'

'More than my fair share, as it happens,' he returned smoothly, but she didn't believe that either.

'You never lost sleep over me, Gray. You didn't care enough about me for that!' It hurt to say it, so she quickly changed the conversation. 'What are you doing out here, anyway?' she asked curiously.

'Same as you, Red. Admiring the view,' he replied mockingly. 'Have you seen enough, or would you like me to take off something else?' he came back wickedly.

Her eyes flashed at him over the top of the mug as she took a sip to moisten a mouth gone suddenly dry. A reckless part of her urged her to call his bluff, but she resisted it. 'I'll pass, if you don't mind. Leave me with my fantasies. Reality turns out to be disappointing.'

'Strange, that wasn't the message I was getting a moment ago,' Gray countered, and she laughed.

'Put it down to a trick of the light. Now, tell me what you were really doing. I thought you were going to bed,' Shelby pointed out.

'Just doing my rounds. Checking the doors and windows are locked for the night.'

'I did that already.'

Gray held up his hands, pacifying her before she took umbrage. 'I'm sure you did, but *I* need to know the apartment is secure.'

She had sense enough to know he was right. She also saw that this was her opportunity to retreat gracefully. 'I'll leave you to it, then. Goodnight.' She crossed the room and thought she had made it safely when his soft words followed her down the hall.

'Sweet dreams,' he said, and Shelby could swear she heard soft laughter follow.

Back in her bedroom, she set the mug of tea down and sank on to the edge of the bed with a groan. Her legs were shaking. This was never going to be an easy situation, but now it was going to be worse. She didn't know what game Gray was playing by telling her he was attracted to her, but she didn't doubt he had a reason. Whatever that reason was, it didn't stop her being drawn to him as strongly as ever.

Going by his past record, she wouldn't put it past him to toy with her precisely because he knew she was still attracted to him. There certainly wasn't anything noble in it. If Gray thought she would fall into his arms like a ripe plum just because he declared an interest, he was mistaken. Not after all he had done.

Unfortunately he could turn up the heat without even trying, because he was so lethally attractive. He didn't even have to touch her to make her want him. All she had to do was close her eyes and she could see him as he was moments ago, standing in her lounge, looking mouth-wateringly good.

Sweet dreams? Oh, no, she wasn't going to have sweet dreams tonight. They were going to be hot and heavy, and very, very sexy!

# CHAPTER THREE

ALTHOUGH she hadn't expected to sleep well, Shelby awoke in the morning to realise she must have fallen asleep almost as soon as her head touched the pillow. If she had dreamt of Gray, she didn't remember it. Which was probably just as well.

Feeling remarkably refreshed, she threw back the covers and got up. She had a long day ahead and a meeting with a new client. After that she had to check on an ongoing project. With such a full day in prospect, she knew she would need a good breakfast as she probably wouldn't find time to stop for lunch.

Provided, of course, she was allowed to do so. Gray would be the fly in the ointment.

Cocking her head for sounds of her unwanted guest, she heard nothing and hoped that meant he was still asleep. She knew he intended to dog her footsteps today, but there was no way she could accept that. She'd have to give him the slip. Technically she would be breaking her word, and she experienced a moment's guilt at doing so, but she could see no other way. Her brain started whirring as she stood there, finger tapping her pursed lips. What should she do? In order to outwit him, she would have to move quietly and fast. It was early yet. With any luck she could be out and away before he knew it.

The thought spurred her on to quickly slip into a lightweight silvery-grey trouser suit and a sapphire-blue sleeveless blouse. Combing her hair into a smooth swathe, she applied a light make-up and was ready to go. All she had to do now was find herself something to eat.

Turning the door handle as quietly as possible, Shelby carefully opened the door.

'Going somewhere?' a voice asked mildly and, totally unprepared for it as she was, she let out a shriek loud enough to wake the dead.

Pressing a shaking hand to her chest, where her heart still thundered like a trip-hammer, Shelby positively glowered at Gray, who was leaning nonchalantly against the door post of her spare bedroom. 'You scared the life out of me! What kind of stupid game are you playing?'

'The very question I was just about to ask you,' Gray responded. He was fully dressed in dark trousers and a white T-shirt that clung to his body like a second skin and outlined every toned muscle of his chest and arms. It also showed off his tanned skin perfectly. A fact her senses noted with every sign of pleasure, judging from the way her own skin prickled and the nerves in her stomach tensed. So much so that it was hard to drag her eyes away—again.

She managed it eventually and rushed to her own defence. 'I'm not playing any sort of game,' she denied, a faint wash of guilty colour staining her cheeks. 'You were the one who was lurking!'

Pushing himself upright, Gray folded his arms across his chest, a move that only served to emphasis the leashed power of the man to Shelby. He had the kind of body a woman could fantasise about exploring, she decided appreciatively, and she should know. She had fantasised about him countless times over the years. At which point she caught herself up sharply when she realised where her thoughts were wandering. This was neither the time nor the place.

'You might call it lurking, sweetheart. I prefer to call it waiting.'

Knowing she was in the wrong, her only defence was

attack. 'OK, what were you *waiting* for?' she asked sharply, chin raised at a jaunty angle.

'Knowing you as I do, I was waiting for you to do something just like this. Where do you think you were going, Red?'

She saw no reason to confirm his suspicions that she had been making a bid to escape him. 'If you must know, I was heading for the kitchen to get some breakfast,' she lied, and started to do that very thing.

Stepping forward with the intention of brushing past him, she discovered that Gray had other plans. He refused to budge. Shelby found her eyes were level with the cleft in his chin. Which meant she only had to angle her head slightly to see his mouth, and somehow she couldn't stop herself doing it.

He had a beautiful mouth. Very male, very tantalising. She had yearned to kiss him again for years, and his closeness sent a shiver of anticipation through her. How would his mouth feel now? she wondered. Would he respond if she were to press her lips to his? Not that she was about to put it to the test. Oh, no. She might long to know, but she had more sense than to show it.

'Cut out the games, Red. Where were you going *after* breakfast?' Gray's frosty tone cut through her musings.

Shelby started guiltily and glanced up, licking her lips in a tiny betraying gesture. Shock ran through her when she saw his eyes drop and follow the movement. Captivated, she tried it again, with the same result. She gasped mentally. In her experience, when a man looked that closely at a woman's mouth it meant he was thinking of kissing her. Could Gray really be thinking that?

Of course, she had to meet his eyes to check it out, and found their blue depths regarding her impatiently. 'Don't try to disarm me with your feminine wiles. I want an answer to my question,' he told her in no uncertain terms, emphasising his words so that she jumped.

Her eyes narrowed. 'Why would I use my feminine wiles? They don't work on you, remember?'

Gray laughed sardonically. 'I know full well what your wiles can do, and they work perfectly. Now stop prevaricating and tell me what I want to know!'

It was amazingly hard to think when Gray had just told her that she did have the power to entrance him. It opened up certain unexplored possibilities, but she didn't have time to consider them.

Shelby contrived to shrug casually. 'I was going to work, of course.'

'Not without me, you're not,' he corrected, equally casually, and her eyes narrowed on his as she frowned.

'You can't go with me.' There was no way. Absolutely no way was he going to work with her.

Gray had other ideas. 'You don't have an option. Either I go with you, or you stay here. Your choice,' he declared firmly, eyes daring her to challenge him on this.

'It's out of the question! You must see that,' she said, appealing for his understanding, but he remained unmoved.

'All I see is that your word doesn't mean very much,' he returned sternly, and the accusation stung, for she knew he had a point. However, this was important so she tried another tack.

'Come on, Gray, be reasonable. I've more than met you halfway. I agreed to a bodyguard. I agreed to your staying in my home. But I can't possibly take you with me whilst I visit a new client. How would I explain your presence?' She might have been talking to a block of stone for all the good it did.

'You can make up any sort of story you like for my being there, but I *will* be there,' he said in a tone that brooked no further argument.

Shelby closed her eyes and counted to ten. What on earth was she going to do with him tagging along at her side? How she would have liked to make a dash for the door, but she knew better than to try. Not only would it be un-dignified, but she had little doubt that he was stronger and faster than she was. He *would* keep her here by force if he had to.

Folding her arms, she stared at him in bitter frustration. 'If this is how you treated your other client that time, I'm not surprised they ended up dead,' she flung at him, and was shocked rather than pleased to see the colour drain from his face as he straightened up, body as tense as a bowstring. With instant compunction she knew she had been unfair, but before she could take it back he spoke.

'The victim wasn't a client but a friend, so I would ad-vise you to be careful what you accuse me of,' he informed her in a tone as hard as granite, and she could tell the subject was still raw.

Biting her lip, she looked at him cautiously. 'I'm sorry. That was out of line.'

'It was,' Gray agreed icily. 'You might not give a damn what happens to you, but I do. I'm prepared to lay down my life to keep you safe. What are you prepared to do?'

Her heart lurched. Would he really do that? she won-dered, but one look at his uncompromising expression as-sured her that he would. It made her feel ashamed. Dear God, she loved him despite everything, and the very last thing she wanted was for him to get seriously hurt. What would she do without him in the world? It didn't bear think-ing about, so she did the only sensible thing.

She looked at him steadily. 'If I agree to let you come with me, would you promise to take care of yourself too?' she countered, knowing she absolutely would not be able to live with his death on her conscience.

The tension drained out of him visibly at her question,

and his inclination of the head was every bit as ironic as his next words. 'I have no intention of shuffling off this mortal coil any time soon, so you have a deal,' he confirmed, holding out his hand.

After a moment's hesitation, Shelby took it. The contact was brief, but the tingling heat which travelled up her arm and along her veins remained long after he had released her hand and stepped back.

'So, does this mean you're beginning to take the whole thing seriously?' he wanted to know, and she shook her head.

'Not exactly. I might despise you, but I wouldn't want anything really bad to happen to you,' she conceded with an offhand shrug. Gray laughed softly.

'I'm glad to hear it, if more than a little surprised.'

Shelby refused to bite, for she had just thought of something. 'As you're planning on going everywhere I go, then you should know I've arranged to meet friends at a charity function tonight.' She'd been looking forward to it and had no intention of staying home. 'I hope you've brought a decent suit with you. It's black tie.'

Having got her compliance over work, Gray knew when to back off. 'Don't worry. I won't embarrass you.'

For all that she hated him, the part of her that still loved him would never be ashamed to be seen with him, for he always looked gorgeous in a suit. Not that she would ever say as much. 'Hah! You're a constant embarrassment to me. If you weren't a necessary evil, I wouldn't be seen d…' She broke off, realising what she had been about to say.

Gray merely looked amused. 'The whole reason for my being here is so that nobody has to see you dead. Now, weren't you saying something about breakfast?'

'Er, yes,' She nodded, not feeling quite so hungry now. 'Have you eaten?'

'Are you offering to cook for me, Red?'

'In your dreams!'

He followed her down the hall and into the kitchen, and she was aware of him every inch of the way. 'Actually, I ate an hour ago.' He saw her looking round for signs of the meal and tsked. 'Sorry to disappoint you, but I'm fully house-trained, Red. I clean up after myself.'

'That puts you in a minority of men, I imagine,' she responded dryly. Getting a bowl from the cupboard, she filled it with cereal and sliced bananas and strawberries on the top, then added milk.

Gray hooked out a chair from the table, twisted it around and sat down, resting his arms on the back. 'I can do any household chore, including cleaning the toilet.'

'Quite a catch, then!' Shelby riposted, sitting down opposite him. With the width of the table between them she should have felt more at ease but, no matter how big the proportions of the kitchen were, they shrank now that he was in the room. Her awareness of him was growing exponentially and, just as she had feared, she knew she would never be able to eat in here without picturing him as he looked now. Far too attractive and tempting as sin.

To prove it, one lazy eyebrow quirked her way, giving him that devastating rakish look she liked so much. 'You don't think a woman would want me for my looks?'

Clamping down on her responsive senses, she sent him a mocking smile. 'You know you're drop dead gorgeous, so stop fishing for compliments!'

Gray's blue eyes took on an intriguing gleam. 'Isn't that a strange way to describe a man you hate and despise?'

Shelby managed to look him in the eye and keep her colour under control. 'It doesn't exactly thrill me that I still find you attractive,' she told him honestly. 'You might be good to look at, but women want more than a pretty face.

You flit from woman to woman like a bee. The truth is you've got no staying power, Gray.'

He raised a lazy eyebrow questioningly. 'Is that so? I hate to contradict a lady, but you'd be surprised at my constancy.'

Shelby had good reason to look doubtful. 'You're seriously trying to tell me there's one woman out there who's important to you? I don't believe it!' she scoffed.

He accepted that with a tilt of his head. 'Nevertheless, she exists. I fell in love with her a long time ago,' he confirmed, and in an instant her heart felt as if it had been violently wrenched apart.

It was one thing to know he didn't feel anything for her other than a strong physical attraction, it was quite another to know there was someone he did care for. Jealousy was a bitter taste in her mouth. A small voice wanted to cry out: why couldn't it be me? The truth was, the heart went its own way. Obeyed its own rules. Swallowing her dismay, she looked at him curiously.

'Why haven't you snapped her up?' she asked the obvious question, to which he grimaced.

'Unforeseen circumstances keep getting in the way, and our lives went in different directions,' he revealed matter-of-factly.

Shelby frowned. 'She doesn't know how you feel?'

Gray's shrug was resigned. 'I never had the chance to tell her.'

Shelby stared down at her breakfast, feeling strangely sad. If he was to be believed, he was in the same boat she was, caring for someone who didn't know they existed. Secretly she shared a moment of empathy with him.

'I'm sorry,' she said simply, and drew an ironic smile from him.

'Pity for the enemy, Red? That's unlike you,' he taunted,

and the moment of empathy was lost under a flash of anger at his response.

'You're impossible. She doesn't know how well off she is,' she snapped back. 'Without a doubt you'd find a way to stab her in the back. You're very good at manipulating situations.'

'Put it down to my training,' he advised in amusement.

Shelby concentrated on finishing what was left in her dish before shooting him a haughty look. 'I had no idea they taught you to lie and cheat women in the army. Even now I can't imagine you in uniform. How could you stand to be given orders when you like your own way so much?'

Gray rubbed a thumbnail along the ridge of his nose and gave her a wry look. 'I was an officer. Which meant *I* gave the orders.'

Tipping her head, Shelby studied him. 'I suppose I should have guessed. Now I come to think of it, you did have shorter hair for a time. You wear it longer now.'

There was a roguish gleam in his eye as he watched her watching him. 'I like women to run their fingers through it,' he said just a tad huskily, and it sent a tiny shock wave along her nervous system.

The thought having been planted in her brain, Shelby couldn't help but wonder what it would feel like. Silky and full of life, was her guess. Of course, her fingers started to itch to test it out, which was never going to happen. 'Thanks for the heads up, but why are you bothering to tell me of all people?'

Cerulean eyes held hers. 'Oh, let's just say for future reference,' he told her, and now her nerves did a spectacular somersault.

She arched her brows mockingly. 'What makes you think I would ever want to run my fingers through your hair?'

'You might decide to try a spot of seduction again.'

Her heart skipped a beat, even though she knew he was

just playing games again. 'Do I look that stupid to you? Can you really see that happening with the way I feel about you?'

Gray shrugged his shoulders. 'Why not? For all that you profess to despise me, you want me. You were even thinking about kissing me a few minutes ago.'

Shelby caught back a tiny gasp as her nerves jolted in shock. She hadn't been expecting him to say that. 'Was I indeed?' she challenged, and he smiled mockingly.

'We both know what you were thinking. Why didn't you do it?'

She had no idea what the purpose of this game was, only that she didn't find it amusing. 'Been there. Done that. You pushed me away that time, remember?'

'You were slightly the worse for drink. What else could I do?' Gray answered and, just as easily as that, there was an unexpected nuance in the air.

That came from way out in left field, and Shelby shook her head to clear it. 'Hold on a second. Are you trying to tell me that had I not been the slightest tad tipsy, you would have acted differently that evening?'

Gray merely shrugged again. 'We'll never know, will we? You *were* slightly the worse for wine, and I have rules about such things.'

She stared at him with a sinking feeling. To know that the Dutch courage she had needed had worked against her was a bitter pill to swallow. It made her response all the more waspish. 'Very noble, I'm sure.'

Gray stood up and replaced the chair. 'You'd be surprised how noble I can be.'

Still inwardly smarting from his confession, and the knowledge that she had come that close to realising her dream, Shelby rose too. Not that it changed anything. She would only ever have been a substitute for the real thing. True, she hadn't known that at the time. She had gone on dreaming, and he had gone on to perpetrate the heinous crime for which she had sworn never to forgive him. Now he was playing a new game, seemingly intent on getting her to explore with him the attraction they shared. It was a potentially hurtful one—though he didn't know that. He had no idea how deep her feelings for him went. She wanted to keep it that way. Which meant she must not let him get too close. A relationship of any kind was out of the question.

'Was it the same nobility that stopped you kissing me just now? We both know you were thinking about it,' she said, firing his own words back at him, and he didn't deny wanting to kiss her.

'No,' he answered with a shake of his head. 'The fact is, mixing business with pleasure is dangerous. Right now I should be concentrating on protecting you, nothing more. Allowing myself to be side-tracked could get you harmed.'

Oh, he certainly knew all the right things to say to reel a woman in. She played along, waiting to see where this was going. 'I had no idea I had such an unsettling effect on you.' If asked she wouldn't have doubted for a second that he was strong enough to keep both parts of his life separate. Yet here he was implying otherwise.

Gray shook his head wryly. 'I knew you were going to be trouble when you were in your teens. Even then you had the power to break a man's resolve.'

To Shelby, who remembered everything about that time with crystal clarity, this was a total contradiction. 'I thought I was a child without the allure to attract a man like you?' she reminded him curtly.

'I lied,' he returned simply. 'Like I said, you were slightly over the limit, and I have rules. I needed to put you at arm's length in a hurry, and that was the quickest way.'

Late in the day though it was, those words were a small

sop to her pride. To know that he had been acting chivalrously healed a wound. However, there were bigger ones that those words didn't touch.

'So, it was nobility that stopped you taking me to bed the other time, was it?' she said, challenging his reasoning, wondering what he would choose to say in mitigation.

He went still, eyes locking with hers. 'Why don't you tell me?' he countered softly.

Shelby's lip curled. 'I think Dad's orders specifically stopped you from going too far, and you followed them to the letter, didn't you? It didn't bother you whether you had me or not. It was all a means to an end!'

Something flared in the depths of his eyes. 'Oh, I wanted you, Red, make no mistake about that. The rest was bad timing.'

'You mean Dad letting the cat out of the bag before you could say anything?' she jeered with a toss of her head.

'I had hoped for more time with you,' he told her, and she affected a look of disbelief, though his words played havoc with her senses.

'What on earth for? Your job was done,' she gibed, and Gray ground his teeth in irritation at her tone.

'Don't put yourself down.' His voice was suddenly serious. 'From an enticing young lady, you'd turned into a stunningly desirable woman.'

Her brows arched delicately as she heard that. 'The kind of woman you'd still like to get up close and personal with?'

'Very close. Very personal,' he admitted with just that husky edge to his voice which hinted at hidden fires and steaming hot passion.

It sent a powerful thrill of anticipation through her system, and it was all she could do to keep a cool head. 'Wow, you really know how to turn up the heat. I guess most women would be falling at your feet right about now?'

His lips twitched. 'Something like that.'

Shelby stared at him, anger starting a slow simmer inside her. She knew the game he was playing now. He wanted her and believed he could have her, if he played his cards right. Well, he was about to find out how wrong he was. She looked him squarely in the eye. 'Unluckily for you, I'm not most women.'

Gray folded his arms and studied her carefully. 'No, you're not,' he agreed, and there was an odd sense of satisfaction in the way he said it that puzzled her.

Walking over to him, she placed her palms against his cheeks, ignoring the prickle of heat which transmitted itself to her senses. 'I wouldn't get involved with you if you were the last man on earth,' she declared witheringly and stepped back with a shudder of distaste.

Gray's nostrils flared as he absorbed the insult, and an intense gleam danced in his eyes. 'That's your pride talking. Don't let it get in the way of what you want,' he advised seductively, and she raised her chin defiantly.

'Wanting and having are two different things. I freely admit to wanting you, and if I went along with your little plan I'm sure the experience would be…ravishing. However, I'd have to live with myself afterwards, and you wouldn't be worth the trouble,' she returned with feline intensity.

To her utter chagrin, he laughed and headed for the door. 'I shall have great pleasure in making you take that back. Once this is over, you'll be purring instead of spitting, little cat,' he added just before he disappeared from view.

Shelby's smile vanished abruptly. She stared at her hands, which still tingled from touching him, and wondered for a wild moment if she might still be dreaming, but she knew she wasn't. Gray really had just turned her world on its head.

He was attracted to her. Had been for a long time. Even

when he had been following her father's orders. That just made the sense of betrayal worse. Even his wanting of her came secondary to his work. Now, he thought, because she was still attracted to him, they could have an affair. Of all the nerve! Her blood was absolutely boiling. She was not going to fling herself into his arms, saying, Take me, I'm yours. Oh, no.

She loved him…though for the life of her she couldn't say why right now. There was no way she could overlook what he had done just because she wanted him physically! How dared he assume she was ripe for the picking? Some way, somehow, she was going to make him sorry for thinking that.

She kept this thought with her as she rinsed her dirty dishes in the sink and stacked them in the dishwasher. Then it was time to go.

Gray met her in the hallway and she couldn't help doing a double take when she saw him. Added to the black trousers and white T-shirt was a black jacket, from where he pulled a pair of designer sunglasses which he slipped on as she joined him. This was not the conservative businesslike Gray she knew at all. This Gray had wow factor! Good enough to eat and heart-trippingly sexy. Not that she was going to allow that to affect her decision about him.

She looked him up and down with a critical eye. 'Who would have thought there was a hunk hidden under all those grey business suits?' she said in mock amazement.

'You approve?'

'There's scarcely a red-blooded woman alive who wouldn't. You'll be beating them off with a stick,' Shelby added with wry honesty.

'But not you,' Gray surmised, holding up her car keys. 'You'll be driving. Try and keep your concentration on the road, not me.'

She shot him a haughty look as she took the keys and

went out ahead of him. 'Oh, please. You're not that irre-sistible.'

'Good. I'd be quite happy with fairly irresistible at the right time and place,' Gray returned, shutting the door behind them.

'And the right time and place would be?' she asked, calling the lift.

'I'll let you know when we reach it.'

Despite her determination not to respond, her nerves gave a tiny leap and she shivered. 'I'll be there, will I?'

'I'm certainly hoping so.' The lift arrived and they stepped inside.

Shelby laughed wryly. 'I'll say this for you, Gray. You're certainly not lacking in confidence.'

His responding laugh was soft and husky. 'It's the only way to get what you want.'

And he had decided he wanted her, she thought grimly. Well, they would see about that.

When the lift stopped, Gray put out a hand to prevent her from stepping out into the car park. He took an all-encompassing look around before taking her by the upper arm and urging her towards their parked cars.

'I feel foolish!' she exclaimed, though she kept her voice down instinctively.

His hold tightened fractionally. 'When you fall at my feet I don't want it to be because someone's taken a pot-shot at you!' he growled back sardonically.

'That isn't going to happen for any reason,' Shelby was quick to point out, using the remote to unlock the car doors as they walked.

'Put it this way, Red. You have to be alive to resist me. Let's keep it that way!'

She said nothing, merely climbed into her car and waited for him to join her. It was going to be a long day.

The journey out to her new client was uneventful, if you ignored the snarl of traffic. Once they were through it, Shelby made good time to the address she had been given. It was a very exclusive area. The understated aura of wealth oozed out from the parallel rows of detached houses. Turning into a manicured driveway, she parked the car before the door and turned to Gray, more in hope than expectation.

'I don't suppose you'll be staying in the car?'

'Not a chance. I need to be where you are,' he answered, just as she had expected.

Shelby reached for her briefcase and took from it a notebook and pen which she handed to him. 'OK, here are the rules. You take these and make notes. It doesn't matter what you write, just look efficient. Above all, don't say anything. Leave all the talking to me. Got it?'

With his sunglasses on she couldn't see his eyes, but the twist of his lips told her he was laughing at her again. 'Down to the last dotted i and crossed t.'

She looked at him doubtfully, but knew there was nothing she could do. 'This is going to be disastrous. I can feel it in my bones!' she exclaimed helplessly as she exited from the car. Climbing up a flight of steps, she took a steadying breath and rang the bell.

The door was opened by an elegantly dressed woman of that indeterminate age which could have been late thirties or early forties. 'Mrs Tyrwhit-Jones? How do you do? I'm...'

'Shelby Greer. I'm so pleased to meet you at last. Do call me Antonia,' Antonia Tyrwhit-Jones finished for her in a breathlessly excited voice. 'Do come in. I've heard so much about you. All my friends tell me how talented you are. I can't wait for you to do wonders with this old house.'

'I'll do my very best,' Shelby responded when she was allowed to get a word in. She could see the woman's eyes going beyond her to study Gray, who had followed them inside, and saw them widen as he drew her full attention. Much to Shelby's annoyance, they then turned decidedly predatory.

'Well, now, who might you be?' Antonia Tyrwhit-Jones asked with rather more than general interest. Fingering the pearls she wore at her throat, she looked Gray up and down with avaricious eyes.

Shelby experienced a violent wave of unadulterated dislike. Her expressed feelings notwithstanding, she took exception to the woman looking at Gray the way she was. In consequence, her reply was designed to put an end to the woman's interest.

'This is Serge. He'll be assisting me today. Taking notes, that sort of thing.' She introduced them.

Speculative eyes looked him over yet again as Antonia held her hand out. 'Pleased to meet you, Serge.' Gray removed his sunglasses and slipped them into his breast pocket, shook hands but said nothing. The other woman looked curiously at Shelby. 'I guess he's the strong silent type. He's very handsome, though. I just adore a man with muscles.'

Shelby pretty much decided there and then that she and Antonia Tyrwhit-Jones were not going to get along. However, she couldn't yet afford to turn away a prospective client. Luckily, there were other ways to skin a cat. Taking the other woman by the arm, she drew her aside, leaning in conversationally as she did so. 'Oh, I know. There's a catch, though. I'm afraid you're not his type.'

Automatically the woman raised a hand to her bleached blonde hair. 'Not blondes?'

Shelby gave her a woman to woman look. 'Not the right sex,' she declared in a loud whisper, and caught the sound of a strangled protest from behind her.

Her client was suitably deflated and looked at Gray with

a shake of her head. 'It can't be true. What a waste! Oh, well, never mind. Now tell me, Shelby, would you like to look at the upstairs rooms first or the downstairs? Or we could have some coffee?'

Having successfully diverted the other woman, Shelby smiled brightly. 'The upstairs rooms first, I think, Antonia. Then I'll make my way down. We can discuss your requirements and any ideas I come up with over coffee later. I like to get an overall feel of the place first.'

'Just as you like. I'm sure you know best,' she conceded, though, as the other woman led the way upstairs, Shelby had the feeling Antonia Thyrwit-Jones was not going to be an easy woman to work with.

Having given them a brief tour of the layout, during which she sent Gray more than one wistful glance, Antonia finally left them alone in the main bedroom, departing with a waggle of her fingers. Shelby let her breath out in a whoosh as she relaxed. The feeling lasted for maybe five seconds, then Gray narrowed his eyes on her.

'Serge?' he queried in disgust, and Shelby couldn't help bursting into a fit of giggles.

She hid her face behind her hands. 'I had to do something. I think she was about to jump your bones.'

'Well, she isn't going to do that now, is she? Not when you told her I wasn't interested in women,' he growled, moving towards her in a purposeful manner.

In the interest of self-preservation Shelby began to back away. 'Take it easy, Gray. It was just a joke!'

'Joke? Do you see me laughing?' he demanded in a tone that set her nerves quivering.

Shelby continued to retreat as he advanced. 'Where's your sense of humour?'

Teeth flashed whitely as he grinned menacingly. 'Lost under a powerful desire to strangle you!'

'Would it help if I apologised?' Shelby asked, just as the

back of her knees came in contact with the bed and, unable to prevent it, she sat down abruptly.

'It wouldn't help if you grovelled from here to doomsday,' he growled, hovering over her so that she fell backwards on to the covers. 'You're going to be sorry you said that, Red.'

Heart pounding, Shelby stared up at him. 'What are you going to do?' she asked breathlessly, moistening her lips with the tip of her tongue. This morning it had been a purely nervous response and she had seen the result. Now she used it as a diversionary tactic, and it worked like a dream.

Gray froze, closing his eyes as he took in a deep breath. 'You had to do it, didn't you?'

Shelby smothered a giggle and blinked, feigning ignorance. 'What?'

Opening his eyes, he speared her on the end of a blue gaze. 'That sexy little trick with your tongue.'

It was highly erotic, lying on the bed with him looming over her, and her breathing went awry as her senses responded to his closeness. 'You mean this?' she asked, doing it again and catching the faint sound of a groan issuing from him. 'It's a nervous gesture.'

'It's damned distracting. That's what it is, you little tease!' Gray corrected as he straightened up and moved away from her.

Sitting up again, hiding an urge to smile, Shelby smoothed down her hair. First round to her. 'I had no idea I could put you off your stride just by licking my lips.' Now that she did, she wondered how she could use it to her advantage.

'Believe me, Red, there are a lot of things you don't know you can do,' he informed her cryptically and, not surprisingly, she was intrigued by the notion. There was more?

'What things?' she wanted to know, but Gray had said all he was going to. When it came to teasing, he had his own methods. Disappointment had her stomach sinking. 'You can't just leave it there.' She wanted to know what powers she had that could be used against him.

He stared at her, a smile slowly curving his lips. 'I have left it there. You can't expect me to do all your work for you.'

Which meant she was going to have to go by trial and error. That could turn out to be hazardous, but he left her no choice. 'I hate it when you say things like that!' she complained with a decided sniff of displeasure. Which was water off a duck's back to Gray, who simply stood there, arms crossed and an inscrutable smile on his face.

'The trouble with you is you've led a pampered life-style,' he told her in the next breath, and Shelby took instant exception.

'I've never been pampered. Indulged from time to time, but never pampered,' she corrected him whilst she opened her briefcase and took out a retractable tape measure.

'You mean none of the men you've dated have ever bought you things?' Gray wanted to know, watching her take measurements with speed and efficiency.

Shelby shook her head. 'I discouraged it. Men who buy you things tend to think they own you,' she explained. 'Make yourself useful and take a note of these dimensions,' she went on, reeling off the figures she had, then going on to add more.

Gray glanced up from the pad he was writing on. 'Some men never learn that you have to let a wild thing have room to breathe and roam. That way they'll come to you of their own accord.'

She looked at him in surprise, having been called many things but never that. 'You think I'm wild? I think I'm insulted.'

He laughed. 'Don't be. You're not wild, but you have spirit. Reining you in would be a crime.'

To her surprise, his words caused a bubbly sensation in her stomach and she pressed a hand over it to settle it down. She couldn't let him see he had touched a nerve. 'So, hypothetically speaking, what you're saying is this. If we were married, you wouldn't tie me down?' she asked lightly.

'Don't get me wrong. I'm male enough to want to make certain you know you're mine but, having done that, you would have all the freedom you craved,' he confirmed, then laughed. 'Realistically, of course, you and I are about as close to getting married as the earth is from the moon.'

Even though it was entirely what she would expect him to say, it cut her to the quick. 'Just as well, as I want nothing to do with you, one way or the other,' Shelby shot back mockingly, hiding her wounds. She turned to the window she had been sizing up.

'If ever there were two people not meant for each other, we're them,' Gray mused, and she glanced over her shoulder.

'Absolutely. Any relationship requires trust, and you've already proved I can't trust you,' she informed him with a frosty smile, turning back to the job in hand.

It was a downright shame, because she knew that, given the chance, she could make him happy. However, he had made it more than clear that what he wanted from her had nothing to do with love. Marriage was not even a remote possibility. Which brought his interest down to pure old fashioned sex. Which she had nothing against, and had an idea that with him it would be fantastic. Her heart, though, would still hunger. She hadn't ever imagined that she would be one to suffer from unrequited love. Life had a way of playing tricks on a person.

'We'd better get on or Antonia will be back. I don't think

I could bear to see her sending you any more disappointed glances.'

Gray made a growling sound in his throat. 'Hell, no. The woman makes me nervous.'

Shelby laughed with genuine amusement. 'Now that I don't believe!'

'Trust me, Red, there's a look in her eye that says she'd like to try and return me to the straight and narrow. You might have to pull her off me,' he said, very much tongue-in-cheek.

She glanced back over her shoulder again. 'Don't worry. I'll protect you. I didn't like the way she was looking at you, anyway.'

One eyebrow quirked. 'I noticed. Why is that?'

She hadn't allowed for the question, but the answer was easy. 'Why? Because you're off limits for the duration, remember?' Shelby declared dryly. 'I'm not suffering this thing on my own!'

'Shame. I thought you might have being going to tell me she was poaching on your preserve,' he said, shooting her a rakish look.

Shelby very nearly cut her finger as the steel tape shot back into its holder. 'Ouch!' she gasped, sucking the damaged digit. 'You've got to be kidding!' she exclaimed derisively.

Gray's lips twitched and there was a wicked light in his eyes. 'It was just a thought.'

She shook her head sadly. 'Well, you can keep those kind of thoughts to yourself in future. You're only here because of this ridiculous threat. It changes nothing between us. You're still a rat. I still despise you, and probably will till the day I die. Which, as you are here to make sure that doesn't happen too soon, leaves years of hating ahead of me.'

Gray heard her out, then had the gall to smile. 'If you

put as much passion into making love with me as you do into despising me, we're in for interesting times. OK, then, what's next?'

Shelby would dearly have liked to throw something at him, but in a client's house it was out of the question. So she satisfied herself by turning her back on him. Lord, let this be over soon, she prayed, because the way things were going she wasn't going to come out of it unscathed!

# CHAPTER FOUR

SHELBY prepared for the charity dinner with extra-special care. Although it wasn't the way she had expected to spend the evening, she was going to be with Gray. That being the case, she was determined to look her best. Actually, her unspoken plan was to knock him totally off balance. She wanted him to see what he was missing. What he was never going to have.

She had already bought a new dress for the occasion before the current situation had occurred. It was a shimmering affair in shades of turquoise and green, with tiny straps to hold it up, and was so light she barely felt as if she had it on. Her reflection in the mirror showed her an elegant young woman with perfect make-up, her red hair piled on top of her head in an ageless and very feminine style. A matching stole draped across her neck and over each shoulder, and sandals and evening purse completed the ensemble.

Shelby thought she looked good, but what would Gray think? Would he be smitten? Not that she seriously wanted him to be. She meant what she had said this morning. However, there was nothing wrong in taunting him. That he did deserve. In spades.

A sharp knock on her bedroom door caused her to turn her head quickly.

'Taxi's waiting downstairs,' Gray called out, and her heart upped its beat all of a sudden.

'I'll be there in a second,' she answered, and pressed a hand over her stomach. Suddenly she felt incredibly nervous. Even her palms felt moist, and she rubbed them on her thighs to dry them. She was crazy! All this anxiety was because she wanted him to like what he saw. More than that, she wanted him to want what he saw. That way, when she rebuffed his advances, the laugh would be on him. And if that wasn't nice of her, too bad. He had been laughing at her for too long.

Knowing that she had taken all the time she could, Shelby took a steadying breath and left the room. In her lounge, Gray was waiting by the fireplace, his hands hidden in the trouser pockets of his dress suit. She must have made some sound, for he glanced round, his eyes automatically running over her. Hers did the same to him, and her heart turned over. He looked—magnificent.

Then her gaze left his clothes and travelled to his face, and there in his eyes she saw what she had long been hoping to see, and it very nearly caused her heart to stop. As their gazes locked she saw the unmistakable heat and flames of a powerful desire. He wanted her. Even though she had been hoping to see it, it sent shock waves rippling along her nerves, heightening her senses, so that she could feel an electric intensity in the air between them.

'Stunning,' Gray declared simply, never taking his eyes off her.

'Back at you,' Shelby responded, holding his gaze and feeling the temperature rise as her blood heated up.

'If it was your plan to make it difficult for me to keep my hands off you, you've succeeded,' he added in that kind of male growl guaranteed to set her nerves fluttering expectantly.

Shelby hastily reminded herself she was not supposed to get caught up in the moment, and ran a hand from her waist to her hip. 'I'm glad you like it.'

He walked towards her slowly. 'I'm going to have my work cut out keeping my mind on my job tonight.'

She was pleased she had achieved her first objective and

knocked him off balance this way. Of course, she hadn't meant to get knocked off balance herself in the process. 'I thought I was your job, and your plan was to keep an eye on me,' she reminded him, her breath hitching in her throat as he stopped mere inches away. Maybe this was not going to be as easy as she'd thought. She hadn't taken the strength of her own responses into account.

'By not looking at you. How can I watch your back if I'm watching your front?' he asked her in that same seductive growl.

He was good at this. She had to remind herself that he was the enemy here. Taking a deep breath, she regained some of her equilibrium. 'Seems like you have a problem. Let me solve it for you. Take the evening off. I promise not to tell,' she added in a confidential whisper.

He shook his head regretfully. 'No can do, sweetheart. I promised your father I'd take care of you.'

The words were all she needed to get her feet back on the ground and return her pulse to normal. She was just a job to him tonight. He was under orders, and she knew how single-minded he was about obeying her father's wishes. Her smile faded.

'Ah, yes, the magic words. You promised Dad. Where would you be without them? When he says jump, your only response is to ask how high!' she responded scathingly, turning towards the front door.

'In respect of you, certainly. You're a responsibility I don't take lightly,' Gray informed her with some impatience as they left the flat and took the lift down to the lobby.

Shelby looked at him mockingly. 'Sounds to me like the job's getting to you,' she taunted, but he merely shrugged the comment off.

'I'll survive. Cold showers usually help. It won't be the first one I've taken because of you, Red,' he added dryly.

Her brows rose in genuine surprise. 'I had no idea.'

One eyebrow quirked her way. 'A man has to have some secrets.'

'So why are you telling me?'

Walking through the lobby, Gray took hold of her arm as they approached the outside door. His steps slowed as he took an all encompassing look round before they passed outside. 'Because now you're intrigued,' he told her, holding open the door of the taxi, following her in seconds later. Giving the directions to the driver, he sat back and glanced at her. 'Women who are intrigued by a man come back for more,' he explained and she tutted reprovingly.

'Said with typical male arrogance. Anyway, should you be revealing your strategy like this?' she asked, frowning as he turned in his seat to study the road behind them. Clearly satisfied with what he saw, he turned back and gave her a sardonic look.

'You already know the best tricks, Red. You use them all the time yourself,' he shot back.

It was true. However, she had never actually tried any of her repertoire on him. She might have, had she known then what she knew now. When he had taken the initiative later she had simply followed her heart. He must be a hell of a poker player because she hadn't got even the smallest inkling that in the first instance he had been attracted and in the second that it was all a ploy. Which had been his intention, and it was something she would do well to remember.

'Why did you always hide this wild attraction you want me to believe you always felt for me?' she asked out of curiosity.

'You're the boss's daughter. Only a fool would mess with that situation,' he responded dryly. She got his point, except for one thing.

'I'm still the boss's daughter,' Shelby pointed out, making him grin.

'True, but you're not eighteen any longer. You're an independent woman.'

'And, as you can't have the woman you really want, you'll make do with what's available?' she rejoined sardonically and received a long cool look for her pains.

'Let's leave her out of this, shall we?' Gray suggested in a voice that said she'd be wise to heed his warning. 'Besides, getting involved with you could hardly be called 'making do',' he added with wry laughter, and took yet another look out the rear window.

Shelby rolled her eyes heavenwards. 'I wish you wouldn't keep doing that. It's driving me crazy!' she complained in mild exasperation.

'Stop complaining or I'll strangle you myself,' Gray threatened lightly.

'Come on, Gray, admit it,' Shelby encouraged, twisting to face him. 'You don't really think somebody is going to shoot at me from a passing car any more than I do.'

She was expecting a grin but he remained serious. 'Not in this country, but we could be followed. An opportunist needs only seconds to act. I don't intend to give him the chance.'

Shelby couldn't help but glance out the rear window herself. 'Are we being followed?' she asked nervously, wondering how she would recognise if they were.

'No, so you can sit back and relax. All you need worry about right now is if your lipstick is still on. Leave the rest to me.'

She subsided back into her seat and sent him a stony glare. 'Don't be so damned patronising. I have a brain, you know.'

'Now would be a good time to start using it, then,' Gray commanded caustically, setting her back up instantly.

'You know what I think? This love of your life could see what you were like, and got out whilst the going was good!' she gibed, and got his full attention. The chill in his eyes was awesome.

'Don't go there, Red. I won't warn you a third time,' he said in a soft voice that struck as hard as steel.

After holding his gaze for a moment, Shelby looked away, swallowing a lump in her throat. She didn't know why she was being so catty about this unknown woman. Which was a lie, because of course she knew. The woman had something she would never possess. His heart. It hurt, proving, if proof were necessary, that she cared. Loved him beyond reason, for reason would have told her to hate him a long time ago. Deciding she was a hopeless case, she sighed heavily.

The remainder of the fairly short journey passed in uncomfortable silence and if it annoyed her that Gray regularly checked the road she wisely kept it to herself.

The hall housing the charity function was ablaze with lights and they joined the crowd mounting the steps, Gray taking a firm hold of her arm and keeping her close beside him. For the first time Shelby actually felt vulnerable for a moment. Her back was a clear target to anyone watching for her, and she was glad when they finally managed to get inside the relative safety of the foyer. So much for her intention not to buy into the situation.

Thankfully, the instant they entered the ballroom she was greeted by numerous friends and acquaintances, and the moment passed off. Most of her friends were already gathered at their assigned table and, seeing the speculation when they saw the man accompanying her, she swiftly introduced Gray, though she fell shy of calling him her date.

'How is it I can never find anyone who looks like you?' her friend Nadia despaired as she shook hands. 'Are you married?'

'Nadia!' everyone exclaimed at once amidst the general laughter.

'How else am I to know?' Nadia went on, unabashed.

Gray laughed softly. 'No, but I'm afraid I'm spoken for,' he told her, giving Shelby a sizzling look at the same time, which sent goose-bumps all over her, even as she tensed at the message he had given out. Having taken her by surprise, she couldn't gainsay him. They were, for tonight at least, an item. Damn him!

Nadia sighed wistfully. 'Shelby has all the luck. When she came in positively glowing I knew you were someone special.'

Shelby's nerves performed a wild lurch. Had she been glowing? She couldn't look to Gray for help, for he had put her in this unenviable situation. All she could do was throw her weight behind it and make him pay later.

'I can't help it. He's absolutely fabulous,' she declared brightly, squeezing Gray's arm and reaching up to plant a kiss on his cheek. It was as well she didn't have to say anything else, for her lips were tingling from the unexpected pleasure and couldn't have formed words anyway.

'I know what you mean. I'd be glowing if I had a man like that holding my arm!' Nadia exclaimed with a wicked roll of her eyes and everyone laughed again.

The next few minutes were taken up with shaking hands and greeting everyone, but finally they gained a breathing space.

'What are you playing at?' Shelby hissed at him once they were seated and the teasing had passed on to somebody else.

'I thought it best to make out we were an item,' Gray responded, shooting her a quizzical look. 'As you left the door open, I decided to get in first, remembering the last introduction you made,' he added dryly.

That brought a warm glow to her cheeks. 'You'd annoyed me,' she excused herself, and he smiled.

'I annoy you a lot. Maybe if you worked with me, instead of against me, we could avoid these little mishaps,' he suggested, and she knew he was laughing at her.

'Thanks for nothing. You realise they're going to be asking questions about you for ever,' Shelby returned dryly, then frowned as she saw the mark of her kiss on his cheek. 'Oops, it looks like I've branded you. Do you have a handkerchief?' He produced one from his pocket, which she shook out and deftly removed the lipstick before handing it back. 'There you are. All gone,' she declared, then caught him watching her and raised her brows questioningly. 'What is it?'

'I know what your friend meant about you glowing. There's something about you tonight that's quite intoxicating.'

Her heart did another of its spectacular flip-flops and she momentarily lost her breath even though she knew it was part of the role he was playing tonight. 'You can stop now. Nobody's watching,' she told him, only to receive a swift, almost invisible, shake of the head.

'Actually, darling, we're being observed by people on neighbouring tables, so you might want to say something nice for a change,' he corrected her assumption under his breath.

The endearment set her heart trotting, but she realised why he had said it when a surreptitious glance around proved he was right. They were being watched. There was to be no relief tonight, it seemed. She had to play the role he had given her to the hilt. To which end she produced a flirtatious smile.

'If I might say so, you're looking quite sizzling yourself.'

Gray rubbed the side of his nose, his expression wry. 'I don't believe I've ever been told I sizzle before.'

She gave a tiny shrug, her body leaning towards him slightly. 'Believe me, you do. It's very sexy.'

Blue eyes danced at her comment and his lips twitched. 'You're very good at this.'

Shelby trailed her fingers along his arm. 'So are you. Aren't we a pair? We're gold medal class in flirtation, but when it comes to relationships we're pushed to come in last!'

Gray captured her hand and turned it over, surveying the lines engraved there. 'Are you still searching for Mr Right?'

A tiny ache settled about her heart as she watched the only man for her trace his finger over her palm. 'I think, when his ship came in, I was at the airport,' she breezed lightly, making a joke of it so it wouldn't hurt too much. Picking up her evening bag, she stood up. 'I need to use the powder room.'

Immediately Gray rose too. 'OK, let's go.'

Unable to say anything with her friends looking on, she had to wait until they were in the foyer again before attempting to pull her arm free of his hand. 'There's no need to go with me. I know the way!' she protested, to no avail.

'Sorry, Red, you know the score. Where you go, I go.'

Shock tore through her as she realised what he was saying. 'You can't possibly come into the ladies' room with me!' she argued, finding it hard to keep her voice down so as not to draw unwanted attention.

'Want to bet?' he shot back in grim amusement, and Shelby came to an abrupt halt outside the powder room door.

'You can't.'

'It's a risk I'm prepared to take,' he informed her blithely, taking charge of the situation, pushing open the door and walking in, tugging her in his wake.

The three ladies in possession of the outer room looked up in surprise.

Gray turned on the charm. 'Excuse me, ladies, but this young woman thought she saw something scuttling about in here, and I've come to check it out. If you could just step outside for a moment, I promise not to keep you more than a few minutes. Is there anyone in the other room?'

The three ladies, who had gathered up their belongings in haste at the mention of scuttling, made for the door he held open.

'It's empty,' one of the women said, answering his question, and received the full force of his dashing smile.

'Thank you for your co-operation,' he told them, closing the door and shooting the lock.

Shelby pressed her palms to cheeks burning red with mortification. 'I can't believe you just did that!' she wailed. 'I've never been so embarrassed in my life!'

'Then you've led a sheltered existence,' Gray retorted, entering the other room, which was empty as he had been told, but checking out each stall to make sure. Reappearing, he stepped away from the doorway. 'It's OK, you can go in there now,' he informed her, and she stared at him, totally stunned.

'You couldn't seriously have thought someone would be hiding in there,' she protested, only to see him shake his head.

'No, as it happens. However, you'll think twice before you ever cast aspersions on my manhood again,' Gray revealed, eyes starting to twinkle triumphantly as he saw understanding dawn on her face.

'You…you…!' she exclaimed, hands balling into angry fists. 'You did this just to get your own back for this morning? What a mean, nasty, horrible…'

A rat-tat on the door interrupted her harangue.

'People are getting impatient,' Gray reminded her, and she drew in a deep breath.

'Thank you, but I no longer wish to go,' she informed

him in a frosty tone, whereupon he walked to the door and opened it.

'Sorry, ladies. Everything is fine; the young lady was imagining things,' he apologised to the small crowd waiting outside.

Shelby had to run the gauntlet of speculative eyes yet again and wished the floor would open up and swallow her.

'That was a rotten trick,' she told him in an aggrieved voice.

'Now you know how I felt,' was all he said in response.

Maybe, but she wasn't about to admit it after what he had just done. 'I may never forgive you.'

He had the gall to laugh. 'Never is a long time. Even you wouldn't hold a grudge quite that long,' he pointed out sardonically, making Shelby grind her teeth.

'I'll give it a damned good try,' she countered, and caught a flash of his grin.

'Now that I do believe.'

She really did hate him sometimes. 'You're impossible.'

'And you're stunningly beautiful when you're angry,' Gray returned smoothly, stealing her thunder and twisting her heartstrings.

'What…? I mean…stop trying to change the subject. I'm mad at you and I want to stay mad,' Shelby harangued him, though her anger had suddenly vanished like magic.

They had, by this time, returned to their table, and Gray held her chair out for her. She sat down but, before moving away, Gray bent down in an intimate gesture and nuzzled her ear.

'Stay as mad as you like, sweetheart. I wouldn't stop you for the world,' he murmured, sending tingles down her spine and curling her toes.

There was no getting away from it, she was a hopeless case where he was concerned, which gave him a heck of a weapon to use against her. The situation this evening gave him the opportunity to use a lot of unfair tactics. If she wanted to compete, she was going to have to take a leaf out of his book.

The chance to do so came along much sooner than she had expected. Having waived the first course of soup, Shelby was quite ready to tuck in to the main course when it was put before her—until she had a whimsical thought.

'Aren't you forgetting something?' she asked Gray, with her knife and fork poised over her plate. He quirked a questioning eyebrow in her direction. 'This food could be poisoned.'

He looked naturally dubious. 'The plate came along with all the others.'

'I know,' she whispered back. 'But the waiter could be in the employ of this nasty individual, and sprinkled poison on my plate. I need an official food taster, and you're it.' Hiding a grin, she cut off a small wedge of meat, speared it on her fork and held it out to him. 'Open up!'

With a resigned sigh, Gray abandoned his cutlery and reached for the fork. 'You realise you're messing with the wrong man,' he growled, placing his hand over hers and making it impossible for her to pull free. He helped her to put the small morsel in his mouth, and all the time his eyes never left hers.

The bottom fell out of her stomach as he savoured the meat and she couldn't look away. It was one of the most intensely sensual moments she had ever experienced sitting at a dinner table, and it had her heart pounding, sending her blood pulsing thickly through her veins. Over in seconds, she knew she would never forget it.

'Mmm, delicious,' Gray declared huskily, eyes hot and sultry. 'Do you want me to try the potatoes?'

Shelby didn't think her system could withstand it. She cleared her throat. 'No, thank you, that will be quite sufficient.' Reaching for her glass with a faintly trembling hand, she took a much needed sip of wine.

Of course, every mouthful she took after that carried with it the memory of watching Gray eat, knowing it hadn't been food he was savouring but herself. There were some things, she decided, that shouldn't be tried in mixed company. Taunting him was one of them.

The evening wore on. Speeches followed the meal, the organisers thanking everyone for supporting the charity so generously. Afterwards the floor was cleared for dancing to a live band, and everyone was left to enjoy themselves as they wished. Much chatter and laughter bubbled round their table, but eventually couples started to drift on to the floor to dance.

After a few minutes, Gray held out his hand. 'Let's dance,' he suggested, and Shelby's brows arched in surprise. It wasn't that she didn't want to, merely that she hadn't expected he would.

'Are you sure?' she queried, keeping her voice low so as not to be overheard.

'It would look odd not to,' he confirmed, getting to his feet, hand still outstretched.

Which left her with little choice other than to put her hand in his and let him help her up. He was quite right, it would look odd. Having given the impression they were a new item, then getting 'closer' on the dance floor would be the natural thing to do. Whilst part of her saw danger signals, there was a stronger part that wanted to get close to him, with a good reason for doing so. Something that had nothing to do with her attraction to him, but was merely playing the game.

Shelby allowed him to lead her through the tables to the dance floor, where he neatly turned her into his arms as they joined the circling mass. She hadn't known what to expect, and it was a curious sensation. Gray was playing it strictly by the book, holding her with the correct distance between them, and after a while she realised that that was not what she wanted at all.

It was like a peculiar form of torture where she was being tantalised by his nearness, her senses awakening to the promise of unexpected delights, but not getting them. Though it would not help her declared intention of not falling into his arms, she couldn't help herself. She wanted to be closer, to experience their bodies touching. She wanted his arms around her, for goodness' sake, and nothing less would do. So when they were bumped the next time she acted swiftly, shifting the hand which was resting on his shoulder and sliding it around his neck, her fingers curling into the silky strands of his hair. At the same time her body came to rest against his, delighting in the feel of his powerful torso. Holding her breath, she waited for Gray's reaction.

After the briefest hesitation his hand which had been on her waist found its way round to her back, settled there and began sending out a wave of heat. Her blood sang, whilst her heart stepped up its rhythm. Lord, what a fool she was to think she could deny herself this way. This was what she had longed for and, without a thought, she lowered her head and rested it on his shoulder.

'Not going to sleep on me, are you, Red?' Gray asked a short while later and, although the tone was light, she could hear a thickness in his voice which told her he was far from being unaffected.

Sleeping had never been further from her mind. Her body was too alive for that and so, she could tell, was his. 'Just setting the scene,' she sighed, rubbing her cheek against the soft fabric of his suit and catching the powerful scent of maleness mixed with cologne. Lord, but he smelt good!

Now, as they slowly circled the floor, their bodies brushed against each other with every slow movement and the effect was electric. It was exactly how she had always dreamed it would be, and she was intoxicated by the sensations. It was glorious, and she wanted to stay in his arms for ever.

'Are you planning to seduce me right here, by any chance?' Gray queried, catching his breath as another bump pressed them closer together and set off sparks.

Still lost in the mood, Shelby laughed softly. 'We'd never be allowed through the doors again,' she said wryly, her fingers playing with his hair.

'Cut it out, Red!' he commanded in the next breath, and she tipped her head up so that she could see him looking down at her.

'I thought you liked women running their fingers through your hair,' she breathed huskily, and she was fascinated to hear him groan and close his eyes for an instant.

'In private, not in the middle of a dance floor.'

She bit her lip but her eyes were sparkling and she received full strength the powerful force of his blue eyes, with the banked fires of desire in their depths. 'I think I'd better stop,' she capitulated, reluctantly bringing herself out of the dream she had been in, back to the here and now.

'You might want to remember for next time that playing with fire can be dangerous,' Gray returned dryly.

With a sharp jolt to her nerves, Shelby knew she had been playing with fire and she was sending messages she had no intention of backing up. 'There won't be a next time,' she insisted, knowing she had been a fool to indulge herself.

Now it was his turn to laugh. 'The way we respond to each other, how can you say no?'

'Because this was just for show. Nothing's changed between us, Gray,' she reminded him coolly. 'I'm not going to get involved with you, no matter how good it feels.'

'Because of the past? Let it go, Red. You won't be

sorry,' Gray argued persuasively, and there was a tiny part of her that was tempted. However, the larger part remembered the hurt of betrayal and could not forgive.

Just at that moment the song came to an end and, in the pause before the next began, Shelby stepped away from him.

'Perhaps we ought to sit this one out?' she suggested, which brought forth the wolfish smile which always managed to send shivers up her spine.

'Oh, I think we can survive another, providing you keep your hands to yourself,' he countered, eyes glittering roguishly as he neatly pulled her back into his arms again and started moving before she could argue.

Had the situation not been so public she would have fought free even if it did cause a scene, but she could not do so here. So she resigned herself to sweating it out. It wasn't easy. Though Shelby kept her hands to herself, Gray didn't. The hand he settled on her back began to make lazy and highly sensuous forays up and down her spine.

'Hmm, this is nice,' he murmured a few minutes later.

It was more than nice. It was the nearest thing to heaven she'd ever experienced. 'You do realise you're not playing fair?' she complained, her voice tense with the effort to remain cool-headed whilst her senses were under siege.

'Fair is for children. The battle between us isn't about winning or losing.'

That was a surprise. She was under the impression that was exactly what it was. 'What is it about, then?'

'It's all about finding reasonable terms for surrender,' Gray explained huskily and said no more, leaving her to wonder if there ever could be such a thing.

This time when the music ended they returned to the table, which was once again full of chattering people. Later, a photographer appeared and took snaps of them all, leaving copies on the table for them to take if they wanted.

Shelby feigned disinterest in the one of her and Gray, but when she went in search of it later before they left, it was gone. Disappointed, she went to join Gray, who had called for a taxi.

Gray's words came back to her then. Reasonable terms for surrender, she mused to herself as the cab whisked them homewards. She had never considered their relationship from that angle. Could she live with that? Could she ignore the past and simply start from now? She yawned, thoughts blurring, and had no idea she had dropped off to sleep until she was gently shaken awake and realised her head was resting on Gray's shoulder.

'Sorry,' she apologised, stifling a yawn.

'You're out on your feet, Red. Do you want me to carry you?' he offered as he helped her out of the car.

She shook her head. 'I can manage. Besides, you need to keep your hands free in order to repel attackers,' she reminded him pertly, then spoilt everything by stumbling over a flagstone.

Gray nimbly swung her up into his arms, ignoring her protest. 'I promise to drop you if the need arises.'

They made it to her floor with little trouble. Gray set her down long enough to open the door, then he picked her up again, shut the door with his foot on the way in and strode to her bedroom, where he gently set her down on her bed.

'Do you need any help undressing?'

'That I can do.'

He smiled wryly. 'OK. You know where I am if you need me.'

'My hero!' she sighed, and he went out laughing softly.

Shelby made one last effort to wash off her make-up and slip into her nightdress, then she collapsed into her bed with a sigh of pleasure. It had been an odd sort of day, with surprising highs. She could hear Gray moving about, making sure everything was secure, but after a while even he grew silent.

As sleep drew ever closer, she marvelled at the knowledge that she was actually contemplating the possibility of maybe having an affair with the man. It hardly seemed possible, and yet it was true. What Gray had said back there on the dance floor made a weird kind of sense. Reasonable terms for surrender, he had said, and Lord, how she wanted to do that. She fought on because he had hurt her so badly. He didn't know that, of course. He thought she was merely holding a grudge. So she could back down and have what she wanted, without him ever knowing there was more to it. If she wanted. Not that she had to decide yet. Nothing was going to happen until all this was over. She could think about it some more. Thinking didn't commit her to anything.

Yawning widely, she turned on to her side, and in seconds sleep finally claimed her.

# CHAPTER FIVE

THE following day was hectic from the word go. Unless Shelby had an early appointment with a client, she always called in to her office every morning. Currently she had two projects on the go, one of which was about halfway along and the other almost completed. With a growing waiting-list, she employed a workforce of three women whom she could trust to work to her plans, but she checked in every day or so to see how the jobs were progressing, and because she loved doing the hands-on work herself.

Her assistant, Paula, was overseeing the final details at their first port of call and ,when Shelby walked in, was hanging curtains.

'Oh, wow! They look great, Paula. I'm glad we went with that pattern,' she declared with satisfaction.

Coming to join Shelby and the ever attendant Gray, who had followed her in, Paula nodded. 'Sets it all off nicely,' she agreed, eyes flickering to her boss's companion with patent curiosity.

'Now, if only we could get those vases for the fireplace, we'd be finished,' Shelby sighed, turning to evaluate the unadorned hearth.

'What's wrong with it as it is?' Gray asked the obvious question and found himself being surveyed like an alien by the two women.

Shelby shook her head sadly. 'Philistine! Paula, this is Gray, an old friend,' she introduced him, having decided it was the only thing she could call him to the people who worked for her. 'He'll be keeping me company for a few days. Gray, meet Paula, my indispensable right hand.'

93

They shook hands, Paula grinning at his confused expression. 'A good designer knows when the job is finished. All this needs is the vases, and that will be it. Perfection. Until then…'

'Don't ask stupid questions,' Shelby finished for her, having circled the room and taken in all the changes since her last visit. 'Gray can't help it. I think he was dropped on his head as a baby,' she added, shooting a mocking glance his way.

Gray slipped his hands into the pockets of his jeans. He had taken his lead from Shelby, who had chosen to wear jeans and a stripy shirt today. 'She'll be sorry she said that later.'

Paula laughed. 'Oh, I see. You're *that* kind of old friend.'

That drew Shelby's attention away from the nearby table lamp. 'Certainly not. He's a friend, full stop,' she denied instantly, sending him a warning glare. Which he promptly ignored.

'That wasn't the impression I got when I carried you to bed last night,' Gray countered smoothly, and her lips parted on a tiny gasp.

'Don't listen to him, Paula, he's making it all up,' she advised the other woman, but Gray simply quirked a lazy eyebrow at her and flashed a smile.

'Calm down, Red. It would have to come out in the end that we're living together,' he went on soothingly, making her blood boil even more.

'Don't you dare tell me to calm down!' Shelby exclaimed wrathfully. What was he playing at?

Paula glanced from one to the other and coughed. 'Um, I think I'll go make us some tea. You two clearly have other things to discuss,' she declared and beat a hasty retreat.

The instant she was gone, Shelby rounded on Gray.

'What on earth do you think you're doing?' she demanded to know.

'I decided that the idea of our being an item would probably work best with your staff. Seeing me here constantly wouldn't seem odd,' he told her reasonably, but Shelby didn't feel mollified.

'You could have at least discussed it with me first! I was happy with you merely being a friend,' she snapped back, breast heaving with anger at his arrogance.

Something glittered in his eyes. 'But we're not friends, Red. We're more than that,' he corrected her in a smoky kind of voice that teased her senses.

Her own eyes narrowed. 'We're not the lovers you want everyone to think we are!' Shelby was so mad she could spit nails.

To add to her irritation, he merely shrugged. 'It's too late now. Nobody will believe you if you try to take it back. You're just going to have to live with it.'

There was, she noted, a certain smug satisfaction in the way he said it, and if there had been a poker on the hearth she might well have used it where it would do most good. However, there wasn't, so she was forced to take a deep steadying breath. He was right, there was nothing she could do, but she didn't like it, and she didn't like him for doing it.

'One of these days you're going to get your comeuppance, Gray Compton, and I only hope I'm there to see it!' she vowed with heartfelt dislike.

Gray's lips twisted wryly. 'If there's any justice in this world, we'll both get our just deserts one day.'

'We can but live in hope,' she added sourly, and he laughed.

'I like the room, by the way. It's very relaxing,' Gray complimented and Shelby took another deep breath and regained her objectivity.

'Thank you. That's exactly what we were aiming for,' she said, unable to prevent her heart swelling rather more than was necessary at the compliment. Though she knew it was ridiculous, she realised she wanted him to like what she did. Wanted him to be proud of her. Loving someone did that to a person. Which once again emphasised just what a hopeless case she was. She couldn't keep her emotions balanced from one moment to the next.

After chatting with Paula for some time, Shelby and Gray finally departed and headed for the remaining project. This commission was to bring a new look to an upmarket apartment. Plasterers, carpenters and electricians had all done their job and now it was up to Shelby and her assistants, Jacquie and Sue, to add the distinctive touch that would make it a Shelby Greer design.

As soon as they arrived, Shelby slipped into overalls to protect her clothes. The lounge floor was covered by cloths and in the centre were pots of paint, trays, rollers and brushes. She went to these and picked up various items plus a can of paint, which she handed to Gray with a winsome smile.

'Since we'll be here for a while, you might as well make yourself useful. You do know how to use a roller, don't you?'

'You actually trust me not to make a mistake?'

She gave him a look. 'Do I have idiot written across my forehead? You'll be applying base coat. Even you can't make a mess of that.'

He grinned wryly. 'I knew there had to be a catch. Where do I start?'

'At the door. Go all the way round the room till you get back to it. I'd offer you some overalls, but we don't have anything in your size,' Shelby said, grinning back at him. 'Have fun.'

She left him to it and went off to make preparations in

another room. When she glanced in some time later, Gray had rolled up his sleeves and was making a good job of the first wall. She was impressed. Clearly he did know his way around a roller and can of paint.

'Didn't anyone ever tell you it was rude to stare?' Gray suddenly enquired, without stopping what he was doing, and Shelby jumped in surprise.

'How did you know I was here?'

Gray cast a glance over his shoulder, eyes locking with hers. 'Your perfume. I'd know the scent of you anywhere. Even over paint fumes.'

Her mouth went dry, and consequently her voice was a tad husky when she spoke. 'I'll have to remember that if ever I want to sneak up on somebody.'.

His lips twitched, eyes taking on that roguish gleam. 'You have an open invitation to sneak up on me any time you like, once this is all over,' he informed her in a highly sensual undertone, and her breathing went haywire.

She arched her brows delicately. 'And why would I want to do a crazy thing like that?'

Gray laughed and turned back to his work. 'Because you want me, Red, just about as much as I want you.'

Shelby couldn't help but give a swift backward glance in case anyone had overheard that nerve-tingling remark. Gray hadn't blurted out that they were lovers this time, but from the way her girls watched them both she knew Paula had been on the phone the instant they had left the other house.

She walked a few paces into the room. 'Would you please keep your voice down!' she commanded, wincing inwardly. Things were getting out of hand and she didn't like it.

This time he turned right around to face her. 'Why? They know, and we both know they know.'

'They wouldn't know anything if you'd kept your mouth

shut. Oh, this is impossible, I can't trust you.' Shelby wailed.

Gray's blue eyes turned steely and there was a hard set to his jaw. 'You can trust me to keep you safe from harm, and that's what I'm doing.'

Shelby threw her arms wide. 'What harm? It's been two days and nothing has happened. Nothing is going to happen, either. I hate this, I hate having to be so close to you!'

Something wild flashed into his eyes. 'No, you don't. What you hate is liking having me close to you. Stop lying to yourself, Red,' he returned bluntly. 'As for the other… Two days is nothing. Even two months of nothing would be too short a time for someone with a grudge and time on his hands. Until we catch him, the danger remains real.'

She knew when she was flogging a dead horse again. 'No wonder you and Dad work so well together. You're two of a kind.'

'You mean handsome, charming and witty?'

'No, pigheaded,' she retorted as she turned and walked from the room.

Hidden from view, Shelby cast a frowning look over her shoulder. He was right, she did hate herself for wanting him so much. Having him so near was pure temptation. It made her forget why she had vowed she would never fall for his lies again. Only this time she could see the desire he had for her, and it wasn't fake. Any relationship they had would be based on mutual attraction. She could have that and know that it was real. It wasn't love, but she wasn't so foolish as to expect that from him. Her heart, though, wanted more, and if she did have an affair with Gray, her heart was going to end up even more bruised and battered. Would it be worth it? Quite honestly, right that second, she didn't know.

By late afternoon all that could be done that day had been accomplished, and Shelby stood back to survey the work with a deep sense of satisfaction. Things were really beginning to take shape now. Gray helped to clear things up ready for the next day. Then, after Shelby had spoken to her assistants about what to do next, she called it a day.

She found Gray waiting for her by the front door. He was leaning against the wall with his eyes closed, his face the colour of putty, and her stomach gave an anxious lurch. 'Are you OK?'

Opening his eyes, he straightened up. 'Just a bit of a headache. Nothing to worry about.'

'Have you taken anything?' She knew from experience there was nothing worse than a pounding headache and working with paint fumes could exacerbate it.

'I've got something back at the flat.'

A memory struck her. 'Is it a migraine?' She seemed to recall him suffering them once.

'If I get the medicine in time, it should stop it developing into a migraine.'

Shelby had never suffered from them, but she knew from friends how debilitating it could be. Which was why she didn't waste time talking, but urged him out of the house and into her car. The headache didn't stop him taking all necessary precautions, though, which made her want to scream. Eventually, they were away and she made as good time as she could back to her flat.

Once there, Gray disappeared into the spare bedroom. She left him to it and did her usual daily checks of the phone and emails. She spent an hour in her workroom-cum-office, answering messages and working on plans, and it wasn't until some time later that she realised the flat was silent. Which was unusual, because Gray tended to prowl around from time to time.

Curious, she went in search of him and discovered him lying on the bed, one arm bent across his eyes. She bit her lip at the whiteness around his lips that spoke of the pain he was suffering.

'Is it very bad?' she asked sympathetically, feeling useless.

'I've had worse. The medication will kick in properly soon,' he answered tautly, and she winced.

Recalling that light was a problem for migraine sufferers, she crossed to the window and drew the curtains. 'Better?'

'Some, thanks.'

Shelby approached the bed, hating to see him laid low like this. 'You're very tense. That can't be helping. Let me give you a massage to relieve the tension.'

He looked at her from under his arm and she was sure he was going to refuse, but then he sighed and rolled over on to his stomach. 'Knock yourself out,' he invited.

Kicking off her shoes, Shelby carefully knelt on the bed and placed her hands on his shoulders. They were so tight that to begin with she hardly made any headway, but by persevering she gradually began to notice a difference. Concentrating hard, she worked out kinks along his spine, across his shoulders and up his neck into his hairline. As the tension oozed out of him, Gray began to utter soft sounds of pleasure.

'Hmm, you have magic fingers,' he sighed, catching his breath as she dealt with another knot.

Smiling to herself, Shelby continued her ministrations. After a while he simply lay there, and it wasn't very long after that that she realised the rhythmical sounds coming from him confirmed that he had actually fallen asleep. Arms and fingers aching, she crept off the bed, retrieved her shoes and left him alone. It gave her quite a kick to know she had helped him to feel better, and she went to make herself a cup of tea feeling a righteous sense of satisfaction.

She had just finished drinking it when the phone rang

and, not wanting Gray to be disturbed, she snatched up the receiver before it could ring again. The caller was the owner of an antique shop she used quite regularly.

'Hi, Shelby,' the woman greeted her. 'You know you were looking for vases for your fireplace. Well, I think I've found the very thing you're after. There has been some interest in them, though, so you'd better get over here and have a look.'

Shelby pulled a face as she turned to look at the closed door behind which Gray lay sleeping. He wouldn't want her to go without him, and yet she was loath to wake him now. On the other hand, it would only take her an hour at most to get to the shop and back again. Nothing was going to happen, and she would be back before he woke, so he would never know.

'I'll be right over,' she promised, and hung up the phone.

It was the work of a moment to gather up her jacket, handbag and car keys, then she let herself out of the flat as quietly as a mouse. Feeling like a schoolgirl playing hookey, she laughed softly as she took the lift down to the garage.

She wasn't laughing some hours later, though, as she finally pulled back into her parking spot. She had reached the shop without trouble and, as the owner had promised, the vases were just what she wanted. She had paid for them and left for home, feeling highly pleased with herself. The vases sat proudly on the seat beside her as she drove along, and she had been wondering how she could explain their sudden appearance at her flat without giving herself away when she had hit the traffic. It was snarled up for miles around and, try as she might, she hadn't been able to find a way round whatever the problem was. She had ended up sitting in her car for over an hour, her mobile still on the mantelpiece where she had left it, knowing that there was no way that Gray would stay sleeping so long. She was going to be in trouble. *Big trouble*!

Which proved to be the case. Gray must have discovered her car was gone and had been looking out for her, because he was in the lift when she walked towards it. Her heart sank at the grim look on his face.

'I know you're mad,' she declared swiftly, hoping to head him off. 'But I can explain.'

That narrowed his eyes as he crossed his arms. 'You can explain? OK, try me.'

Shelby's heart skipped a beat, but she waited to speak until after the lift was carrying them both upwards. 'How's your head?' she asked and could have sworn she heard his teeth grind.

'My head is fine. Don't change the subject,' he went on doggedly, and she thought she knew how his squaddies would have felt when they incurred his wrath.

'My guess is there was a really serious accident, because the traffic was stacked up like you'd never believe,' she told him in a rather breathless rush. It got her nowhere.

'And this, somehow, makes it all OK, does it?' he growled, to which she tried a casual shrug.

'I would have been back otherwise,' she explained simply, walking out of the lift ahead of him and pulling a face that he couldn't see.

'So, if you had made it back before I woke, everything would have been OK?' They entered the flat and he shut the door forcefully behind them. 'Of all the downright stupid things you've ever done, this is the worst. I could wring your silly little neck for you! What in hell did you think you were doing?'

'Picking up these vases,' she declared brightly, holding them up for him to see. 'A contact phoned me whilst you were asleep and, as I didn't want to wake you, I simply popped out to collect them. Aren't they just perfect for the fireplace?'

His response to that was to swear, and Shelby jumped so much she nearly dropped her precious vases. Hastily she set them down on the sofa where they would be safe.

'When is it going to get through to you that your life has been threatened, Red? What you did was irresponsible and reckless. Not to mention downright selfish,' Gray railed at her and, because she knew he was right, she got angry too.

'Oh, come on. We both know nothing's going to happen to me.'

His hands opened and closed several times as if he was fighting the urge to shake her till her teeth rattled. 'No. We don't know that. You have no right to play fast and loose with your life and worry the people who care about you. I thought you had more sense than that, but I can see I was wrong.

The reference to her father stung, as it was meant to do, and she raked an uneasy hand through her hair. 'OK, OK, I agree I shouldn't have done it, but nothing happened, so can we let it go now?'

He looked at her for a long moment, then took a deep wrathful breath. 'Only if I have your solemn word you won't do anything like it again,' Gray returned hardily, and she stared at him in frustration.

'I don't like being kept a prisoner in my own home,' she complained, though she knew it was an exaggeration.

Gray's expression said he knew it too. 'That's coming it too strong. Nobody's stopping you going out, you just don't go alone. You're making this far harder than it need be. So, what's it going to be? Do I have your word?'

'Yes, if it means anything,' she agreed grudgingly.

Having gained her acquiescence, Gray relaxed his angry stance a little. 'It doesn't have much value right now. You have to prove it's worth more,' he told her bluntly as he headed for the kitchen. 'I'm making tea; do you want a cup?'

'Yes, thank you. Milk, no arsenic,' she retorted, regaining some of her spirit, which had been rather quashed in the face of his justifiable anger.

'Don't tempt me,' he shot back immediately and, realising she had got off lightly, Shelby thought it wise to make herself scarce for a while and went off to work in her office.

The mood between them was rather strained for the rest of the evening. They ate together, but conversation was somewhat stilted. She didn't like it, and regretted that she had been the cause of the worsening state of affairs.

It was probably her troubled conscience that made her so restless that night. After an hour or two of tossing and turning with only brief snatches of sleep, she threw back the covers and sat up. It was hopeless. She needed something to help her drop off. Coffee would only keep her awake and she didn't care for milky drinks, but there was always the crossword. It was guaranteed to have her eyes crossing in next to no time.

She had left the newspaper on the coffee table but, so as not to disturb Gray, she decided to pick it up and take it to the kitchen. Having worn her grey cotton vest and shorts to bed tonight, she didn't bother to put on her robe, but padded about as she was.

With the curtains drawn, at Gray's insistence, there was very little light in the lounge. Not surprisingly, Shelby stubbed her toe on the coffee table, stifled a yelp of pain and hopped about on one foot rubbing at the injured digit. That was when, out of the corner of her eye, she saw a dark shadow detach itself from the deeper shadows by the wall and head straight towards her. Caught like a rabbit in the headlights of a car, she stared in horror as the shadow took on a human outline, but she barely had time to open her mouth to scream when it launched itself at her, catching her around the arms and carrying her down on to the nearby sofa. Terrified, and unable to move her arms, she did the only thing she could do and screamed out.

'Gray! Help me! Oh, God…!'

That was all she was able to utter as a large male hand was pressed over her mouth, but it left one arm free and she used it to pound at the back of her attacker. At the same time she thrashed around wildly with her legs, kicking out, and knew she had landed a painful blow when the man on top of her grunted in pain.

Her movements unsettled them and they rolled off the sofa on to the floor, thrusting the coffee table out of the way. Silently she screamed for Gray to come and help her, then set about trying to save herself. There was little she could do. He had stopped her kicking by winding his legs around hers, but his hand had slipped slightly, enough for her to get a good grip with her teeth and bite down hard.

'Ouch!' the man yelped, releasing her mouth, and she took swift advantage.

'Gray! Gray! Help me!' she yelled at the top of her voice, before her breath was taken away when her attacker rolled them over, subduing her with his weight.

'Stop yelling, for the love of Mike, or you'll wake the whole neighbourhood!' a familiar voice growled in her ear.

Shock sent her heart lurching in her chest. 'Gray?' she croaked out in disbelief.

'Right here,' he confirmed, and she could hear the irony in his voice.

Sick fear turned to righteous anger as she slowly realised that her attacker was none other than Gray himself. 'I could kill you. What were you playing at? I was absolutely terrified!'

'That was the general idea,' he retorted mockingly. 'Perhaps now you'll take the situation you're in seriously. That could have been someone else tonight. Someone who wanted to do you serious harm.'

Fury surged up in her like an exploding volcano. 'So you thought that gave you the right to scare me half to death? Get off me, you brute,' she added for good measure, and it was the laugh he gave that tipped her over the edge.

Gray had freed her arms and she was able to rain down blows wherever she could reach, whilst at the same time writhing in an attempt to get him off her. He was far too strong to move, however, and in no time she was exhausted, but she managed to land a good few blows before he could capture her wrists and hold her hands to the floor on either side of her head.

'Don't expect me to apologise, Red,' Gray told her bluntly. 'I just gave you a lesson you needed to learn.'

Shelby glared up at him bitterly, able to see that it was him now that her eyes had adjusted to the light. 'It was a despicable trick,' she snapped, and because his head was just above hers she could see his teeth flash as he grinned.

'So you lost a life. You've got eight others. And you needn't bother complaining to your father. He agreed you needed a salutary lesson.'

'You spoke to him?' she gasped.

'What did you think I would do when I found you missing? I had to check out all the places you might have gone, and your father was first on the list,' Gray explained and her heart sank to her boots.

'So Dad was in on this?' How could he? She felt... betrayed.

'He agreed something had to be done. The method he left up to me. Even I didn't know what I was going to do until I heard you come out of your room tonight. I was already in the lounge, so I took the opportunity to give you a scare,' he enlightened her drolly. 'I'm happy to say you surprised me, Red. You fought like a wildcat.'

She was too angry to be mollified by the praise. 'If I'd known it was you, I would have scratched your eyes out!'

'Cheer up. You've almost certainly given me a black eye,' he returned, pressing the spot on his cheekbone and wincing.

'Does it hurt?' Shelby asked, with false contrition.

'Like hell.'

'Good,' she said with satisfaction. 'Now get off me.'

'Why? I'm quite comfortable,' he countered in a faintly husky voice, and her eyes shot to his.

She could see the faint glitter in his eyes and her stomach lurched. She had been too busy fighting to be aware of him, but now that they lay still his position on top of her made her think of other things entirely. Her anger ebbed away as she slowly became aware of the sensual pleasure of having his body pressed so closely to hers. Her mouth dried up as her body reacted to his. Deep inside a pulse began to beat insistently as her blood surged through her veins and her breasts swelled, her nipples turning into aching buds that longed for more pressure, not less.

The air about them became charged, waiting, expectant, and in the stillness of the room she could hear her ragged breathing mingling with his.

'Maybe…' She started to speak, but then his head lowered and his lips brushed the line of her jaw, and all at once she forgot what she was going to say.

Again and again his lips brushed like butterfly wings up towards her chin, stealing her breath away at the shivery delight. There they paused, hovering over her lips as if debating whether to kiss her or not. Silently her body screamed yes, and she looked at him from beneath weighted lids. Then, just when she thought it wasn't going to happen, Gray uttered a strangled sound and lowered his lips to hers.

It was like magic, the gentle touch out of proportion to

the reaction which went on inside her. She had waited such a long time for this to happen again that for a second or two she actually felt dizzy. It was everything she remembered, and more. His lips explored hers in tantalisingly soft brushes, but then his tongue swept across the same spot, tasting her, and Shelby gasped, her lips parting at this newest pleasure to bombard her system. Immediately he took advantage of the situation to deepen the kiss, his tongue gliding between her lips to begin a sensual exploration.

Shelby gave a sighing moan as she angled her head the better to accommodate him. Shivers of pure delight travelled along her nerve endings, instantly arousing, and she met his tongue with her own, engaging in a dual that stoked the fire until it threatened to burst into flames. She had no intention of stopping, for she wanted to experience this, to know all there was to know about making love to Gray, but he had other ideas. From somewhere he found the strength to break the kiss and pull away enough to look down at her.

'I shouldn't have done that,' he confessed none too steadily. Rolling off her, he sat up.

Shelby sat up beside him, feeling bereft because he was no longer touching her. 'No, you shouldn't,' she agreed gruffly.

He glanced sideways at her. 'Why didn't you push me away?' he asked curiously, and she was glad the darkness hid the flush on her cheeks.

'Put it down to temporary madness,' she riposted dryly.

'This situation is enough to drive anyone insane, Red,' he agreed ironically as he rose to his feet and held out a hand to help her up. 'It's late, we'd better get some sleep.' Sighing, she allowed him to pull her to her feet. 'Have you learned your lesson?'

'Oh, yes,' Shelby agreed, turning away before he could catch a glimpse of her expression.

She *had* learned a lesson tonight, but not the one he thought. She had learned that despite everything that had happened between them, she was still beyond hope where he was concerned. He only had to touch her and she forgot all the reasons why she shouldn't let it happen. He had kissed her, and all thought of fighting him had vanished like morning mist.

She took the memory of that back to bed with her. As she lay there, recalling every vivid second of it, she knew he was her destiny. Her life was inextricably bound with his, and it was time she stopped fighting fate.

# CHAPTER SIX

THE next day was pretty much the same as the previous one, only this time Shelby didn't make any solo trips. The vases did look good on the fireplace, and Gray wisely forbore to mention how they had been acquired. A strained peace settled over them.

They were back at her apartment by late afternoon, and Shelby was busy getting her notes up-to-date and writing herself reminders of what she had to do tomorrow, when the telephone rang.

'Shelby Greer,' she identified herself into the receiver and waited for a response. When it didn't come, she held the receiver away from her ear and frowned at it, as if that would make a difference, then tried again. 'Hello, this is Shelby Greer. How can I help you?'

Again there was no answer but, for a second, she thought she could hear breathing before there came the sound of the receiver at the other end being carefully replaced. She blinked in surprise and slowly returned the receiver to its rest.

'What's wrong?' Gray wanted to know. He had been standing by the window staring out, but when she glanced his way she saw he was now watching her.

She shrugged. 'Nothing, really. They just hung up without saying anything, that's all.'

Gray took his hands from his trouser pockets and came over to her, a frown etched on to his brow. 'You actually heard the phone go down?' he asked sharply, and her nerves skittered.

'Yes, I did. And, before that, I could swear I heard

breathing,' she added, and even before she had finished speaking he had taken up the phone and was busily dialling.

When his first call was fruitless he dialled another number and had a briefly worded conversation with someone at the other end. Then he set the phone down and waited. Shelby had no trouble picking up his tension, and the reason for it sprang instantly to mind.

'Do you think it was him?' she asked shakily. This was the first time she had had contact with the person who was making threats against her. It made it real suddenly.

'Unless you're in the habit of receiving hoax calls,' he said by way of confirmation.

Shelby pressed a hand to her stomach, which suddenly felt rather queasy. 'He's never contacted me directly before. Why would he do that?'

Gray looked at her steadily and didn't hold back the truth. 'Because he's upping the stakes. This is what I was afraid of.'

Her breathing grew ragged and her heart was racing like mad. Unable to sit still, she stood and paced about the small room. 'You think I'm in even more danger now?'

He nodded solemnly, not troubling to remind her that he had always thought she was in danger. 'Unless we get a lucky break and the friend I called can trace the call. The hope was to catch him before he put his words into action. Seems as if we're going to have to go to plan B.'

She was rapidly coming to realise that she had taken the whole thing far too casually. 'We're on plan A at the moment, then?' she asked, and received a nod of assent. 'What's plan B, and is there a plan C?'

'Plan B is to get you away from here to a safe place,' he informed her in the serious tone she was used to getting from him.

'Is there such a place?' Suddenly she didn't feel as if she could be safe anywhere.

He must have picked up something in her tone, for he gave her an encouraging smile. 'I know of several, but don't worry, I intend to keep you safe and well. You'll be OK. Trust me.'

'I do,' she replied honestly. The instant she said it, she knew it was true. It was because she trusted him that he had hurt her before.

He stared at her for a moment, a strangely arrested look on his face, then he smiled. 'Good. That should make plan C easier to accomplish.'

'You think it will come to that? We'll have to go to plan C?'

He shrugged. 'You never can tell, but it's best to keep the option open.'

The telephone rang again and Gray snatched up the receiver. He listened intently and Shelby could see from the expression on his face that it was not good news.

'They couldn't trace the call,' he told her when he hung up the phone.

Feeling chilly, Shelby ran her hands along her arms, trying to instil some warmth into them. 'Do you have any idea who this man is?'

'Oscar had been able to narrow it down to a handful of possibles. Of those, one has dropped out of sight. This is the one we're concentrating on,' he enlarged, surprising her, for she hadn't known any of this. Then again, she hadn't taken it seriously. If she had, maybe her father would have told her.

'Does he have a name?'

'Keith Mobley. Does it ring any bells? He has some pretty radical ideas, which your father refused to print in his papers. Mobley didn't take kindly to that and threatened to make him pay.'

Shelby shuddered. 'Why wasn't I told all this?'

'Oscar chose to keep the full details from you because he didn't want to worry you.'

She could almost hear her father telling everyone, Don't tell Shelby. He wanted to protect her, but it had meant she hadn't taken the threat seriously. One creepy phone call had changed that. 'What do we do now?'

'Exactly what we have been doing, only more so. Meanwhile, I'll set the wheels in motion for getting you away. Are you OK with that, or are we going to have a fight about it?' he asked her ironically.

She shook her head. 'My fighting days are over,' she declared vehemently, only to hear him laugh.

'That will be the day.'

Shelby cast him an indignant glare. 'I shall be as good as gold from now on,' she promised, which once again failed to have the desired effect.

His eyes carried that familiar roguish gleam she rather enjoyed seeing. 'Not too good, I hope,' he goaded and she folded her arms with a huff.

'I'm being serious now, Gray!'

His smile appeared. 'Honey, so am I.'

Her hands slapped down on her thighs in a helpless gesture, and she was just about to take issue with him when she realised what he was doing. 'OK, I get it. You're trying to distract me.'

Gray's lips twitched. 'You *were* looking a little frantic.'

Shelby shifted uncomfortably. 'Yes, well, I suddenly realised that anything could have happened to me whilst I wasn't taking the threat seriously. It was a lesson. I'm sorry I gave you and Dad such a hard time.'

Thankfully for her pride, Gray didn't say, I told you so. 'Tell him that next time you see him. Now, if you've finished with the phone for a while, I'd like to make some calls.'

'Could you use the one in the lounge? I still have work to do.'

'Sure, no problem,' he agreed, and left the room.

Shelby sat down at her desk, but it was a while before she could concentrate on her work. She felt foolish for not believing her father. He wouldn't make a fuss about nothing, and she should have accepted that long before this. She owed him a very big apology. Not to mention Gray, who had had to take all the flak.

Eventually she managed to get back to her designs, and was amazed to find hours had passed when she finally shut her computer down. The flat sounded quiet and, curious, she went in search of Gray. She found him sitting at the end of the couch, talking into the telephone. He put it down after a moment or two and must have sensed her presence for he glanced up as she walked towards him. One eyebrow raised questioningly.

'Everything OK?'

Shelby looked at him, really looked, and saw the strain and tiredness around his eyes and mouth. His concern was etched there, and she was annoyed with herself for not seeing it before.

'I'm fine. How are you? You look…tired,' she asked in return, sinking down on to the seat beside him.

He shrugged that off. 'I'll be fine as soon as we catch this creep. He's gone to ground. Talk about *déjà vu*!' he added in an undertone, rubbing a hand around the back of his neck, easing the strain.

Shelby bit her lip. She had forgotten that this was not the first time he had been through something like this. Her attitude must have given him nightmares.

'Was it like this that other time?' she asked, and when his head shot round she hastened to qualify her question. 'I'm not just being nosy. I would like to know what we're up against.'

His jaw set. 'I prefer not to talk about it. Brings back too many bad memories,' he returned grimly, and she leant towards him.

'Have you ever talked to anyone? Shared the pain? Bottling it up can't help,' she probed gently, and his mouth twisted wryly.

'It's hardly a topic for conversation at dinner.'

'True,' Shelby proceeded carefully. 'But there's just the two of us here. Can't you talk to me? I'm a good listener, and I have a vested interest. Besides, I've made things worse for you, and I would very much like to put that right. Please talk to me, Gray,' she pleaded earnestly, and he sighed, closing his eyes, leaning his head against the back of the couch.

'It's not pretty,' he told her in a low voice.

'I can handle that. Believe me, I don't have to have everything sugar-coated,' she returned equally softly. 'Who was being threatened?'

Gray ran his hands over his face, as if to ease the stress of remembering. 'The family of an old friend. We were in one of those warring African states. Piet had something the rebels wanted, but he refused to hand it over.' He took a deep breath. 'So they threatened his wife and children. Piet called for my help, but I failed him.' The statement was made with such bitter self-recrimination that it made her gasp.

'What do you mean, you failed him? I don't believe it,' she protested, instinctively protective, and he looked at her with angry eyes.

'What would you call it when I let his wife die?' Gray demanded grittily, and shock was a lump of ice in her stomach.

'H-his w-wife?' she stammered, and his lips twisted into an ugly line.

'I told you it wasn't pretty,' he grated, and Shelby drew in a steadying breath.

'Tell me,' she urged, knowing it was not as simple as that. Could not possibly be.

Gray leant forward, head bent over his knees. 'Maybe we should leave it there,' he suggested, but she couldn't, for his sake.

'How did she die?'

He glanced at her sideways in silent debate, then sat back again. 'It happened when Piet was away making the arrangements to get his family out. The rebels broke into the compound one night and set fire to the house. We'd had no rain. Everything was a tinderbox. In minutes we had an inferno. I had been sleeping at the front of the house; Jen and the children were at the back. The children were nearest, so I went for them...' Gray's voice tailed off, and Shelby knew what was coming. He took a long breath before continuing. 'I got them out, but when I tried to go back for Jen, I couldn't get in. I don't know how many times I tried before some neighbours managed to pull me away. I failed.'

Shelby's eyes burned with unshed tears, and she drew in a ragged breath as she absorbed his pain. It was the most tragic thing she had ever heard. 'You didn't fail. You saved the children,' she said unevenly, placing a soothing hand on his arm.

'Jen died,' he returned harshly, and she bit her lip, wiping away a tear before it fell.

'Yes, she died, but you saved her precious children. She would have wanted you to do that. Any mother would. You didn't *let* her die. It was a tragedy that could have been so much worse. You've got to forgive yourself, Gray. There's only so much any one man can do, and you did it.' Her heart ached. She wanted to hug him until all his pain was gone, but could only sit there, watching.

Gray didn't respond immediately. Instead, he rose to his feet and crossed to the window, looking out, though Shelby doubted he saw much. Finally, he spoke over his shoulder.

'Now do you see what a determined person can do?' he asked her, and she sighed.

'Yes, and I'm sorry for the crass things I said.' She had just wanted to hurt him as he had hurt her. She hadn't known what she was dealing with.

He turned to her then, expression determined. 'If you mean what you say, then the best apology you can make would be to watch out for yourself.'

Shelby stood up, holding his eyes with her own. 'I will. Thank you for telling me.'

Gray closed the gap between them, reaching out to tuck a stray twist of hair behind her ear. 'You were right, you are a good listener.'

She smiled faintly as her heart expanded with pleasure that she had been able to help him in some small way. 'I'm glad I could help. Listen, I'm going to grab a quick shower before dinner. Shall we order something in?'

He smiled for the first time in ages. 'Leave it to me.'

Shelby retreated to her bedroom. What an awful thing to have happened. Her heart went out to him. The knowledge that he lived with that on his conscience made her want to cry. Nobody deserved to feel such pain. Especially not Gray.

How she wished she could have gone to him and held him, but that was impossible. All she could do was listen and try to heal the wound. She knew all about wounds, having one of her own. Because of it she had carried a grudge, and what good had it done her? So what if Gray didn't love her? To say no to what he was offering would be cutting off her nose to spite her face.

She was, above all else, a realist. You couldn't love to order, nor make someone love you. And though that often made her heart ache, given a choice, she would rather have this moment with him now than a lifetime of nothing. *Carpe diem*. It was that simple. Seize the day. Life was short, and who knew what was around the corner. So she would take what she could. There would be time enough later for regrets. At least this way she would always have some good memories to warm her heart in the long winter of the rest of her life.

The following morning Gray didn't reveal much about the plans he had been making the night before. All he would tell her over the breakfast table was that they were progressing nicely and, with luck, they would be leaving within the next few days. They could have gone now, but he wanted the security checked out first.

Shelby tried to play twenty questions, to get some idea of where they would be going, but all she got in response was a smile and a shake of the head. Finally she sighed testily. 'How will I know what clothes to take if you don't tell me where we're going?' she complained with feminine logic, and received a long look for her pains.

'It's summer, Red. Take a wild stab at what clothes you'll need,' he suggested dryly, and she very nearly threw her cup at him. 'What plans do you have for today?'

'I need to spend time on the Tyrwhit-Jones woman's design. Lord, I keep thinking of her as the Awful Antonia. It would be just my luck to say it to her face. What else? Oh, yes, I have to call in on another client in the wilds of deepest Sussex. She isn't quite sure about something, so I promised to put it right. We'd better do that first. I'll drive.'

Two hours later they finally left suburbia behind and could bowl along the fairly empty country roads. The only car in sight was the one far behind them.

'Connie's a dear, but she lives in the back of beyond!' Shelby exclaimed, though not really complaining.

'Connie?'

'Lady Constance Cosgrove. Connie to her friends. You'll adore her. She's the friendliest natured woman you'll ever meet.' Pausing, she cast him a twinkling look. 'She'll adore you, too. She's the most dreadful flirt. No handsome man is safe.'

Shelby glanced into the rear-view mirror and frowned. The car which had been some way behind them appeared to be closing the gap rapidly. Thinking the driver wanted to pass, she slowed down to give him room, but he tucked in behind her with scarcely room to breathe. So she sped up, whereupon the other car did the same, keeping itself dangerously close.

'What's he doing?' she asked sharply, and Gray glanced round. What he saw made him swear and turn back to her.

'We need to get off the road. Look around for a drive... anything. Hurry!' he urged her, glancing back again.

Shelby's heart leapt into her throat. A quick glance in the mirror showed the car looming large behind them. She didn't have to ask who or what, she knew. It was him! Somehow he had followed them from the city and whatever he had in mind didn't bode well. Trying not to panic, she searched for somewhere they might go to get away from their pursuer, but before she could do so there was an almighty crash from behind which jerked her backwards and forwards. The car swerved dangerously across the road and it was only with Gray's help that they straightened up.

Minutes later the man drove his car into their rear for a second time and again they fought to stay on the road. Shelby searched frantically for somewhere to pull off, but up ahead the road opened up with fields on either side.

'What shall I do?' she cried to Gray, who was watching the car swerve out and speed up alongside them.

'Brace yourself!' he shouted above the noise, just as the

other car swerved violently, crashing into the side of them, sending them plunging off the road.

The car bucked and leapt over deep ruts that jarred her spine. Up ahead, someone had been digging out a fallen tree, leaving an enormous hole in the ground, and they were heading straight for it. Braking like fury, she struggled with the wheel, but there had been rain recently and the earth had turned to mud. Unable to gain purchase, the car shot sideways into the hole with enough force for her head to slam into the window.

A black hole opened up before her and she tumbled into it, knowing no more.

Shelby stirred, eventually, a few days after the accident which had brought her to the hospital bed she lay in. Not that she knew it was a few days—or what kind of bed she was in to begin with. She wasn't really aware of anything much, except that the world seemed a little fuzzy around the edges, and she hadn't even opened her eyes yet.

She accomplished this with surprising difficulty. It seemed her eyelids were carrying lead weights, and she couldn't imagine why. That was her first inkling that something wasn't quite right. The second followed fast on the heels of the first. Her nose was assailed by an unmistakable scent that meant only one thing—hospital.

She was in hospital? What on earth was she doing there? The as yet only mildly alarming and rather more intriguing realisation had her automatically trying to check out her limbs for movement. The discovery that, firstly, she could barely move and, secondly, that even a small amount sent a shaft of pain through her head, caused her to desist immediately.

Well, at least she knew what she was doing here, she mused wryly, taking short breaths to ease the pain, which thankfully began to fade away. She must have had a run in with something a great deal larger than herself —and come off the worst for it. However, her attempt to recall the event did nothing but make the headache increase. It seemed to have turned her thought processes to mush at the same time. Anyway, it took too much effort to think right now. She would reminisce later.

What she could do was take a much more careful inventory of her injuries. Bracing herself for pain, she managed to raise her arms and legs some inches off the mattress, which reassured her that her body was intact, even if it was one big aching bruise.

'It's OK, you're all in one piece,' a familiar male voice declared from somewhere on her right, giving her an almighty shock, for she had believed herself to be alone. 'Sadly, I can't say the same for your car,' the voice added dryly.

'Gray?' she queried faintly, turning her head in the direction she thought his voice emanated from, but he was just beyond her field of view. 'What on earth are *you* doing here?'

'Keeping an eye on you, of course,' he came back with his usual irony, which she didn't have the strength to make a riposte to right then.

'Oh! When did you get back?' By rights he should have been on the other side of the world.

'Back?' Gray countered somewhat cautiously, and she sighed.

'You were in Sydney the last I heard,' she reminded him a little testily, because her body hurt every time she moved. The next instant she heard a creaking of furniture as her companion stood up.

'The Sydney business was cleared up quickly,' he informed her evenly.

Shelby loved the rich texture of his voice. Loved him, full stop. His looks matched his voice, and so far as she was concerned he was the sexiest thing on two legs. It was a pity he had proved to be such a louse. As ever, though, being close to him sent a tingle through her system. Or maybe that was just the painkillers wearing off.

His presence partially explained, she struggled to recall something odd he had just said. 'My car?'

'The one you crashed in your attempt to avoid hitting a dog,' Gray invented cautiously, checking out a theory.

Shelby frowned. She didn't remember crashing the car. The dog didn't register either. 'Did I hurt anyone?' she croaked, and tried to swallow, but her mouth was as dry as a desert.

'Only yourself,' he informed her, stepping into sight. Her lack of contradiction was setting off alarm bells like crazy.

Unaware of his concerns, Shelby had her own path to follow. Oh, yes, she thought for the umpteenth time, he was sexy all right. Black-haired and handsome as the devil. All she could actually see was his top half, but that was more than enough to impress her. He had the kind of chest that invited a woman to snuggle up close. Quite a hunk, in fact. Many a night she had fallen asleep imagining how it would feel snuggling up with him. The one time she had thought dreams would become reality, she had been rudely disillusioned. She had vowed never to forgive him for what he had done.

'Thirsty?' Gray asked, cutting through her bitter meanderings, and she nodded, wincing at the thump the action created.

Gray winced in sympathy. 'You had a lump the size of a goose egg on your head, but it's going down,' he told her as he reached for a button somewhere beyond her vision, but which raised the head of the bed and put her in a more comfortable sitting position. 'Try some of this.'

He was holding out a glass of water, and she allowed him to put it to her lips so that she could drink. It was warm but wonderfully refreshing. When she had had enough she pulled away, risking a faint smile of gratitude.

'Thanks,' she said, her voice sounding much more normal now. 'Seriously, Gray, why are you here? I can imagine Dad hovering by my bedside, but not you.' Unless her father had ordered him to be here. Now that sounded more like it, she thought waspishly.

Gray momentarily froze in the act of replacing the glass on the bedside table. He was worried but dared not show it. If Shelby didn't know why he was here, then she must have a memory problem. That being the case, he couldn't blurt out that she was in danger. He had to be cautious and still try to work out what she did or didn't know. The simplest way to do that was to talk about a supposed change in their relationship and take it from there.

'Why not?' he challenged casually, his eyes watching every flicker of emotion on her face. 'I've always cared what happened to you.'

She frowned in total surprise. 'Since when?' she queried sceptically. She knew exactly how much he didn't care about her. Sluggish as her brain was, it was working enough for her to wonder what he was up to now.

Gray replaced the glass and slipped his hands into the pockets of his jeans. 'For a long time, as it happens, but more recently since we put aside our differences and developed a closer relationship,' he explained, choosing his words with care.

Shelby's lips parted in a tiny gasp of surprise. 'We have?' She wondered if she was still dreaming for, much as she had always wanted more from him, she had learned the hard way that it was like reaching for the moon. To her further surprise, he nodded.

'It's why I'm here, waiting for you to wake up. I didn't expect that when you did you wouldn't remember about us.'

She could feel her eyes grow as round as saucers. 'Us?' The word was little more than a shocked whisper. What was he saying? There had never been an 'us' for them. How could things have changed so suddenly, and how could she not remember it?

Gray carefully picked up one of her hands and held it in his. 'I know it's a lot to take in, Red, but you and I are most definitely us.'

'But we can't be. I'd remember!' she pointed out, staggered by the simple act of his taking her hand. Her mind was reeling. He just didn't do that sort of thing. She had to be going crazy.

His lips twitched, but his expression remained rueful. 'You'd think so, but clearly you don't. I think it must be due to the accident. You had a heck of a bang on the head.'

Because it was the one thing she had always desperately wanted—loving him as she did—she knew it couldn't be true. It had to be a lie. So she shook her head emphatically. 'Oh, no, I don't think so. This is just another rotten game you've decided to play on me. Well, I don't think much of your timing. You and I an item? I'd sooner believe the earth was flat!'

'I'd prove it to you in a way that would expel all your doubts, but you're in no fit state to be kissed,' he assured her, but Shelby shook her head.

His certainty was countered by her own knowledge that he had played such a trick before. 'Kissing me would prove nothing. Why should I believe you, when I know what lengths you can go to?'

Gray sighed, his expression sombre. 'I explained about that. True, your father came to me for help, but I said no. You see, I'd been waiting a long time for you. And when the opportunity arose to change the nature of our relationship, I took it. Unfortunately, Oscar returned and got the wrong end of the stick. You believed him.'

Shelby listened to him in consternation. Oh, she remembered everything so clearly. Gray romancing her, her father telling her it had been at his request. Hurt, she had raged at Gray, because she had believed her father. Now Gray was telling her it had all been a mistake. He hadn't agreed to help her father at all. She hadn't given him a chance to explain. If that were true, then all the time she had spent hating him had been for nothing.

Her heart lurched. Could she have been wrong? 'I believed all this?' she asked doubtfully.

'After we'd discussed it for a while, yes,' he confirmed, watching her carefully.

One thing he said stuck in her mind. 'You've been waiting for me?' It was an incredible thing to believe, but if it were true...

'Just about as long as for ever,' he quipped, smiling faintly.

A lump lodged in her throat and she had to swallow hard to shift it. 'You're serious? This isn't just some, *Let's make a fool out of Shelby* ploy?'

'I am, and it's not.'

'You and I are...?' Understandably, she wasn't quite sure what term to use. Gray supplied one.

'Involved.'

Shelby took a steadying breath, eyes searching his for any hint of a lie. She knew what her heart wanted to believe. Dared she, though? Just on his word? Lord, how she wished she could remember him telling her all this before! She loved him, she should trust him, but she had been wrong before. Except, he was telling her she hadn't been wrong. What did she do?

'This is too incredible!' she exclaimed. She didn't know what to believe. How could she accept what he said at face value? And yet...what if it was completely true?

The sensible thing was to keep an open mind. For now

the only thing she could do was accept what he told her, be cautious and wait for her memory to return. The truth would come out then. So, she could take it on trust for now and let matters take their own course. And if it turned out he was lying…Well, she would deal with that then.

'OK, I accept that what you're telling me may be true. I'll know one way or the other when my memory returns, so you'd better not be lying,' she told him cautiously. She had to protect herself, for her heart was so very vulnerable to him. Please God, let it not be a terrible mistake! 'Is there anything else I should know?' she asked calmly, though the question set her heart thumping anxiously.

'About us? Well, we're still in the exploring stage, Red. Getting to know each other better,' he said, flashing his roguish grin.

Shelby almost howled. After wanting something for so long, it was just her luck that when it finally happened she couldn't remember it! How could fate do this to her? Something must have shown on her face, for Gray reached out and brushed his knuckles gently over her cheek.

'Don't worry about it. Besides, there's another side to look at. We can always start all over again,' he teased gently, then sobered. 'First things first. There are a few things I need to ask you. First and foremost, I take it you do remember your name?'

She managed a faint smile. 'If I can't remember that either, I'm really in trouble. My name is Shelby Greer. How was that? Do I pass?' Her spirit, which had been knocked for six by his revelation, was rallying.

He returned her smile with a slightly ragged one. 'Thankfully, yes. I admit to being worried. OK, we've established you know your name. What is the last thing you remember?'

The last thing? She frowned, probing the mists. 'I remember Dad telling me you'd gone to Australia. That was the last time I saw him.'

Gray nodded, his suspicions well and truly confirmed. 'That was over two months ago, Red. It seems to me that bump on the head has taken away the memory of several weeks of your life.'

It was a shock, even though she had been half prepared for it. 'That long?'

Gray squeezed her hand bracingly. 'Look at it this way, it could have been worse. You could have lost your memory completely.' He lay her hand back on the covers gently. 'Listen, sweetheart, I'm going to leave you alone for a time whilst I go and get a doctor to look at you. I must ring Oscar, too. In the meantime, try not to get too alarmed. I'm sure it must be scary, but try to stay calm. I won't be long.'

He went out, leaving her alone with her thoughts. They were, to put it mildly, in a state of confusion. OK, so she knew people often forgot things after an accident, but it had never happened to her before. It was alarming not being able to recall what had happened just a few days ago. She had no memory of the crash and, what was more important, she had no memory of them! It was so unfair!

Which brought her back to them. Was she accepting the truth of it too quickly? Quite possibly, because she wanted it to be true. Because, for all his faults, she was sure Gray wouldn't lie about this. And yet... She cut the thoughts off, knowing she was going round in circles. It was an impossible situation and the best thing she could do was what he said—remain calm.

Gray, meanwhile, had asked one of the nurses to get hold of Shelby's doctor, and was in the process of phoning her father. As soon as Oscar picked up the phone, he told him the news.

'Shelby's awake.'

'Oh, thank God. Thank God!' Oscar Greer exclaimed emotionally. 'Is she all right?'

'Physically, she has some painful bruising. The trouble is, she appears to have lost her memory of the last few weeks. She doesn't know anything that's been going on. What do you want me to do?'

Her father's response was immediate. 'You can't tell her, Gray. You know Shelby. She'll fight it like she did before, and we don't have time to win her round a second time. You've got to find a way to keep her safe without alarming her. Can you do that?'

Gray grimaced, knowing he had already provided himself with the perfect means of doing so. 'To test her memory, I told her the two of us were an item. She believes it to be true,' he explained, wondering how that would go down with his boss. How Shelby would deal with it in the long term, he didn't dare to contemplate. Time enough for dealing with that when he had to. He just wanted to keep her safe.

Oscar didn't even query it. 'Excellent. You must keep her believing it, my boy. Do whatever you have to do to keep her out of harm's way. Keep her safe for me, Gray.'

'You have my word on that, Oscar. I'll take her away to the country like we planned. You'd better pack some clothes for the pair of us and bring them down with you.'

'Will do. Tell her I love her and that I'll be there as soon as I can. How are you bearing up?'

'Better now she's awake,' Gray admitted. 'I'd better go. I told her I wouldn't be long.'

'I'll let you go. Take care of yourself, Gray. Goodnight.'

Gray said goodnight and hung up the phone. The die was cast. Not the way he had planned it, but he had long ago learned to take a situation as he found it and turn it to his advantage. There were risks involved, but again he was prepared to take them. Not with Shelby's life, though. Priority number one was keeping her out of harm's way. What happened after that—well, he was good at thinking on his feet. All might work out right yet.

# CHAPTER SEVEN

SHELBY was just beginning to think she had been abandoned when a doctor, complete with white coat and stethoscope, strode into the room. He sat himself down on the edge of the bed and smiled at her in a friendly way as he examined her with his eyes.

'Awake at last, I see. How do you feel?' he asked in that brisk way doctors had.

'My body aches and my head hurts,' she told him, though her gaze was on Gray, who now entered the room and took up a position by the window. Folding his arms across his chest, he smiled at her encouragingly and gave her a thumbs up.

'Well, that's what you get for driving into a hole in the ground. Fortunately, no irreparable harm was done. We did fear concussion when we saw the size of the lump on your head, but that's reducing nicely. You're a very lucky woman,' the doctor pronounced whilst listening to her heart and taking her pulse. Finally he set her hand down and looked at her soberly. 'I'm told you have a problem remembering.'

He made it sound so everyday that she laughed. 'You could say that. I seem to know everything that has happened up to a few weeks ago. Is that normal?'

'Temporary memory loss after the kind of knock on the head you had is not unusual. In most cases the memory returns after a short while,' the kindly doctor informed her paternally.

'How long must I wait? Days? Weeks?' she wanted to know, and he smiled.

'There is no magic number. When it's ready, your memory will most probably return, though there are some instances where it doesn't, but let's not go there just yet. What I do know is that trying to force it doesn't help. You must learn to be a patient patient,' he added, laughing at his own joke as he rose off the bed. 'I'll arrange for someone to come along and talk to you about it. The dos and donts, as it were. In the meantime, I'll leave you in the safe hands of your..er…um…husband.'

The doctor left, but she didn't notice. His parting words had make her eyes widen. She stared at Gray, still standing by the window, whose expression was wryly amused.

'Husband?' she queried dryly, and he smiled. The action brought warmth and a light of twinkling mischief to his eyes. It also had its usual effect on her. Her heart turned over and a bubble of emotion swelled up inside her. She loved him so much. Beyond reason. Beyond anything. For the moment, at least, he appeared to be hers. That was what he was telling her—but her husband?

'We're not married, but we are living together. I imagine the doctor didn't know what to call me,' Gray teased lightly, inviting her to share the joke, but she was too busy taking in what he had just told her.

'We're living together?' Somehow, in her thinking, she hadn't got them quite that far. They were lovers, then. How cruel not to know it when she'd waited so long.

'At your flat for the present,' Gray confirmed, collecting a chair as he came closer. Setting it by the bed, he pulled out his wallet and searched inside it for a moment before handing over a photograph. 'I thought this might interest you. It was taken at a charity function we both attended,' he enlarged as he sat down and waited for her reaction.

Shelby stared at the photograph. It had obviously been taken at a party, and showed the pair of them standing together, laughing at the camera with raised hands holding glasses of champagne. Her doubts eased a fraction at this tangible proof.

'We seem to have been having fun,' she remarked, handing the photo back. Her throat felt tight. It hurt so much to know that they had finally become lovers and yet she couldn't recall even the simplest kiss or caress.

Gray took the snap and replaced it in his wallet. 'Making up for lost time.'

'We don't fight any more?' she asked curiously.

A wolfish grin tweaked at her heart. 'Not in the same way, no,' he confirmed and Shelby felt her cheeks grow warm.

'You're not going to tell me we're engaged too?' Nothing would surprise her.

'We haven't got around to it yet,' Gray responded, then unfastened the pocket of his shirt and reached into it. 'You do have rings, though.' Holding his hand out palm upwards, he revealed a simple gold wedding band and a solitaire engagement ring. 'Do you recognise them?'

Shelby looked down at the rings and smiled. Abruptly her eyes filled with emotional tears, which she knew must be due mostly to the accident, for she had no memory of their owner, save in a few tattered photographs. 'They were my mother's. Dad gave them to me on my eighteenth birthday.'

'The nurse took them off to clean you up. I've been looking after them until you woke up.' She took the rings he tumbled into her palm and slipped them on to her right hand.

She glanced up, smiling. 'Thank you.'

'You once told me you felt lost without them,' he told her simply, and she sighed, twisting the rings around her finger.

'I do.' She recalled the occasion. He had been holding her hand across a dinner table and the sky hadn't yet fallen in on her dreams. 'It's the only real contact I have with her. I wish I could have known her,' she said softly.

'I should imagine she was very much like you,' Gray declared with a faint smile, and she lifted an eyebrow.

'You mean annoying, self-opinionated and spoilt?' she challenged, using some of the words with which he had described her over the years.

He tutted. 'I was thinking of strong, passionate and compassionate,' he countered pointedly, and her nerves jolted.

'Is that how you really see me?' she asked in surprise. She couldn't recall him ever saying anything so complimentary. Unless you counted the time she'd believed he'd been lying, but which now turned out to have been the truth. A convoluted thought that made her wince inwardly.

'When you're not being the proverbial pain in the backside,' he added, tongue-in-cheek, and Shelby laughed. This was more like she remembered.

'I knew you couldn't change your spots entirely.' Gray laughed too and they shared a moment of total empathy, which left her feeling both uplifted and sad. 'I can't remember this 'us' you talk of.' She tried again, hoping something would miraculously click into place, but nothing happened. It was all still depressingly blank. And her head was beginning to ache with the effort. 'Damn. You'd think something so momentous would do the trick!'

'You can't rush it, Shelby, but I'm not surprised you're trying to. You always were impatient.'

'Well, of course I only have your word for that,' she said dryly, trying to make light of the situation she found herself in, and it brought a wry smile to his lips.

'See, you're sounding more like your old self already! Using every trick in the book to your advantage.'

'Don't start with me, Gray. I'm poorly, remember?' she said faintly, pressing a limp hand to her brow, and that made him laugh again.

'That will only get you so far with me, Red. *I* haven't forgotten anything!' he told her sardonically, and she frowned at him from under her hand.

'How kind of you to remind me. I must try to return the courtesy one day,' she promised direly, but he didn't look in the least worried.

'I'm sure you will, darling,' he agreed with good humour.

The endearment tugged at her heart. It was possible he had said it countless times in the past few weeks, but this was the first time of hearing it for her. 'I like the way you say that,' she told him whimsically, feeling almost shy. It was hard to respond naturally when she wasn't totally sure it wasn't a mistake.

Blue eyes smiled kindly at her. 'What—darling? You'll be hearing it a lot.'

She looked at him a little uncertainly. 'Good. Maybe it will help me believe…' She broke off, biting her lip as she realised her remark was casting doubt on him. Gray merely nodded consideringly.

'Make you believe I'm telling the truth? I hope so.'

About to respond, Shelby found herself unable to hold back a yawn. It had been a fraught few hours, and now she was being overwhelmed by a feeling of exhaustion. 'Lord, I'm tired,' she muttered, closing her eyes. She didn't want to sleep yet. There were so many questions she still had to ask. Her body, however, had other ideas.

Gray pulled his chair up beside the bed, making himself as comfortable as he could. 'Go to sleep, Red. I'll still be here when you wake up,' he promised, and received a breathy little sigh in response.

A few minutes later he could tell from the rhythmical sound of her breathing that she was asleep. He brushed the hair away from her face and raised himself enough to press a soft kiss on her lips.

'Hell, Red,' he declared softly. 'What have we got our-selves into this time? I'm taking a hell of a risk here. All I hope is that, when the dust settles, it will turn out to have been a risk worth taking.'

Sighing, he made himself as comfortable as he could in the chair, placed his hand over hers on the cover, and closed his eyes.

He had to be really uncomfortable, Shelby thought as she stared down at the sleeping figure of Gray in the chair be-side her bed. It was dark outside and from the lack of sounds beyond her door she knew it must be late. She must have slept for hours and certainly felt better for it. She had finally awakened to find Gray slumped in the chair, and had lain looking at him ever since.

For the nth time she wished she could remember what had finally brought them together. Her brain had been working overtime since she'd stirred. Sure, Gray had said that he had been attracted to her for a long time, but why had he made no attempt to tell her the truth before if she meant that much to him? The answer made her lips twist. Probably because she had been so busy hating him that she had never given him the chance! Until when? Something must have happened to change that. Something in the last few months. But what? It was so frustrating! What if…? No! She had to stop with the 'what if's. They would drive her mad. She had to wait and see. Had to give herself time.

Looking at him now brought a smile to her lips and gave her a warm feeling around her heart. Gray had hinted that they were lovers, but had she told him she loved him? Did he love her, or was this just an affair? Lord, she hated the not knowing. If only she could remember, she'd have an-swers to all her questions!

'Trying to make yourself remember generally has the reverse result.' Gray's sleepy voice interrupted her thoughts and she turned her head to look at him. He looked rumpled and dog-tired and endlessly endearing.

'I know, but in my position you'd do the same thing,' she pointed out, and he gave her a lopsided smile of acknowledgement.

'Probably. How are you feeling now?' he asked as he stood up and stretched, trying to smooth out the kinks the chair had put in his body.

'Much better. My head has stopped aching. What time is it?'

He glanced at his watch. 'Way past the witching hour. Getting on for three in the morning. We're probably the only ones awake.' He flexed his back and shoulders, easing the cramped muscles.

'You can't be comfortable in that chair. Why don't you go home?' she suggested, though she didn't relish the thought of being here alone. Hospitals gave her the heebie-jeebies.

'I probably would, if we were anywhere near home,' he agreed with her, and Shelby couldn't contain her surprise.

'Where are we?' She had assumed, obviously wrongly, that she was in her local hospital.

Gray smiled wryly. Now they were coming to the crunch point. He planned to keep as close to the truth as possible, without causing her to smell a rat. Hopefully she would accept the story without question.

'Sussex. We were on our way to visit one of your clients. After that we were going to head off for a holiday.'

'Oh,' she responded faintly, naturally not remembering, though she knew she had a client in the county. 'Have I spoiled our holiday?'

He shook his head. 'Put it off for a few days, that's all. As soon as you can leave hospital, we'll on our way. You'll need a little rest and TLC after this.'

'How, if I wrecked the car?' she wanted to know, and Gray grinned.

'There are other forms of transport. I called in a favour from a friend,' he informed her, then found himself having to smother a powerful yawn of his own. 'Sorry about that,' he apologised.

'You really need to get some decent sleep, Gray. Why don't you ask if there's a room here you could use?' Shelby said in some concern.

'It's OK. I have a room booked at a nearby hotel. I haven't used it much because I wanted to be here when you woke up,' he explained. Running a hand over his chin, he winced. 'I could do with a shave, too.'

'Well, I'm awake now and you can see I'm fine, relatively speaking. Go. Have a shave, get some sleep and come back later. All I'm going to do is sleep, anyway,' she urged him.

After a moment, when it looked to her as if he might argue, Gray shrugged. 'You're right. I'm out on my feet.' Coming to the bed again, he bent over her. 'See you in the morning, darling,' he said softly and pressed a kiss to her forehead.

When he made to move away, however, he discovered Shelby had grabbed two handfuls of his shirt and was holding on tightly. He looked down into her eyes.

'If you think you're leaving after that, think again. I didn't hurt my lips, you know.'

His eyes dropped to her mouth, and his own lips twitched. 'No, I can see that.' Letting out a sighing breath, he took her lips in a gentle yet provocative kiss that sought a response from her then stopped once he had got it. Drawing back, he smiled wryly. 'Better?'

'Much,' she agreed huskily. The tingling his lips had started still washed along her veins. 'Goodnight,' she said, suddenly reluctant to see him go.

He sensed it and gave her hand a reassuring squeeze. 'Close your eyes and I'll be back before you know it,' Gray promised, and crossed the room in a couple of strides. At the door he paused briefly to give her a wave, then vanished from sight.

Shelby turned her head on the pillow and stared out of the window where the sky was already beginning to lighten in the distance, a faint smile curving her lips. Lifting a hand, she ran a finger over lips that still tingled. Gray must have kissed her in the last few weeks, but this was the only one she remembered. This kiss, brief though it had been, told her a lot. They were an 'us' all right. Another layer of doubts vanished, easing her mind.

Maybe dreams really did come true. On that thought she closed her eyes again and before very long had drifted back to sleep.

Outside in the corridor, where he stood leaning against the wall, Gray rubbed his hands over his face in a battle-weary gesture. He couldn't actually leave until his relief turned up—a good friend he could trust to look out for Shelby whilst he got some much needed rest. Jack was at the hotel and had promised to be there in ten minutes. In the meantime, he waited.

He found himself caught in the sticky web of truths and half-truths he had woven in order to keep Shelby safe. It wasn't going to be easy treading the fine line that had been drawn. She might think they were a couple; yet, however much he wanted her, the one thing he couldn't do was act as if the fiction was a reality. Only a scoundrel would take advantage of the situation and, though appearances were to the contrary, he wasn't a scoundrel.

He laughed wryly. He was going to be in for a hell of a time and he only hoped his self-control would last out. Once he would have been certain, but things had changed and now he wasn't quite so sure.

Shelby was discharged from the hospital forty-eight hours later. There wasn't anything wrong with her that wouldn't heal in time—even her memory. She had spoken to a counsellor and the sensible advice she had been given had helped her a lot.

Gray arrived to pick her up mid-morning. Shelby had been up, champing at the bit, for hours, and she virtually pounced on him when he walked in the door.

'It's about time. I thought you were never going to get here,' she grumbled, and he shot her a resigned look.

'You must be feeling better. You sound more like you already,' he gibed as she grabbed the bag of clothes he had brought with him and started to ransack the contents.

'I'm sorry. I just want to get out of here. I can't stand this place.'

'You never did like hospitals,' a dear voice declared gruffly, and Shelby glanced up in surprise as a tall, greying man stepped into the room.

Tears of emotion sprang to her eyes. 'Dad!' she exclaimed in a choked voice and abandoned the clothes to hurry over to him. 'It's good to see you.'

Oscar Greer smiled and held out his arms. 'It's good to see you awake and alert. The last time I was here you were unconscious. Come and give me a hug. I need it badly. You scared the life out of me.'

'I'm sorry,' Shelby apologised, hugging him tightly.

Oscar released her to arm's length and gave her the once over. 'You're looking much better. Gray has been keeping me appraised of your recovery, but I had to come and see for myself before you went away. Have you remembered anything yet?'

Shelby shook her head. 'Not a sausage. I rang the studio to see how my projects were going and I don't remember doing half of what Paula was talking about. Really I should go and see her before going anywhere,' she declared, going back to her bag of clothes.

Oscar and Gray exchanged a speaking look, and it was Gray who answered.

'Only you're not going to. You're going to obey doctors' orders and take it easy for a while. Understood?'

She had had no intention of doing any such thing, until he tried to take charge. 'You can't order me about, Gray Compton,' she told him, chin raised to a belligerent angle.

He swatted the words away like flies. 'No, but I can throw you over my shoulder and put you in the car. It's your choice. What's it to be?'

Shelby folded her arms and stared at him hard. 'You'd do it too, wouldn't you?'

Blue eyes gleamed back at her. 'In a heartbeat,' he confirmed hardily.

She looked at her father. 'Are you going to let him get away with this?'

Oscar hid a smile behind his hand, then cleared his throat. 'I'm afraid I agree with Gray on this. The girls are fully capable of managing without you for a while.'

'Traitor,' she accused her parent, but knew he was right. She had chosen her assistants because they could work unsupervised. That wasn't the point of the disagreement.

'Now that that's settled,' Gray declared triumphantly, 'I'm going to take Oscar down to the cafeteria for coffee whilst you get changed, OK?'

Shelby shrugged indifferently. 'OK, that's fine. I'll be here. Nowhere else to go!' she retorted grumpily, and scowled when they abandoned her to her mood and walked out again.

Alone, her glum expression soon changed to a catlike smile. He might think he had won, but only because she hadn't been serious about staying. How could he think for one second that she would prefer to stay and work when the opportunity to be alone with him was the alternative? During the last couple of days she had come to terms with the situation. Gray was so attentive, so supportive...so caring, she couldn't believe it was simply a game. So she was heeding her own advice, taking everything as it came and not looking too far ahead.

She could feel excitement building up inside her. It was all due to the fact that she and Gray were going away together. They were going to be alone and, no matter what had happened before, it would be the first time for her. She had dreamed of such a moment. Had longed for it with all her heart, and now it was going to happen. The circumstances could have been better, but she wasn't about to look a gift horse in the mouth.

When Gray and her father returned, Shelby was dressed in jeans, an emerald T-shirt and deck shoes. She had everything packed and waiting on the bed and was pacing the room impatiently. They left immediately, Shelby holding her father's arm, with Gray bringing up the rear with her belongings. She had planned to say goodbye to some of the nurses on her way down but, to her surprise, found herself swept out of the hospital and into a waiting car in a matter of minutes.

'Just a second. I wanted to say thank you to the staff,' she protested as Gray got in beside her, blocking her attempt to clamber back out.

'There isn't time, darling. You have a plane to catch,' Oscar argued reasonably as he took his place beside the driver. 'OK, John. Take it away.'

She subsided because she was not about to fling herself out of a moving vehicle. She would make sure she sent a card and gift for all the staff on her floor to share.

Gray cast a look out of the rear window before making himself comfortable beside her.

'Did we forget something?' Shelby asked curiously, looking back herself, but he shook his head.

'Just checking,' he explained easily. 'Force of habit,' he added, and she sat back again.

'Where are we going?' she queried once they had been driving a while. She knew the area from visits to her client, but couldn't work out where their route would take them.

'The local airport. There's a plane on standby there,' Gray returned smoothly.

She frowned at him, wondering if he had just misunderstood or was being deliberately obtuse. 'I meant, where are going? What's our final destination?'

'It's a surprise,' he divulged noncommittally, and something suddenly struck her as odd, though she couldn't say why.

'Why do I get the feeling something's going on?' she asked, and was surprised when both Gray and her father turned to look at her sharply. Then she found the driver's eyes watching her in the rear-view mirror, which was the most startling thing of all. What on earth…?

It was her father who answered. 'Listen, darling, all that's going on is that Gray arranged this surprise for you. Now, if he tells you, it won't be a surprise. So why don't you stop worrying about nothing and enjoy the journey?' he advised her.

'That's all very well, but I'm not sure that I like surprises,' she argued, momentarily diverted, and everyone laughed, including the driver.

'That one will never fly, sweetheart. We all know there's nothing you love more than springing a surprise on your nearest and dearest,' Gray pointed out mockingly. 'This time, the surprise is on you.'

There was nothing she could say to that. It was, after all, true. Sighing heavily, she made an attempt to concentrate on the passing scenery, and it was as she was doing so that she felt Gray take her hand and thread her fingers through his. She looked round at him questioningly.

'The thought of flying makes me nervous,' he told her, and her eyebrows rose incredulously.

'I happen to know that you have your own pilot's licence,' she countered dryly.

He grinned faintly. 'OK, the truth is I needed an excuse to hold your hand.'

'You've never needed an excuse to do anything in your entire life,' she pointed out, but didn't take her hand away. It felt good. Right. She probably held his hand all the time these days, and one day it would all come back to her.

Gray looked at her, a strange light in his eyes. 'Haven't I? You'd be surprised.'

She looked at him questioningly, waiting for more, but that was all he said. She puzzled over what might unsettle his supreme confidence, but couldn't come up with anything, and in the end had to let it go.

The airport was small and the plane they were using a private one, so it took no time at all to pass through the checks. Shelby hugged her father at the departure gate.

'Please don't worry. I'll be fine,' she reassured him.

'I know you will, darling. Gray's a good man.'

She glanced round at Gray, who was standing just outside, carrying their luggage, which had been in the boot of the car. 'I guess that's why I love him so much,' she agreed softly, and saw the stunned expression that settled on her father's face. It was then that she realised she had spoken a little too loudly. Her secret was out.

'Shelby?' Oscar exclaimed, and she hastily stood on tip toe to kiss his cheek.

'Oh, Lord. I didn't mean to say that! It's a secret. Please, please, please don't tell him I said so because I don't think I've ever told him,' she pleaded, then gave him a crooked smile and hurried to join Gray.

Oscar Greer stood watching her in somewhat of a daze. Then he smiled, and the smile slowly broadened into a grin. He laughed, shaking his head in wonder and wry amusement. His gaze fell on Gray and his merriment deepened. Well, well, well, he thought, rubbing his hands together in glee. Who would have thought it? This couldn't have worked out better if he'd planned it himself.

Oblivious to it all, the two sources of his amusement were concentrating on each other.

'Everything OK?' Gray asked her as they walked towards a gleaming white jet.

'He's worried, but he knows I'll be fine,' she answered him distractedly, her attention on the aircraft. 'A Lear jet? You can't be serious!'

'Ever been on one?' he asked, and she shook her head, virtually speechless.

'I wish!'

That roguish smile twinkled down at her. 'Then you're in for the flight of your life,' he declared, helping her to mount the steps into the luxury jet. 'Sit anywhere you like. I'll just stow the luggage away.'

Shelby took a seat by the window and Gray had just joined her when the pilot walked through from the cockpit. He retracted the steps and locked the door before speaking to them.
Good morning, Mr Compton. Mr Ross sends his compliments. You'll find refreshments in the galley, and the rest room is just beyond that. We'll be taking off in a few minutes, and I hope you enjoy the flight.' With a respectful nod he went on his way and disappeared forward.

Shelby took an appreciative look around the luxurious interior. 'How do you know somebody who would lend you his Lear jet?'

Gray shrugged lightly. 'I got him out of a jam once and he's returning the favour.'

She was impressed. 'It must have been some jam!' she exclaimed ironically.

Gray merely smiled, and as the engines started at that moment, Shelby promptly forgot all about the mysterious Mr Ross. Having buckled herself in, she reached across and slipped her hand into Gray's. When he looked a question, her lips twitched.

'Flying makes you nervous, remember?'

Blue eyes gleamed back at her. 'So it does,' he responded, and tightened his grip.

Shelby felt her heart swell, and turned her attention to the world flashing by outside with a sigh of satisfaction. Now, if only she could get her memory back, life would be just about perfect.

# CHAPTER EIGHT

THEY arrived at their final destination in the late afternoon. All Shelby knew was that they were in Scotland, and from the airport where they had landed Gray had driven them west in a hired Range Rover. The scenery was breathtaking and constantly changing as they travelled up the coast, then headed inland until finally he drew them to a halt before a house set on a hillside overlooking a loch.

A smiling woman came out of the house to meet them as they climbed out of the car.

'Mrs Menzies?' Gray queried, walking forward to shake hands.

'Aye. And you'll be Mr and Mrs Compton,' she confirmed in the lilting, softly spoken manner of the locals. Shelby shook hands, deciding there was no point in correcting the woman's error about their married state. 'Now, here are the keys. I've made up the bed for you and set the water heater. By the time you go to bed, there will be plenty of hot water. You'll find food in the refrigerator and logs for the fire are down in the cellar. It can get a wee bit chilly at night up here. If you need me for anything, you'll find me at the farm on the other side of the loch there.' She pointed to a collection of buildings in the near distance.

'Thank you, Mrs Menzies. You've been very kind,' Gray responded, taking the keys.

'You and your wife enjoy your stay, now,' Mrs Menzies declared with another friendly smile, then picked up a bicycle which had been hidden by the wall and rode off on it.

Shelby watched until the woman was out of sight, then

took a good deep breath of the fresh scented air. 'This is fantastic. How on earth did you find it?'

'Through a friend of a friend,' he answered vaguely.

'I never knew you had so many friends!' she declared, eyes dancing. 'Look at all those colours in the heather. Oh, I wish I had my sketch pad with me. I need to get this down on paper!' she exclaimed, receiving a sensory bombardment every way she looked.

Gray cast her a curious look out of those blue eyes. 'You paint?'

'One of the few things I inherited from my mother. I'm not a Turner or a Constable, but I get by,' she confirmed, sighing happily. 'You couldn't have chosen a better spot, I love it!'

'I don't want to dampen your enthusiasm, but we didn't pack any painting gear. We should be able to pick up a pad and some watercolours in the nearest town, though. Will that do?'

Shelby rubbed her hands together, enthused by the prospect of painting the myriad views. 'I can't wait.' Turning to him with a excited smile, she slipped her arms around his neck and sighed. 'Thank you for bringing me here,' she said huskily and, in a spontaneous gesture, raised herself on tiptoe to kiss him.

There was a fraction of a second when Gray didn't respond, but just when she was beginning to wonder at his reluctance his arms snaked round her, drawing her close. He took her simple thank you kiss and returned it with a searching one of his own. His teeth nipped at her lips, then his tongue soothed them with a silken glide. When she gasped at the tingle of pleasure, he took the opportunity to gain entry to the warm cavern of her mouth, searching out the sensitive spots with his tongue, urging her to meet him halfway, which she did with a sigh of satisfaction.

For mindless minutes they stood locked in each other's

arms, their kiss slowly but surely growing in passion until the need for air caused Shelby to break the contact. 'Wow!' she exclaimed with a husky laugh. 'What was that for?'

Gray's eyes only slowly lost their heated gleam. 'It's been a long dry spell between kisses, and I couldn't resist it any longer,' he confessed wryly and she smiled tenderly, her hand cupping his cheek.

'I'm glad you didn't. We must have had a lot of practice,' she teased, and something flickered across his face too quickly for her to interpret.

'Well, you know what they say, Red. Practice makes perfect,' he joked back as he gently ran his hands up and down her back.

'Mmm. In that case I'll definitely be finding out how perfect you are later,' she flirted, only to frown when his hands stopped their gentle stroking. 'What? What is it?'

'We shouldn't forget you were in an accident mere days ago and only got out of hospital today. You don't want to rush things,' he advised her, stepping back so that her arms fell to her sides.

Not surprisingly, she looked at him oddly. He had initiated this, so why was he pulling back? 'The doctor said I was in perfect health, except for the odd bruise or two. I'm not an invalid.'

Gray's response was to ruffle her hair. 'I know you're not, sweetheart, but it still hasn't been long.'

Shelby wasn't at all happy with that answer or the action. 'Don't you want to make love to me?' she demanded to know, going straight to the heart of the matter, and Gray uttered a dry laugh as he shook his head.

'Hell, Red, you have no idea! I want to do that so damned much it hurts,' he told her gruffly, and there was such a powerful look of desire in his eyes that she really couldn't doubt his answer.

Moving closer, she placed her palms on his chest and

fluttered him a come-hither look. 'In that case there's nothing stopping you,' she declared alluringly.

Groaning, Gray placed his hands over hers, lest they threaten to stray enticingly. 'I only have so much control here, and you're enough to tempt a saint. Give me a break, Red. I'm trying to do what's right, which is give you time,' he added reasonably.

Her tongue peeped out to moisten her lips, causing him to catch his breath, which set her nerves jumping again. 'Thanks, but I don't want it,' she insisted and he closed his eyes for a moment.

'You've got it anyway.'

She stared at him in silence and with a lurch of her heart she thought she might have the real answer. 'There's something wrong with this relationship, isn't there? Something you're not telling me. That's why you're holding back,' she accused tightly, her heart starting to thump anxiously in her chest. Oh, God, could she have loved him and lost him all in the space of the weeks she couldn't remember? Was he just being kind until she did remember?

Gray looked at her for a long moment, then dragged a hand through his hair. 'There's nothing wrong between us, Red. Our relationship is as… strong as it ever was.'

As far as Shelby was concerned, he could be saying what she needed to hear rather than the truth. She had no way of knowing, and had never felt so vulnerable in her life. 'Is it? How do I know you're telling me the truth?' Her eyes were a little wild now and she was disastrously close to tears.

Swiftly taking her by the shoulders, Gray looked her squarely in the eye. 'Listen to me, Red. This is why I want to give you time, because your emotions are still recovering from the shock. Think. You have to know I wouldn't lie to you.'

Shelby held his gaze, reading the message he was trying

to send her. She had to believe he wouldn't lie or she was lost. She was overreacting, and it was all due to the accident—as he had told her.

Slumping against him, she rested her head on his chest and sighed. 'I'm sorry. It's just…not remembering us makes me nervous. Of course I believe you, Gray,' she said and felt his chest rise as he drew in air in a ragged sigh of his own.

'Thank you for that,' Gray responded gently, slipping an arm across her shoulders and starting them walking towards the house. 'Listen, darling, we're both a bit strained after all that's happened. That's why we're here. We need to relax and take things easy. How about we start with a hot cup of tea?'

Tea sounded just about perfect right then. 'Let's do a deal. I'll make us some tea whilst you bring the luggage in. How's that?' Shelby offered, raising her head to twinkle a smile up at him.

Laughing, Gray handed her the keys. 'I should have known you'd get out of the hard work somehow. Milk, no sugar,' he enlarged helpfully. Catching her chin in his hand, he held her steady whilst he dropped a kiss on her lips. 'Just a little something on account,' he grinned, then turned on his heel and headed back to the car.

Left to her own devices, Shelby went exploring. The house itself was old, but the interior had been improved to suit modern day needs. She found the kitchen easily enough, and set the kettle on to boil whilst she reconnoitred the rest of the ground floor. The sitting room was the cosiest she had ever seen, set about with rugs and comforters and deep-cushioned chairs and a settee just made to curl up in. On the upper floor there were four bedrooms, but only one ready for use. The main bedroom had an *en suite* bathroom and a spectacular view over the loch. As soon as she saw it, Shelby couldn't imagine sleeping anywhere else.

Humming cheerfully to herself, she jogged back downstairs and retraced her steps to the kitchen. With the tea brewing in the pot, she hunted through the cupboards for something to go with it and discovered a tin of home-made shortbread. It had to have been left there by Mrs Menzies, and Shelby made a note to thank her the next time she saw her.

They drank their tea in the garden, munching on melt-in-the-mouth shortbread whilst watching the world go by on the loch below. The bustle turned to a trickle and eventually died away as the sun slowly sank in the west, and it was only the first chill of evening which finally sent them inside.

Later they dined on soup with chunks of fresh bread and a fine red wine. Gray found an old movie channel on the television and Shelby curled up beside him on the settee, her head on his shoulder, an arm tucked behind him, her hand slipping beneath his shirt.

'This is nice.' She sighed comfortably. 'Do we do this often?'

'Not often enough,' he replied huskily, and shifted so that his arm was around her shoulders. 'Better?'

'Hmm, much,' she confirmed with a tiny sigh, a flirtatious smile hovering unseen about her lips. Slowly but surely her fingers began to trace lazy circles over his skin. For a while he appeared to ignore it, but then she felt the tension start to mount in him.

'Cut it out, Red,' he ordered gruffly, and her lips twitched.

'Cut what out?' she asked innocently, ignoring his command.

'You know what you're doing,' he countered, then gasped as her fingers found a particularly sensitive spot.

This time she laughed out loud. 'I most certainly do.'

Gray's hand found her chin and raised her head until

their eyes met. 'I give you fair warning, sweetheart. You're messing with the wrong man,' he growled.

Her eyes flirted with him recklessly. 'That's good!'

Swift as blinking, Shelby found herself lying on her back on the settee with Gray half leaning over her, his mouth twisted into a wolfish grin.

His teeth gleamed whitely as he said, 'You're playing a dangerous game.'

'It's the only type worth playing,' Shelby flirted wickedly. She might not recall how they had come to be lovers, but flirting with him like this felt as right and comfortable as an old pair of shoes—only far more exciting.

'You know, there are two ways this can go,' he informed her, insinuating his hand beneath her T-shirt, causing her to catch her breath this time.

'Is that so?' she murmured breathlessly, her pulse beginning to trip faster in her ears.

His fingers glided upwards until they brushed the lower slopes of her breasts. His voice became huskily sensual. 'I could kiss you, or…'

Her eyes widened expectantly. 'Or…?'

'I could simply do this,' he went on in an altogether different tone and, before she could stop him, he began to tickle her ruthlessly.

'No!' Shelby exclaimed before she was overcome by tickle-induced laughter. She bucked, writhed and squirmed, all to no avail. Gray was stronger than she was and he knew just where to tickle her to undermine her best efforts at escape. One of her flailing arms caught him around the ear and, to avoid getting hit again, he buried his head in her neck. Just as it got to the point where it was hurting her to laugh, he stopped, raising his head to look down at her.

'Had enough?'

'H-hardly,' she puffed. 'I'm just getting my second wind!'

Laughing, Gray rested his weight on his elbows and looked at her admiringly. 'I'll say this for you, Shelby Greer. You're a real terrier when it comes to defending yourself.'

Shelby was beginning to get her breath back now. 'That had better be a compliment.'

The look in his eyes softened. 'It was.'

She let out a sighing breath. 'I wanted you to kiss me,' she told him with a faint pout and he smoothed it out with the brush of his thumb, sending a tingling throughout her body.

'I know,' he replied softly. 'To tell you the truth, Red. I could keep on kissing you from now until for ever and never get tired of it. That isn't the problem.'

'Then what is the problem?' she asked him, her heart melting.

Removing his thumb, he replaced it with his lips, gently rubbing, nipping and teasing with teeth and tongue. 'If I get started, I won't want to stop.'

Shelby's lids fluttered down over her eyes as she sought to return each caress. 'Me neither.'

Her lips parted and he breached her defences, searching out her tongue with his own, enticing her to join him, which she did gladly. He groaned deep in his throat.

'You're so damned addictive. I want you so much, it's driving me crazy.' The powerful words were enough to ignite their mutual passion, which was never far from the surface.

Shelby cradled the back of his head with her hand and gave herself up to the infinite pleasure of kissing him. She knew how he felt, for she felt it too. As the kiss deepened, became more and more arousing, her whole body thrummed with need. Kiss followed kiss, each wilder and more passionate than the last, and she moaned, wanting more, needing him to touch her. As if he could read her mind, Gray's hand once more slid beneath her T-shirt, but this time to caress, not to tease. As he sought out her breast, she arched into his touch, gasping at the shaft of pleasure that swept through her.

This, she thought, as her hands clung on to him, was what she was born for. To be with him. To experience everything with him. It felt so gloriously, wonderfully right, that she wanted it to go on for ever. Yet, even as she thought it, she could sense Gray drawing back. She knew it wasn't easy for him to break free of the passion which threatened to overwhelm them, yet he did it, pulling back so that once more he was looking down at her, but this time the coals of desire still burned in his eyes and he was breathing hard.

'You see what I mean?' he growled. 'Every time it gets harder and harder to call a halt.'

'But I told you it wasn't necessary,' she reminded him.

With a deep sigh, Gray pushed himself up and away from her, combing faintly trembling hands through his hair. 'I know, but I have rules, Red, and one of them is not to take advantage of the situation.' It would help a great deal if she didn't keep trying to seduce him.

'I'm starting to hate rules.' She sighed as she too sat up and restored her clothes to a semblance of order. 'Tell me how we came to get together, instead,' she compromised, settling herself back beside him.

'Shouldn't you be remembering that on your own?'

'Probably,' she agreed with a grimace. 'But what if I never remember? I want to know, Gray.' She looked up at him, green eyes large and pleading.

Caught in their spell, he knew he had to say something, even if it did blow up in his face later. It wouldn't be the truth, but it could have been, had luck been on his side. And there was always the chance that one small seed could fall on fertile ground. He was taking so many risks, what did one more matter?

So, making himself comfortable, he drew her close. 'It was after one of those dinners at your father's, just after I returned from Japan. We were having one of our customary exchanges of words. You accused me yet again of playing games with you, and my patience finally snapped. I told you how wrong you were, that I'd wanted you for years, and that if you'd ever bothered to ask me my side of the story, things might be different between us.'

It sounded entirely plausible to Shelby, recalling how convinced she had been of his guilt. She had refused to listen. 'What did I say to that?'

'You were lost for words to start with. A miracle in itself. After a moment you demanded I explain what I meant,' he told her, glancing down to see how she was taking it, and saw her bite her lip.

For her part, Shelby could picture herself with her arms crossed defensively, glaring at him so he shouldn't see her consternation. When you'd been hurt you wouldn't easily be won over, even if you longed to be. 'What did you do then?'

A nerve ticked in his jaw as he answered. 'Like I told you the other day, I explained that, whilst Oscar had asked me, I had refused. The reason I sought you out was because I wanted to. I'd waited long enough.'

That had her sitting up and looking at him. 'So how come you pushed me away when we were out on the terrace, and said you weren't attracted to me?' she challenged him.

He smiled ruefully, though his gaze was watchful. 'Exactly what you asked me the last time we had this conversation, and the answer is still the same. I lied.'

'You lied?' she charged incredulously, and Gray shrugged.

'You had had too much to drink,' he was swift to point out, and Shelby rolled her eyes helplessly.

'Of course I had. To bolster my courage. I'd never tried to seduce you before!'

One eyebrow quirked. 'Really? I didn't know you'd needed Dutch courage. I always imagined you had the gall to do anything.'

Not where he was concerned. Her heart was involved, and that changed everything. 'Yes, well… For your information, I'm not the hussy you take me for.'

He smiled faintly. 'If I thought anything about you, Red, it was that you were the most alluring woman I had ever met. You still are.'

One look at his face told her he wasn't joking, and it did her heart a power of good. It wasn't that she was expecting him to declare he loved her. She was too sensible for that. However, she could begin to hope that this attraction between them would not easily be satisfied. Having accepted they had a relationship, time was what she needed now. Time to make memories. Then, when it was all finally over, she could open up the secret place in her heart and warm herself on the old flames. However, that was ahead of her. She had to concentrate on now.

'So it's true what they say: third time's the charm. Here we are, together at last. Who would have thought it? What will become of us, do you think?'

He smiled, eyes searching hers for something she couldn't tell if he found or not. 'Time will tell, sweetheart. Time will most surely tell.'

Suddenly the future was full of unknown possibilities, and she was glad she hadn't given in to doubt. 'Let's go to bed,' she suggested, then, seeing the look on his face, laughed huskily. 'I didn't mean that. I'm tired.'

Gray rose at once and helped her to her feet. 'You go

on up whilst I check everything's secure down here. I've put your bags in the main bedroom.'

'Don't be long,' she urged him as she headed for the stairs.

'I won't be,' he promised.

Up in the master bedroom, Shelby decided against drawing the curtains as there was hardly likely to be anyone looking in, they were so isolated. Looking at the comfortable bed, she was suddenly aware of just how tired she was. It had been a long day, mostly spent travelling. Much as she would like to have clambered into the bed as she was, she rummaged in her case for her wash bag, a towel and her night things, and took them into the *en suite* bathroom.

The shower was blissfully warm and she was tempted to stay under it. Yet she had no idea just how much hot water there was so, after washing, she stepped out and dried herself off, slipping into a blue silk nightie. Towel-drying her hair, she wandered back into the bedroom, and it was only then that she noticed that Gray's bags were missing. The towel dropped to the floor as she crossed to the fitted wardrobe on the off-chance he had unpacked his things already. It took but a moment to discover that the wardrobe and dressers were empty.

Then she heard the sound of a door closing and followed the sound to the room opposite. Gray must have come up whilst she was in the shower, for he was in the process of unpacking his clothes in that room. Standing in the doorway watching, her heart sank.

'What's going on?' she asked abruptly, causing him to glance round.

He straightened with a small stack of clothes in his hand. 'I thought I'd sleep in this room,' Gray informed her evenly. 'Just until you're healed.'

'I am healed,' Shelby told him tautly. 'There's no reason

for you to sleep anywhere else—unless you don't want to sleep with me. Is that what you're really trying to say?'

Gray dropped the clothes back into his bag and rubbed a weary hand around his neck. After a moment he sighed and shook his head. 'No, that isn't what I'm trying to say at all. Shelby, this whole situation is complicated enough without adding more pressure.'

A tiny bubble of anger started to expand in her chest. 'The situation wouldn't be complicated at all if you started acting naturally. We're lovers. What could be more natural than us sleeping in the same bed?'

Gray settled his hands on his hips and stared at her hard, a nerve ticking away in his jaw. 'I've already told you I'm trying to do the right thing.'

Down by her sides, Shelby's hands curled into fists. 'I don't want the right thing, I want you. Sleeping beside me in our bed! If you're worried about me pouncing on you, don't be. I've already accepted that we're going to wait.'

His chest rose and fell as he drew in a long breath. 'Did it ever occur to you that I might be worried about me pouncing on you?'

She folded her arms at that. 'Don't be silly. You wouldn't!'

Her confidence had his brows lifting. 'Oh, wouldn't I?'

'No,' Shelby declared emphatically. 'No matter what the provocation, you'd never do anything like that.'

Gray closed his eyes and gave his head a swift shake as if to clear it, then he laughed wryly. 'Thanks for the vote of confidence, but it changes nothing.'

Shelby narrowed her eyes on him. 'You're determined to sleep here?'

'For tonight,' he confirmed.

'Oh!' she muttered direly and, spinning on her heel, marched out of the room.

After a moment or two Gray returned to his unpacking,

but he was hardly any further forward when Shelby marched back into the room, a pillow clutched in her hand. Giving him a fiery look, she walked round him, tossed her pillow on to the bare mattress, followed on after it and made herself comfortable on her side with her back to him.

'What do you think you're doing?' Gray asked shortly, and she answered without looking at him.

'If Mohammed won't go to the mountain, the mountain must go to Mohammed!'

'You can't possibly sleep here like that!' he argued, and saw her shrug.

'If you can, I can.'

There followed a moment of fraught silence where all that could be heard was the gnashing of Gray's teeth.

'There are two other bedrooms in this house,' he declared finally and at that she did glance over her shoulder at him.

'I'll follow you wherever you go. I intend to sleep with you, Gray, so you'd better make your mind up to it,' she advised him, turning back and struggling to find a cosy position.

Maybe it was a stupid stand to take, but to Shelby it was important. She wanted to be close to him. Needed it, for she didn't remember any of the closeness that they must have shared. All she wanted was to lie in his arms and go to sleep. That wasn't too much to ask, was it?

The next thing she knew, two arms were slipping beneath her, lifting her up. With a cry, she began to struggle.

'Quit that,' Gray ordered as he strode with his belligerent armful into the master bedroom. He fell short of dumping her unceremoniously on the bed, setting her down gently in view of her recent accident. Immediately he released her, though, Shelby made a bid to scramble off the bed on the other side.

Gray had to dive across the bed and catch her arm.

Shelby stared him out. 'Stay where you are, damn it!' he growled angrily.

Shelby froze, but remained poised for action. 'I'm not going to sleep here on my own!' she told him bluntly, which received a snort of dry amusement from Gray.

'You won't be. You've won,' he told her shortly. Releasing her he strode from the room and, as she blinked rapidly in amazement at her victory, then hastily slipped beneath the covers, she could hear him moving about.

Seconds later he came back in with her pillow under one arm and holding his bag in the other. He kicked the door shut, dropped the bag on the floor and tossed the pillow in her general direction.

'Don't say another word,' he ordered, stabbing a finger towards her. 'Or, so help me God, I'll give you the spanking you never got as a child!'

Shelby clutched the pillow to her chest and watched him. He put away his clothes with the minimum of effort, gathered together what he would need for the night, and disappeared into the bathroom. Her breath escaped on a tiny sigh then. Maybe she had gone a little too far, she thought regretfully. She hadn't wanted to make him angry. She just wanted to be near him.

Sighing again, she put the pillow beneath her head and waited. Ten minutes later, dressed only in a pair of shorts, Gray returned, snapping off the bathroom light and then the bedroom light as he went. Shelby caught the merest glimpse of supple tanned male flesh before the room was plunged into darkness and he slipped into the bed beside her. She lay quiet, the gap between them seeming as large as an ocean.

Suddenly the bed rocked as Gray moved closer. Then a long arm reached out, pulling her into his side.

'Neither of us will get any sleep with you over there and me over here,' he growled huskily and a wave of relief swept through Shelby, bringing a smile of happiness to her lips.

Without a word, she curled up against him, resting her head on his shoulder, her hand placed over his heart. Minutes later, she was asleep.

Sensing it, Gray laid his arm across his eyes and prayed for the same to happen to him. Yet inside he knew that the desired sleep was going to be a long time coming.

# CHAPTER NINE

WHEN Shelby awoke next morning she was alone in the bed. Reaching out to run her hand over the place where Gray had slept, she found it cool, proving he had been gone some time. Stretching with that particularly feline type of feminine pleasure, she felt refreshed, full of energy for the day ahead.

She wondered where Gray was. Though she listened hard, she could hear no sounds coming from downstairs. Throwing back the covers, she rose and padded over to the window. For a moment or two the spectacular view claimed all her attention, but then she caught some movement out of the corner of her eye and glanced down.

Gray was steadily jogging up the road towards the house. When he reached the car he stopped, and Shelby was impressed by the fact that he was hardly puffing at all. Right now he was wearing a khaki coloured vest, black shorts and running shoes. He looked handsome and rugged and set her senses tingling in no time at all.

Opening the window, she leant out. 'Good morning,' she called brightly, and he turned, looking up at her with hands on hips. 'Isn't it an absolutely glorious day? Why didn't you wake me?'

'You looked too peaceful,' Gray answered. 'Besides, I didn't think you were into jogging.'

She laughed. 'I'm not, but I would have enjoyed watching you. Did you know you've got really sexy legs?'

He grinned back at her. 'Come down here and tell me again,' he ordered, and she gave him a wary look.

'I don't know if I should. You look a bit dangerous!'

'All the more reason to come, then,' Gray returned, flashing that roguish smile of his and sending tingles down her spine.

'Well, seeing as you put it like that…' Shelby said, laughing, and left the window to go in search of her clothes.

Less than ten minutes later, having washed and dressed in shorts, top and trainers, she tripped down the stairs and went in search of him. She found him eventually, leaning against the fence that marked the boundary of the garden, talking on his mobile phone. He beckoned her over and, as she drew closer, she could hear his side of the conversation.

'It was who we thought, then? Which station? Let's hope they throw away the key… My pleasure, Oscar, and I hereby notify you I'm taking a long leave of absence.'

Shelby's ears perked up at that. 'Hey, are you talking to Dad?' she asked, and Gray nodded, holding out his hand for her to come closer.

'Yes, that's Shelby you can hear. She finally decided to get up. I think she wants to talk to you. Hold on.' He handed over his phone, then slipped his arms around her.

'Hi, Dad,' she greeted her father cheerfully, resting her weight against Gray.

'Hello, darling. You sound more chipper today. Feeling better?'

'Much. It's probably got something to do with the company,' she added, winking at Gray, who quirked an eyebrow back at her.

Oscar Greer laughed. 'Of course it has. I remember how it felt to be with the right person. Nothing to compare with it. You take care now, and enjoy yourself. Oh, and tell Gray something for me. Faint heart never won anything.'

Shelby frowned, more than a little confused by that. 'OK, I will. Bye, Dad, See you soon.' Closing the phone down, she handed it back to Gray, who slipped it into the pocket of his shorts. 'Dad said to tell you faint heart never won anything. Do you understand that?'

'It's a private joke,' he responded inscrutably.

'Yes, but what does it mean?' she insisted.

'I'll tell you one day,' he told her unhelpfully. 'Now, what were you saying about my legs?'

Her smile broadened into a grin. 'I like a man with long legs. They're very sexy.'

He grinned back at her, and there was a rakish gleam in his eye. 'Mmm. I was just thinking the same thing about you. I've been imagining you wrapping them around me when I make love to you,' Gray added huskily, and a powerful wave of heat started in the pit of her stomach and swept through her entire body.

Shelby made a growling sound. 'I love it when you say things like that. Tell me more.'

'Do you really feel better today?' he asked instead, and the prosaic question made her tut.

'Much. Why?'

Gray lowered his head towards hers. 'Because I'm badly in need of sustenance. I've been starving for your kisses for far too long.'

The tone and texture of his words caused Shelby to shiver in anticipation. 'Then you'd better not waste time talking,' she invited, and he needed no further encouragement.

Gray took her lips with a depth of need that blew her mind. Of the kisses she could remember, nothing compared to this. It might have been shocking if she hadn't felt an equal hunger. He sought and she gave, revelling in the release of his pent up passion. She had wanted him to kiss her like this, and it gave her the freedom to kiss him back without reservation.

When they finally broke the kiss, her heart was thundering wildly and she could scarcely breathe. Yet it felt won-

derful, for beneath her hand she could feel the rapid thud
of his heart and could see the way he had to drag air into
his lungs.

Gray rested his forehead against hers and strove for a
measure of calm. 'Now do you see why I had to hold
back?' he asked thickly, and her nerves responded instantly.

Oh, yes, she saw. 'Is it always going to be like this?'

'What do you think? My passion for you can never be
moderate,' he confessed in a husky growl her senses instantly responded to.

'I'm glad we got over the past. Think what we would be
missing. Do you feel foolish for turning me down all those
years ago?' she just had to ask, but he shook his head.

'No. It wasn't the right time. You had a lot of growing
up to do.'

Naturally she frowned at that. 'Oh, I did, did I? What
makes you think I didn't know my own mind?'

'Oh, you knew your own mind, all right. Which is why
you were having so much fun playing the field,' Gray responded, and she knew she only had herself to blame for
his thinking. She had covered her tracks well.

'Maybe you're right,' she conceded. One day, if their
relationship should turn out to be more than an affair, she
would tell him the truth.

At that point her stomach growled, and Gray released
her. 'Come on, Red. Let's drive into town for breakfast.
Then we'll buy your painting equipment and drive up into
the mountains.'

'That sounds like a wonderful idea,' Shelby agreed instantly.

Fifteen minutes later they were in the car and on their
way. It turned out to be the most perfect day she could ever
remember. After a lazy breakfast, having found the things
she needed, they stopped off to buy a picnic lunch then
headed inland. Everywhere they looked was a feast for the

eyes. They were so spoilt for choice that in the end Gray simply parked the car and they walked.

Whenever Shelby saw something she just had to sketch they would stop. Whilst she painted, Gray stretched out beside her. Sometimes he would watch her work, and at others he closed his eyes and dozed.

By mid-afternoon Shelby was beginning to feel hungry again. Gray found them a sheltered spot, miles from anywhere, and spread out the blanket he had carried from the car. Here they could eat and look at the stunning view at the same time.

Some time later, Shelby sighed. 'I should have done this a long time ago. I've been so busy focusing on my career I'd forgotten what it feels like to really relax.'

'So the knock on the head saved someone having to knock you on the head to get you to take a holiday?' Gray teased lightly, and she threw the crust of her sandwich at him.

Taking two plums from a bag, he handed her one, then lay down and made himself comfortable with his head on her lap. Shelby leant back against a convenient outcrop of granite and slowly ate her plum, and all the while her fingers idly combed through his silky black hair.

'Oh-oh. You've got a grey hair!' she exclaimed, tossing the stone of her plum back into the bag.

'I'm surprised there's only one,' Gray replied dryly, handing her his plum stone to deal with. 'The amount of worry you give me, there should be more.'

'When have you ever worried over me?' Shelby wanted to know, putting the plum stone in the bag along with her own.

Gray captured her hand on its way back to his hair. 'More times than I care to remember.' One by one he began to lick her fingers clean of plum juice.

Shelby caught her breath at the sensuousness of it. 'Are

you sure you want to be doing that?' she asked, finding it highly arousing. 'It's giving me ideas.'

'I hoped it might,' he responded, moving his tongue in lazy spirals round her index finger.

'I'm shocked!' she gasped, stifling a groan of pleasure. He was turning her on as easily as if he had flicked a switch.

Gray abandoned her fingers in favour of tracing lazy circles around her palm with his tongue. 'Brace yourself, Red. You ain't seen nothing yet,' he promised.

'You always seem such a gentleman,' she retorted, biting her lip as his tongue discovered the pulse at her wrist.

He looked up at her then, eyes gleaming hotly. 'You bring out the beast in me!'

Her smile at that was a study in provocation. 'Thank God. I thought I might be losing my touch.'

Gray shook his head. 'That will never happen between you and me. You only have to touch me and I go up in flames.'

It was an opportunity not to be missed, and Shelby swiftly bent down and kissed him. She took her time, tasting his lips before slipping her tongue inside and wreaking her own brand of sensual havoc. When she was done, she raised her head just enough to see him. 'Like that?' she asked softly.

He smiled wickedly, deliberately misunderstanding. 'I liked it so much you can do it again.' Raising his hand, he curled it around her nape and urged her head down.

This time the kiss was mutual and all the more potent for it. The more time they took, the swifter was her body's response. Her heart had quickened its beat, sending her blood pulsing thickly through her veins. Every nerve was aroused, aching for more.

'Gray?' His name was an aching plea against his lips and drew an immediate response.

'Yes,' he confirmed tautly, moving so that she was lying down and he was bending over her.

The weight of his body resting on hers was an indescribable pleasure. Her breasts swelled in response, her nipples hardening to sensual points that craved to be touched. When one hard male thigh slid between hers, she uttered a moan of pleasure and arched against it instinctively. Her hands sought to touch him wherever she could, tangling in his hair one moment, tugging at his T-shirt the next so that she could explore the tanned flesh beneath it.

It was incredibly satisfying to feel him shiver beneath her touch. To know that she could affect him so strongly. When his hand slipped beneath her top in search of her breasts she could hardly bear the suspense of waiting, and when his fingers finally brushed the lacy bra aside and claimed her aching flesh he felt it in every inch of her body. He subjected her to the most delicious torment, teasing her with lazy circles of his thumb until she wanted to scream. Then and only then did he take the time to swiftly remove her top and bra and claim the turgid peak with his mouth.

Her head went back as his tongue laved her sensitive flesh, teasing her with flickering strokes that stole her breath until at last he began to suckle, drawing her deep into his mouth until she groaned deep in her throat at the pure unadulterated pleasure. Then he began to repeat the process on her other breast, and she was helpless to do anything other than close her eyes and succumb. Yet eventually that was not enough. She wanted to touch him, to make him feel what she was feeling, and she began tugging at his T-shirt, pulling it up until Gray was forced to stop what he was doing and raise himself enough to allow her to pull the top free and toss it aside.

Their eyes locked then and oh, so slowly he lowered himself until their skin touched. It was an instant of pure pleasure that stole their breath and left them, for vital aeons, not daring to move. Shelby breathed in deeply, her arms gliding around his neck.

'Mmm, that feels so good,' she murmured huskily.

'Almost too good,' Gray agreed, tracing a line of kisses along the tender lines of her shoulder and neck. His hand made a slow exploration down the curve of her waist, only to be frustrated by her shorts. 'You're wearing too much,' he growled, nimbly dealing with the button and zip.

'So are you,' she pointed out, and he moved.

'That can soon be put right.'

Shelby raised her hips to allow him to remove the last of her clothes and then he dealt with his own. Seconds later he lay down again and, with nothing between them, everywhere they touched flash-fires started to blaze. The freedom to explore was intoxicating, the pleasure given and received beyond anything either had experienced before. It was hard to tell where one body ended and the other began as they writhed together, each kiss and caress drawing gasps and sighs of pleasure as they drove each other closer to the edge.

When his hand found her intimately and began a stroking caress, it was so overwhelmingly erotic that Shelby could feel her body tighten, the pressure rapidly building and spiralling upwards towards the inevitable.

'No. Wait,' she gasped urgently, but it was already too late. She had no power to hold back an explosive climax that had her arching into his hand and crying out. The waves of pleasure pulsed through her as she collapsed, and conflicting emotions surged through her. As much as she had enjoyed the release, it wasn't how she had wanted it to be. She had wanted them to come together.

Sensing her disappointment, Gray settled himself between her legs, taking his weight on his arms as he looked down at her flushed cheeks and glittering eyes. 'That's only the beginning, darling. Stay with me,' he urged and with infinite care he began to arouse her again.

Shelby knew he was right when within minutes she could feel her body starting to turn molten again. Her desire had only died back, not been put out, and soon it was a growing fire in the pit of her stomach. Determined that he should not get off scot-free, she used her lips and hands to caress him wherever she could reach, and it was highly arousing to hear him gasp beneath her touch and shudder with the pleasure.

When he entered her she was ready for him, and it was the most beautiful moment of her life. He didn't just fill her physically, he filled her emotionally too. He completed her, for in her heart they were two halves of a whole. Only in these precious moments was she totally whole. She wanted to capture the moment in her memory for all time, but when he started to move thoughts flew from her mind and there was only feeling.

Folding her legs around him, she held on, moving to meet his thrusts. They were slow at first, measured by the strength of his control, but as need grew she could feel his control slipping away, until finally he abandoned it altogether in the search for mutual satisfaction. It came in a white-hot explosion that shattered her first and then Gray. They cried out at the sheer perfection of the moment.

Tears sparkled like diamonds in her eyes as she slowly floated back down to earth. Nothing could really have prepared her for what she felt then. The tears were of joy, for she knew that this was what she had dreamed of for so long. Gray was hers, and she was for ever his. Nothing could ever replace this. She wouldn't even try.

Gray somehow found the strength to roll on to his side, his chest rising and falling rapidly as he strove for breath. Turning his head, he looked at her and something knifed through him as he saw one perfect tear trickle from the corner of her eye.

'Hey. Are you all right, Red?' he asked, concern making his voice raspy.

Her response was to turn on her side to face him, her lips curving into a beatific smile. 'I'm perfectly fine,' she told him, searching his eyes for any signs of how he felt now.

'Why the tear?' Gray wanted to know, using a long finger to wipe the moisture away.

She sighed, so replete she felt as if she was lying on cotton wool, not a rough blanket. 'Because that was so beautiful. Wasn't it?'

His hand cupped her cheek, and at last he smiled rather bemusedly. 'It was surely way beyond my expectations. I always knew that you and I could have something special.'

The words surprised her. 'Isn't it always like that?' she asked, and Gray went still before uttering an odd laugh.

'Trust me, Red. What we just shared was one of a kind,' he assured her swiftly.

Shelby looked at him soberly. 'I have to trust you. You're the only one with a link to what I can't remember.'

Very gently he rubbed his thumb over her lips. 'Hey, forget what you can't remember. What we just shared is what counts. It has to mean something.'

'Perhaps it means we love each other,' she suggested, knowing that that was what she would like it to mean, but Gray could have other ideas. She had no reason for thinking his feelings towards her were anything more than physical.

An odd gleam shone from the back of his eyes. 'Perhaps it does,' he agreed lazily.

As an answer it left a lot to be desired, but she pursued it. 'Are we in love?'

'What do you think?' he countered, and his voice took on a husky edge.

She frowned at him, hard. 'Do you have any idea how aggravating it is to have your question answered with a question?'

His smile was roguish. 'I've a pretty good idea.'

Shelby narrowed her eyes at him. 'You're avoiding the question!'

'Yes,' he admitted at once, and she sighed helplessly.

'OK, so I have to make my own deduction. We're not in love, and you don't want to tell me because you don't want to hurt my feelings by telling me before I remember for myself. Right?'

'Wrong,' he batted back instantly, and Shelby's heart did an almighty flip-flop in her chest as his answer registered.

'Are you…' she began croakily, then had to stop to moisten her mouth. 'Are you telling me we do love each other?' she asked incredulously.

'Not exactly. It would be truer to say one of us loves the other,' he enlarged, moving closer to her.

The bottom of her stomach dropped out. Oh, God, did he mean he knew she loved him? It would be excruciatingly embarrassing if he felt nothing for her but, having come so far on an idle remark, she had to go on.

'Meaning…?'

Sapphire eyes looked directly into hers. 'Meaning I love you,' he said simply, and she lay there, stunned.

'You do?' She couldn't help the question sounding so doubtful, but it was the last thing she had expected him to say.

'As God is my witness. I love you, Shelby Greer. I'm hoping that maybe you love me too.' His words as well as his expression reflected hope muted by doubt. It was this uncertainty that convinced her he really wasn't joking.

Her spirits suddenly soared as it dawned on her that her wildest dream had just been answered. Love shone from her like a beacon. 'But of course I love you, Gray. I always have!'

It was his turn to show surprise. 'Always?'

Laughing, she nodded. 'Yes. Always.'

'Hmm, as I recall, you weren't too enamoured of me for a while,' he reminded her.

'True, but even though I hated you for what I thought you'd done, I loved you too,' she admitted, causing his smile to turn wolfish.

'I'd never have guessed. Remind me never to play poker with you,' he declared, running his hand caressingly over her hip, inflaming senses that had barely died down.

Shelby inched closer till their lips were a mere breath apart. 'Keep that up, mister, and you'll have to pay the consequences,' she warned him, letting her own fingers trail down his chest until they found a flat male nipple which they began to tease into a hard nub.

Gray's arm snaked around her waist, holding her to him as he rolled so that she lay atop him, her legs straddling his hips. 'Do your worst, Red. I've been dreaming of what it might be for a long time.'

With a husky laugh she took him at his word, using her hands, lips and tongue to explore her way down his firm male body. Gray allowed her free rein, and it was highly arousing to Shelby to hear his moans and feel the results of her caresses in his involuntary movements. When she found his aroused flesh and closed her fingers around the velvety shaft, he jerked wildly, hips leaving the ground as if he had just been given an electric shock.

'Hell's teeth!' he growled tautly, breathing fast, then groaned deeply as she let her fingers slide up and down with excruciating slowness.

Sensing that it was taking all his control to lie still and allow her this freedom, Shelby took pity on him. Rising, she settled herself over his hips and lowered herself on to him until he was deep inside her. Only then did she begin to move, rocking her hips rhythmically, rising and falling, intent on slowly stoking the fire that was growing inside them. Yet Gray had other plans. His hands trailed from her hips up to her breasts, teasing her nipples into aching peaks, then snaked down again to seek out the hub of her passion. The sensual stroking shattered her control and sent the throbbing coils of desire spiralling upwards towards release. She fell forwards and he caught her, rolling so that he was on top again, and with powerful thrusts of his hips he drove them both over the edge a second time.

When he had recovered enough to move, Gray eased his weight off her but kept his arm around her.

'How was it for you?' he asked with a faint laugh, and Shelby answered with a groan.

'Pretty spectacular, actually. Was it my imagination or did fireworks go off?' Making love with him was an experience she could never have imagined. None of her dreams had brought her anywhere close to the reality.

'I think it was a twenty gun salute,' he returned wryly.

Shelby blinked up at the clear blue sky. 'I can't move,' she said happily. 'You should carry a government health warning. Making love with this man seriously damages your strength!'

Laughing, Gray sat up, bringing her with him, and began reaching for their clothes. 'Much as I would like to stay here with you all day, it's going to get colder pretty soon. We'd better cut along back to the house.'

Reluctantly, Shelby slipped back into her clothes. She had wanted the moment to last for ever, but knew he was right. There was nothing in the least romantic about being up on a mountain when the sun went down.

When she was dressed, Gray held out a hand and pulled her to her feet and into his arms.

'You were worth waiting for, Red. No regrets?' he asked,

eyes searching hers with a sudden intensity she couldn't explain.

'None,' she responded at once. 'I love you.'

His smile didn't appear and his expression remained serious. 'I love you too. Remember that.'

Shelby frowned. 'Why would I forget?' she asked, and he sighed heavily.

'We none of us know what's round the corner,' he replied mysteriously, releasing her to pick up their belongings.

Shelby puzzled over what he had said as they made their way back down to where they had left the car, but had to give it up as a bad job. Whatever he meant was doomed to remain a mystery, for she couldn't foresee any reason why she would forget. Besides, she had other things to think about, such as the fact that, against all the odds, they loved each other.

One day she would want to know how and when he had fallen in love with her and why he had taken so long to tell her. However, for now, just knowing it was enough. For the first time since her accident, the future didn't seem so scary.

# CHAPTER TEN

THERE were times in the next few days when Shelby had to give herself a pinch in order to convince herself she wasn't dreaming. She was so happy that half the time she felt as if she were walking on air. She had never seen Gray so relaxed. It was wonderful being with him. The days were a joy, the nights a revelation.

There was a quality to their lovemaking that she had never felt before, and she knew it was because she loved him. Love gave everything they said and did a different nuance. She couldn't have explained it in words; she just knew it was there because of her feelings for Gray and his for her. Life had never been more perfect.

Towards the end of the week, Gray decided to drive into the village to pick up some much needed groceries. Shelby opted to stay behind to do some washing. They had got through most of the clothes they had brought with them. It brought a smile to her lips as she set a load on to wash, remembering just how some of the clothes had got grubby. Humming to herself, she went upstairs to change the sheets and see if there was anything else that needed freshening.

The bed having been stripped and remade, she glanced round for anything she had missed. There was a towel and some other items of clothing draped over the chair in the corner of the bedroom and it was as she gathered them up that something fell off on to the floor. Glancing down in surprise, Shelby discovered it was Gray's wallet and he would need it to pay for the groceries. Tossing the washing on to the bed, she reached down for the leather case. It had fallen open and she realised, as she picked it up, that the reason it didn't close properly was because he kept a folded-up handkerchief in it.

Shelby hadn't intended to pry but her curiosity was piqued. Unfolding the linen square, to her surprise she found a smudge of lipstick on it. Her brows rose. Why on earth was he keeping a dirty handkerchief in his wallet? The answer swiftly followed the question. She hadn't considered Gray to be an overly sentimental man, but the handkerchief and its smudge had to mean something to him.

She couldn't exactly say why, but her heart lurched anxiously. The happiness she had been feeling faded away as she slowly folded the linen back as she had found it. She was about to replace it when the corner of a photograph caught her attention next. Gray had shown her a photograph before, and she wondered if this was it. She was sure he wouldn't mind her taking another look.

Easing the photo out, she took it across to the window for a better look. Yes, it was the same one. As she angled it, sunlight caught on something outside the window and reflected it back into the room, blinding her temporarily. Pain shot through her head and she winced, pressing a hand to her temple. Whatever the flash had been, it left her with a nagging background headache.

Doing her best to ignore it, Shelby examined the photo again. She smiled. Apart from the incident in the toilet, it had been a great evening. There had been a photographer doing the rounds of the tables, taking snaps. She hadn't realised he'd kept this one...

Her breath caught in her throat as she realised what she was thinking. She could remember this photograph being taken, and that could only mean one thing. She had got her memory back. There was a seat built into the window embrasure and she dropped on to it, probing her brain for the hitherto elusive memories. They all came flooding back as the gates were opened. The threats. Gray. The accident.

Some things were a little fuzzy, but basically she recalled everything.

Including the events after the accident.

It was as if a fist had fastened on her heart. She stared at the picture, feeling sick. There was no 'us'. This wasn't a photo of the two of them together because they were in love with each other. It was all lies! Everything he had told her in the hospital had been a lie, and that meant these last few days had been pure fabrication too.

Shelby pressed a hand to her mouth. Oh, dear God. She had told him she loved him. He had said he loved her too. Yet how could he? They had been attracted to each other, but it wasn't love—for him. Everything was suddenly very clear. He had invented that because of her accident. He had needed to keep her safe, and he had needed to be with her. The best way to accomplish that was to say they were lovers already.

Her head swam with the enormity of it, and she was hit by an intense wave of hurt. He had lied and she had believed it. She would have gone on believing it, had her memory not returned by looking at the photo he had left behind with his wallet when he'd gone out.

Her head came up at that, alerting her to a new fact. Gray had gone out. He had gone out and left her here. Alone. The one thing he had been careful not to do. Which could only mean the situation had changed. There was only one thing which could do that. The man had been found. He was no longer a threat. Of course it was a relief to know she was out of danger, but it couldn't alter the fact that the world she had believed to be so perfect had just collapsed around her like a house of cards!

The creak of a board caused her to look round and her heart lurched painfully when she saw Gray standing in the doorway. His eyes went from her stricken face to the washing, his wallet and then the photo she still held, assessing the situation in an instant. He took a deep breath, his expression becoming watchful.

'I forgot my wallet,' he told her simply, and Shelby nodded. It was probably the sunlight flashing off something on the car that had triggered the whole thing off.

'I found it in the washing and thought you wouldn't mind my looking at our photo again,' she said flatly. 'I wish I hadn't, though,' she added, slipping it back into the wallet and holding the leather case closed.

'Why? What's happened? You're acting a little strangely,' Gray observed, taking a few cautious steps into the room, the better to see her.

She laughed unevenly, but responded with a question of her own. 'Do you think it was wise to go off and leave me alone like that?'

As if he had somehow been expecting it, he made the logical conclusion instantly. 'You've remembered.'

Rising, Shelby walked over to him and held out the wallet, her eyes never leaving his. 'Everything,' she confirmed pointedly.

Gray frowned faintly, not quite following. 'Surely that's a good thing? You wanted to remember.'

She shrugged. 'I did, until I discovered it was a curate's egg. Only good in parts.'

His frown faded and was replaced by an encouraging smile. 'It was bound to be a shock, sweetheart,' he began, reaching out to take her by the shoulders and offer comfort.

Shelby took a swift step backwards, shrugging him off. 'Don't touch me!' she ordered, and Gray allowed his hands to fall to his sides again.

'What's the problem?' he asked bluntly, visibly drawing himself up ready to respond to whatever she said next.

''What's the problem?'' she parroted with a scornful laugh. 'The problem, darling, is you!'

He folded his arms over the chest she had fallen asleep

on any number of times these past few days, and it speared
her heart to recall it.

'Spit it out, Red. Let's hear it,' he commanded tautly,
and suddenly the atmosphere in the room could be cut with
a knife.

'I understand that you were only doing your job,' Shelby
replied, pacing away to the window, then turning to face
him, hands rubbing up and down her arms in her agitation.
'Faced with the fact of my accident, you had to do something,' she accepted in a scratchy voice. 'Some lies were
inevitable, but did you really have to go so far as to tell
me you loved me?' There, it was out, the lie that hurt her
to her core. The lie she would never forgive him for.

Gray responded by closing the gap between them, eyes
burning into her. 'What makes you think I don't?'

Her own eyes flashed angry sparks at him. 'Because I'm
not a fool. It was all a lie. All part of the act that would
keep me docile until my memory returned!'

His head went back, as if her words had struck a physical
blow, then his nostrils flared as he took in a steadying
breath. 'And if I tell you you're wrong?' he countered hardily, and she laughed harshly.

'I wouldn't believe you. You lied to me, Gray, and I'll
never forgive you!' she declared passionately, her chin
wobbling disastrously.

'No,' Gray argued with a shake of his head. 'Let's get
this straight. It isn't the supposed lie you won't forgive, is
it? It's that I know you love me. Or are you going to tell
me that was a lie too?' he countered tensely.

Her breath hitched in her throat at his insight, and she
stared at him. She wanted to say it, to salve her pride, but
couldn't. 'It wasn't a lie,' she gritted out through her teeth.
'You were the one who lied. How could you?' She began
her nervy pacing again.

The accusation made his jaw clench. 'How could I lie?

By saying we were a couple to protect you from some madman—easily! How could I love you? God knows, right now I don't know how I could, but I do!' he declared in a raised voice that halted her in her tracks.

'Stop saying that,' Shelby ordered, feeling confused and shaken. This wasn't at all the way she had expected him to react to her having discovered the truth. He was the one in the wrong—wasn't he? He was the one who had lied, so why was he acting so hurt and outraged? He ought to be apologising to her, trying to explain his actions.

Gray propped himself against the nearby wardrobe and folded his arms, looking prepared to stay there for ever. 'No. I can't take it back, and wouldn't if I could. You want the truth and so do I. I'm tired of having to pretend I don't care. When I told you I loved you, it was the honest truth. I love you, Shelby. What are you going to do about it?'

That struck a nerve with her. 'What do you know about pretending you don't care?' she charged scornfully, and his brows rose mockingly.

'What? You think you have a monopoly on hiding your feelings? Dream on, Red. I fell in love with you when you were eighteen years old!' he informed her in a tone that was way short of lover-like.

Shelby's lips parted on a sharp intake of breath. 'You couldn't have,' she protested, for that was when she had fallen in love with him.

He smiled grimly. 'Couldn't I? You have no idea. I held out my hand to help you out of a taxi, like I'd done countless times before, but this was different. You looked up at me with those big green eyes of yours, and I fell head over heels,' he confessed, shaking his head at the memory. 'I spent the next ten years hiding the fact.'

She was totally stunned. If he was to be believed, they had fallen in love with each other at the same moment. It was incredible. She had told nobody, not even her father, so there was no way Gray could know the how of it from her or any other source. Which meant everything he had just told her had to be his truth. If that was so, then it would mean he hadn't lied. Her hand rose to her mouth and she stared at him over it, her eyes huge with wonder and uncertainty.

'That was when I fell in love with you,' she told him in an awestruck voice, all the anger draining out of her in the face of his confession.

At her words it was Gray's turn to be dumbfounded. He straightened up abruptly. 'What? You're kidding?' he challenged in disbelief.

Shelby shook her head. 'No. You took my hand, and…' She allowed the rest to tail off. He would make his own connection.

Gray took a deep breath, then dragged a very shaky hand through his hair. 'You know what this means, don't you? We've loved each other for ten years and hid it so well that neither of us even guessed! If you believe I really do love you, that is?' He looked a question that made her wince.

'Yes, I believe you. There's no way you could have made that up,' she told him honestly. 'Like you, I worked so hard not to give myself away. When I thought I had, because of your lie, I struck out. I'm sorry.'

Gray allowed himself a faint smile. 'You were hurt. It's understandable.'

'How can you forgive me so easily?' she just had to ask, and his smile softened.

'Because I love you, Red. It's as simple as that,' he told her, and this time when he went to take her in his arms she didn't pull away. 'For the record, I hated having to lie to you. Unfortunately it was necessary.'

Shelby slipped her arms around him and held on tight. From the depths of despair just moments ago, she was discovering happiness was within her grasp again. 'I understand now. It was just such a shock—remembering that way. That picture...' She fell silent for a moment, recalling other things. 'You kept the photograph?' She frowned up at him and his lips twitched.

'You looked beautiful in it.'

Her heart did a tiny skip. 'And the handkerchief?'

'It was my way of holding on to your kiss,' he told her simply and brought tears to her eyes.

'I think that's the most romantic thing I've ever heard!' Shelby exclaimed, her heart swelling with love for him.

Gray looked at her seriously. 'You're very precious to me, Red,' he told her in a husky voice. 'When Oscar told me about the threats, I couldn't get back to you fast enough. When you refused to take it seriously, I wanted to throttle you. If you had died, my life would have been over. That was when I decided I had to partly show my hand. I couldn't face losing you, so I had to find out if there was ever going to be anything between us. When I realised you wanted me as much as I wanted you, I decided to go for it. If a love affair was all it would turn out to be, hell, at least I would have had that.'

A tiny laugh escaped her. 'We're too much alike. I was thinking the same thing.'

He groaned a wry acknowledgement. 'So, here we were, supposed lovers, with me knowing we weren't and you fully expecting us to be sharing a bed. You pushed my resolve to its very limits. I don't know how long I could have held out if I hadn't got that phone call from your father.'

Shelby leaned back slightly so she could see his face. 'Of course. Now I get it. I didn't understand. I thought you'd given in to the inevitable. Dad gave you the all-clear, didn't he, and that meant I was no longer off limits. That's why you made love to me!'

Gray dropped his forehead down to rest on hers. 'Thank

God for that call. I was going out of my mind. Another night like that one and I wouldn't have been accountable!'

Laughter bubbled out of her at that. 'And there I was doing my best to seduce you. But you could have made love to me, Gray. I wanted you to, and I didn't remember we hadn't actually got that far.'

'Which only added to my torment,' he admitted dryly. 'But I couldn't have made love to you, Red, for the very reason you pointed out. You didn't know what was a lie.'

'Yet we did make love,' she reminded him, and he sighed.

'True. After which I told you I loved you. I hoped the truth of that would outweigh the lie in the end.'

She recalled something else. 'You told me to remember you loved me. I didn't know why, but I understand now. It was because you feared something like this happening, wasn't it?'

Gray pulled her back into his arms and rested his chin on her hair. 'When I told you I loved you, I didn't expect you to tell me you loved me back. Hoped for it, but didn't expect it. When you told me, I realised that your lack of memory had made you vulnerable to the truth when you finally remembered it. I hoped that my words would soften the blow.'

Shelby sighed wistfully. 'It would have done if I'd remembered what you said. I do love you, Gray. So much that I can't put it into words. When I think of all the time I wasted, going out with those other men. Pretending I was having a grand old time, when really I was pining for you.'

'That makes two of us, darling,' Gray confessed. 'Those women were for show. The only one I wanted was you. I think your father guessed I had a soft spot for you. That was why he told me that being faint hearted wouldn't get me what I wanted.'

A light went on in Shelby's brain. 'I think you're right.

When we were at the airport on our way here, I let slip to him that I loved you. He must have realised that the pair of us were hopeless cases and decided to do a little match-making of his own!'

Gray's laugh was wonderfully light-hearted. 'Thank goodness he did.'

'You know he's going to think he engineered the whole thing, don't you? We're never going to live it down.'

'He'll tell the children too,' Gray added with a laugh.

'Whose children?' Shelby asked, heart tripping as she looked up at him.

Blue eyes smiled down at her. 'Ours, of course. Providing you marry me.'

Happiness was a huge bubble inside her. 'Are you asking me to marry you?' she teased lightly, never having any intention of saying anything other than yes.

'You're the only woman I ever intend to marry, so yes, I'm asking. Will you marry me, Red?' he asked solemnly, and her love for him overflowed.

'Oh, yes. A thousand times yes,' she accepted, reaching up to kiss him.

Gray kissed her back, and for a moment the world outside stopped existing as they sealed their vow. Then he broke the kiss and swept her up in his arms, carrying her over to the freshly made bed. There was a wealth of love and laughter in his eyes as he laid her down and joined her.

'We'll do the shopping later. Right now I have an urgent need to make love with you.'

'Now that sounds like a plan,' she sighed, then frowned. 'Talking of plans, you never did tell me what plan C was,' she reminded him, and Gray grinned that wonderfully seductive wolfish grin of his.

'Plan C, darling, was to get you to fall in love with me,'

he informed her ironically. 'It's now redundant, I'm happy to say.'

Her fingers found their way into his hair and teased the silky strands. 'Hmm, I'm so glad I have you at last.' She sighed happily.

'You've always had me, Red. From the moment I set eyes on you getting out of that taxi, I was hooked,' he admitted without a trace of regret. 'I only agreed to help your father that time because the man was bad news and I wanted you for myself. I intended to woo you and ask you to marry me then, but Oscar's confession got in the way and I was forced to retrench. I didn't know how long I would have to wait to try again. Do you forgive me for lying to you? I had the best intentions.'

'I was wrong not to let you explain, and I've regretted that. Of course I forgive you. I love you; what else can I do? Let's put the past where it belongs. We've a lot of time to make up for,' Shelby pointed out, reaching for the hem of his T-shirt, and he laughed. 'What's so funny?'

'You told me once I'd never find out how passionate you are in bed,' he reminded her, and she grinned.

'You shouldn't have said that. Now I'm going to have to make you pay for it,' she threatened.

Gray lay back with a husky laugh. 'I was hoping you were going to say that.'

# ONE NIGHT WITH
# THE TYCOON

BY
LEE WILKINSON

**Lee Wilkinson** lives with her husband in a three-hundred-year-old stone cottage in a Derbyshire village, which most winters gets cut off by snow. They both enjoy travelling and recently, joining forces with their daughter and son-in-law, spent a year going round the world 'on a shoestring' while their son looked after Kelly, their much loved German shepherd dog. Her hobbies are reading and gardening and holding impromptu barbecues for her long-suffering family and friends.

Don't miss Lee Wilkinson's exciting new novel, *Claiming His Wedding Night*, available this month from Mills & Boon® Modern™.

# CHAPTER ONE

HER smile as sparkling as a tiara and her heart as heavy as lead, Rebecca Ferris stood in attendance while her eighteen-year-old stepsister married the only man she had ever loved.

Holding the bride's bouquet, she waited while Lisa and the Honourable Jason Beaumont, newly pronounced man and wife, kissed each other. Then, stiff as any robot, she followed them and the rest of the wedding party, into the vestry for the register to be signed.

After an unusually cold, wet start to the summer, the long-range forecast for mid-July had predicted a warm, dry spell, and the wedding day had been set for the sixteenth.

Helen, the bride's mother, had arranged for a late cere-mony and an evening reception. As the weather was holding wonderfully the photographs were taken outside Elmslee's old grey church, with a backdrop of ancient yew trees.

Guests stood around in little groups in the early-evening sunshine, discussing what a handsome pair the newlyweds made—the bride, blonde, petite and beautiful, and the slimly built groom, tall, fair and with matinée-idol looks.

When the photographer was finally satisfied, ribbons flut-tering on the white wedding cars, they were driven through the picturesque village and back to Elmslee Manor, the Ferrises' family home for more than three centuries.

Lisa, who as a very small child had come with her mother to live at Elmslee, had been impatient to get away. Much preferring the bright lights of nearby London, she had moved into Jason's Knightsbridge flat at the very first op-portunity.

Rebecca had been born at Elmslee. She loved the small

Elizabethan manor, with its mullioned windows and barley-sugar chimneys, and had missed it sadly when she left.

Now it was to be sold. Helen had put Elmslee on the market and was planning to take a flat in London to be near her newly married daughter.

Knowing how much her father would have hated the idea, Rebecca had ventured to protest.

Her stepmother had said sharply that, money aside, now Lisa had gone, the ten-bedroomed manor was much too big for her, and far too quiet.

Today, however, Elmslee was anything but quiet. The house and gardens were *en fête*.

A large marquee had been set up on the south-west side of the house, with its smooth lawns and dark cedars. There were space-heaters on the terrace, just in case it turned cool, and a lively orchestra ready for the evening's festivities.

A paved area in front of the old orangery was to be used as an extra car park, floodlights were in place in the grounds, and coloured lanterns had been strung between the trees.

The second Mrs Ferris, well-used—after sixteen years—to playing her part as lady of the manor, had excelled herself. All the arrangements for the reception had been put into place with astonishing speed and efficiency.

Before Jason had time to change his mind again, one of the aunts had observed cattily.

In a hall beautifully decorated with huge swags of flowers, the wedding party lined up to greet the guests as they filed in.

It was an ordeal Rebecca had been dreading but, head held high, she was managing to smile her way through it when Great-Aunt Letty was announced, and began to move down the line.

After presenting her leathery cheek for a kiss, the old lady grumbled, 'I don't know why the ceremony had to be so late. Fashion, I dare say. It'll be nearly my bedtime before we get to eat.'

Then in a piercing whisper, 'I was most surprised when I got a wedding invitation with Lisa's name on it. I understood that *you* were engaged to young what's-his-name...'

Rebecca swallowed hard. 'Well, yes, I was, but—'

'What on earth were you thinking of, letting that spoilt brat of a stepsister steal him from you?'

Seeing the stricken look on her great-niece's face, Letty patted her hand consolingly. 'Never mind, love. Take it from me, there's as good fish in the sea as ever came out of it. You might even say better.'

Letty moved on, and, lifting her chin, Rebecca continued to smile and shake hands with people she scarcely knew. Then thankfully the last guest was announced, one that she recognised as being her stepmother's special crony.

During a sudden lull in the general noise level, she heard Helen say clearly, 'Of course, poor Rebecca's terribly disappointed. But really there was no point in trying to cling to a man who's never really wanted her. So humiliating...'

Well-aware that everyone within earshot was listening avidly, as a couple of waiters began to circulate with trays of champagne, Rebecca slipped away and escaped through a side-door.

Half blinded by a combination of low sun and tears she was struggling not to let fall, she hurried down the garden, her ankle-length, lilac-coloured dress brushing the clumps of summer flowers that edged the paved path.

Stumbling a little in her haste, she skirted the marquee and made her way past the shrubbery to the old, circular summer house that stood on a little knoll. Disused for a long time, the place had been neglected in recent years, and even more so since her father's death.

Climbing the steps, she pushed open the creaking door of what, as a child, had always been her sanctuary when she was feeling unhappy or misunderstood, and sank onto the wooden bench that ran around the walls.

After several days of sunshine the musty air was quite

warm, and it was blessedly dark, the grimy windows covered on the inside by spiders' webs, and the outside by rampaging ivy.

While Lisa had flitted from boyfriend to boyfriend since the age of fifteen, Jason was the only man Rebecca had ever wanted, and for the first time since losing him she lowered her guard and let the bitter tears run down her cheeks unchecked.

Suddenly the creak of the door opening made her look up sharply. A bright shaft of low sunlight slanted in, dazzling her. All she could make out was a tall, dark shape filling the doorway.

'I've been told that women always cry at weddings, but don't you think this is overdoing it a bit?' a male voice asked drily.

Mortified, she shielded her face with her hand.

He closed the door with his heel, and set his back to it.

'I'd like to be alone,' she informed him thickly.

Mockingly, he said, 'You sound like Greta Garbo.'

'Go away! Please go away,' she begged.

After a moment, hearing no further sound of movement, she glanced up.

Leaning nonchalantly against the door, he was holding a bottle of champagne by the neck, and two long-stemmed flutes.

She couldn't see his face clearly in the gloom, but his hair was very dark and his teeth very white as he smiled at her.

'What do you want?' she demanded.

'I'm here to offer my condolences.'

Though his words *might* have been described as sympathetic, his tone certainly couldn't.

She wasn't sorry. The last thing she wanted was to be pitied by a perfect stranger.

*Though he obviously knew who she was.*

'Who are you?' she demanded.

There was the slightest pause, before he told her, 'My name's Graydon Gallagher.' Getting no reaction, he added casually, 'Most of my friends call me Gray.'

Coming over to sit by her side, he looked at her carefully in the half-light.

Her ash-brown hair was taken up into a chignon and adorned with a circlet of fresh flowers. Around her neck, which was long and slender, she was wearing a single string of pearls.

Despite the careful make-up her heart-shaped face looked pale and drawn, her wide-set almond eyes were brimming with tears, and mauve shadows beneath them suggested that she hadn't slept properly for weeks.

In most of the photographs he had seen of her, her face had been serene, her amber-coloured eyes clear, her mouth wide and full, but with hardly any bow at all, looking as if she might smile at any moment.

Though it was not beautiful in the conventional sense, he had found it a fascinating face, full of character, and had thought cynically that Jason's taste was improving enormously.

A lot of the females he had got entangled with in the past had been glamorous gold-diggers, out for all they could get, with beauty their only asset.

This woman, Gray had felt sure, was different. She had brains and—he would have bet any amount of money—strength and resilience.

Though she could be—and considering the family's circumstances, probably *was*—after Jason's money, she looked the sort that might make that feckless young man a good wife.

In the event she had been pipped at the post by her young stepsister, and was obviously not relishing it.

As he studied her she sniffed, and wiped away a tear that was trickling down her chin.

With a twisted smile at the triteness of it, he felt in his pocket with his free hand and passed her a folded hankie.

'Thank you.' She blew her nose and scrubbed at her wet cheeks. 'Are you a friend of Jason's?'

'I've known him all his life. For a time we lived in the same London square, only a few houses apart.'

'And you've stayed close?'

'Yes, you could say that.'

During the weeks that she and Jason had been engaged, he had jealously wanted her all to himself.

Not particularly gregarious, and head over heels in love, she had been pleased by this show of male possessiveness. But because he had neglected his usual social circle, she hadn't met all that many of his friends.

His voice ironic, Gray pursued, 'I had thought that when he got married he might ask me to be his best man, but...' Broad shoulders lifted in a shrug.

Thinking back, she remarked, 'I didn't see you amongst the guests.'

'Unfortunately my plane was delayed on take-off at JFK, so not only did I miss the actual service, but I was also rather late arriving at the house.'

Frowning, she said, 'So you weren't announced?'

'No. After parking my car, I came in by the rear entrance. I was just about to join the merry throng when I happened to overhear your stepmother's rather unkind remarks.'

'Oh.' She flushed hotly.

'I noticed you slip away.'

'And you followed me? Why?'

'You looked so unhappy that I thought a drop of vintage champagne might help to alleviate your—er—disappointment.'

At close quarters she could just make out that his face was lean and attractive, with a strong chin and a fine straight nose. He must be in his late twenties or early thirties, she guessed. Though his eyes gleamed brilliantly beneath dark brows, she couldn't tell whether they were grey or light blue.

He set the glasses on the bench and, his movements deft, began to open the bottle, observing gravely, 'Remarkable restorative powers, champagne.'

Stripping off the foil, he untwisted the wire, and used his thumb to gently ease out the cork. 'Transporting it may have made it a little lively. However, I'm sure we'll cope.'

'Thank you, but I really don't want any champagne.'

'Now, is that nice?' he demanded plaintively, as the cork came out with a loud pop and ricocheted off the wooden ceiling. Pouring the foaming wine, he added, 'To save wounding my feelings you could at least *pretend* to be grateful.'

'I am, of course. But I—'

'You don't look a bit grateful,' he objected, peering at her closely.

Becoming convinced that he was just having a bit of cruel fun at her expense, she said raggedly, 'I'd be *very* grateful if you'd just go away.'

'I'll think about it when you've had at least one glass of champagne,' he promised.

'I don't *want* a glass of champagne…any more than I want your company.'

'You may not *want* my company, but I'm convinced you *need* it.'

'Why should I need it?'

'To bolster your ego. It must be quite deflating to be ditched for one's stepsister. Though I gather you all stayed friends, as you're the chief bridesmaid?'

When she said nothing, he observed with mock sympathy, 'It can't be easy being a bridesmaid when everyone knows you should have been the bride.'

In truth it was the hardest thing she had ever done. Only her pride, allied to a lifetime of concealing her feelings, had made it possible.

It was that same fierce pride that had allowed them all to 'stay friends'. Determined that no one, least of all Lisa and Jason, should know just how devastated she was, she had struggled to hide her anguish behind a façade of calm acceptance.

'However,' her companion was continuing blandly, 'I do think you should make an effort to put in an appearance at the reception.'

Her hands balled into fists. 'After what Helen said, I can't…I just can't!'

'So what *do* you plan to do? You won't be able to hide out here indefinitely. The minute the sun goes down it'll start to get chilly, and, while the marquee appears to be heated, this place certainly isn't.'

'As soon as everyone's eating, I'll slip back to the house.'

He clicked his tongue reprovingly and asked, 'How can the evening's festivities—which must, incidentally, have cost your stepmother a bomb—go with a bang when the chief bridesmaid will be hiding in her room indulging in tears of jealous rage?'

Her hand itched to smack his good-looking face.

Barely managing to repress this sudden, quite untypical urge to violence, she said curtly, 'I'll be doing no such thing.'

'You can hardly deny that you're hiding now.'

Watching her bite her lip, he went on, 'You should be out there celebrating with them. While the occasion may not be quite as joyful as you'd hoped, at least, between you, you've managed to keep Jason in the family.

'No small triumph. Quite a lot of other women have tried and failed.'

Handing her a glass of champagne with such calm assurance that she automatically took it, Gray suggested, 'But in the circumstances, instead of toasting your stepsister's success, what if we just drink to the future?'

At that precise moment, her future looked cold and bleak and empty.

When she made no move, he raised a level brow. 'Or perhaps that doesn't appeal to you?'

'No, it doesn't.'

'Why not?' he challenged. 'Though you may have lost one prospective husband, you've plenty of time to find another. You're still quite young. Twenty-one? Twenty-two?'

'I'm twenty-three,' she said, and instantly regretted telling him.

'Five years older than the blushing bride! Dear me, no wonder you're absolutely furious. With all that extra experience you should have been able to hold on to your man.

'Though in all fairness, I must say that where Jason is concerned it might not have been easy.

'He's always had a roving eye, and because of his wealthy background and his title, not to mention his looks, he's had more women chasing after him than you could shake a stick at.'

The 'roving eye' stung, and, her voice trembling with rage, she cried, 'You're absolutely hateful!'

Looking completely unmoved, Gray said, 'But don't despair. Though you may not be a raving beauty like your stepsister, as far as I can see in this light you're still very attractive—'

'Thanks,' she said glacially.

'So you surely must have plenty going for you.'

'Funny how I can't think of a single thing.' The bitterness came through.

'Then let's drink to one another, and a change of fortune.' He raised his glass. 'Here's to us, and whatever makes us happy.'

Feeling goaded and driven, with an unaccustomed recklessness, she took an incautious gulp of the fizzy champagne and promptly choked.

As she coughed and spluttered, he patted her back solicitously, enquiring at length, 'That better?'

Unable to speak, she nodded.

'Why don't you try another drink?' he urged.

This time she was a great deal more careful, and after a couple of sips managed a husky, 'Thank you.'

'Is that genuine gratitude, or just good manners?' he enquired quizzically.

'Good manners,' she flashed back. 'As I said earlier, if it's genuine gratitude you want, you'll go away and leave me alone.'

'So you can start crying again?'

'I'll cry if I want to,' she retorted. Then groaned inwardly, aware that she had sounded childish.

'I suppose I can't blame you,' he said magnanimously, 'hurt pride can be the very devil. And the fact that your chance to marry into money has been snatched away must be galling.'

'Money has absolutely nothing to do with it. I loved him.'

'Past tense?'

'No, I still love him.'

Gray frowned. 'You sound as if you mean it.'

'I *do* mean it.' She took another drink. 'He was the only man I've ever loved, and I thought he loved me.' But it seemed she'd been wrong.

At the best of times champagne tended to make her a little tipsy. Now, not having eaten all day, it was going straight to her head, and making her feel light and floaty.

But at least that was better than the leaden weight of misery that had weighed her down since she had discovered Jason's and Lisa's perfidy.

Replenishing her glass, Gray suggested, 'Suppose you tell me all about it?'

Used to hiding her emotions—even from her family and friends—she had no intention of opening her heart to this rude and abrasive stranger.

Reading her expression, he said coaxingly, 'Go on, you may as well. It'll do you the world of good to get it off your chest.'

She half shook her head.

'At the very least it'll help to pass the time. Start by telling me how you and Jason met.'

Already the champagne was loosening her tongue, and without meaning to she found herself saying, 'We met at work.'

Responding to his undoubted interest, she continued, 'My father died at the beginning of last year. After his death, Bowman Ferris, the finance company his great-grandfather had helped to found in the early nineteen-hundreds, was bought out by Finance International.

'PLFI, as it's widely known, is an Anglo-American banking corporation owned by Philip Lorne, Jason's uncle, and Jason was brought in as the new MD of the London branch.

'A few months later when Miss Swensen, his American PA, asked to be transferred back to the States to be closer to her terminally ill mother, I got the job.'

'I see,' Gray said smoothly.

'If you're thinking it was because he fancied me—'

'Knowing Jason, I must admit that the thought had crossed my mind.'

'I was given the post because of my experience.'

A gleam in his eye, he drawled, 'I don't doubt it.'

Colour tingeing her cheeks, she told him angrily, 'I'd been my father's personal assistant for well over a year.'

'Ah!'

'It was a job I enjoyed.'

'And, after Bowman Ferris changed hands, I take it you continued to enjoy working for Jason?'

'I did. But now I have to leave.'

'Why do you have to leave? So long as your work is still up to scratch there can be no possible grounds for getting rid of you. If by any chance he tried, you could always appeal directly to Philip Lorne.'

Tightly, she said, 'You don't understand—I *want* to leave. As things are, none of us, particularly Lisa, likes the idea of Jason and me having to see each other on a regular basis.'

'Presumably you've managed to cope since your engagement came to an end?'

'I handed in my notice then, but Jason begged me to stay on, for his sake.'

Gray frowned. 'I don't quite see?'

'He said that in spite of all his precautions the rest of the staff knew we'd been "friendly", and if I left suddenly there was bound to be gossip that might reach his uncle's ears.'

'Hmm… So what did you do?'

'I agreed to stay on for a while—'

Almost savagely, Gray said, 'Jason has always traded on his looks and his charm to get exactly what he wants.' Then with a sigh, 'Go on.'

'But only if I could work for someone else… As luck would have it, Mrs Richardson, the Assistant Managing Director's PA, was absent on maternity leave. Jason arranged for me to take her place temporarily, and his own secretary to do my work until Miss Swensen returned.

'It didn't stop a few tongues wagging, but when it became clear that we'd stayed on friendly terms the speculation died down.'

'And how do matters stand now?'

'I handed in my resignation last month, ready to leave as soon as Mrs Richardson and Miss Swensen came back. They're both due to return to work next Monday, so I won't need to go in again.'

Hearing the bleakness in her voice, Gray asked, 'Have you another post lined up?'

'Not yet. There don't seem to be many jobs going. But Jason has given me good references, so I'll find an opening somewhere.'

'How long have you been working?'

'I joined Bowman Ferris when I left college two years ago.'

'Why?'

When she looked at him blankly, he asked, 'Wouldn't your father have given you an allowance?'

'Oh, yes, he offered me one.'

'Why didn't you take it?'

'I didn't need an allowance. I wanted to work.'

His tone bland, Gray observed, 'The other two ladies seem to prefer a leisurely existence.'

'Surely that's up to them,' Rebecca said steadily. 'I'd always intended to have a career. That's why I chose to go to a business college.'

'If she hadn't got married, would your stepsister have gone to college?'

When the subject had once been mentioned, Lisa had looked disdainful. 'Why on earth should I want to join the ranks of scruffy, poverty-stricken students? I don't need a career. I've every intention of getting myself a rich husband.'

Displaying an uncanny accuracy, Gray queried, 'Or perhaps she was more interested in trawling the social waters in the hope of catching a good-looking, unattached, hopefully generous millionaire?'

Stiffly, Rebecca said, 'Since Lisa left school she's been helping Helen with her various committees and charity lunches.'

'Bully for her.' He sounded anything but impressed. Then thoughtfully, 'I notice you don't call your stepmother "Mother".'

'She's never wanted me to. When she and Dad got married, she was barely nineteen.'

'And you were how old?'

'Seven.'

'So your stepsister was just two?'

'Yes.'

'How did you get on with your stepmother?'

'Quite well.' That was something of an exaggeration. Though Helen had seldom been unkind to her, at the best she'd felt tolerated, provided she stayed in the background.

'I heard a whisper that she's always put her own daughter first.'

'It's understandable,' Rebecca said simply. 'I can't blame her for that.'

'What *can* you blame her for? Apart from today's bitchy remarks?'

'Nothing really...'

'The "really" convinces me there's *something*.'

'She's put Elmslee Manor on the market,' Rebecca said in a rush.

'I see. Did she give a reason?'

'She said it's too big for her. And of course, even apart from the mortgage repayments, it takes a lot of upkeep—' Rebecca stopped short, biting her lip, then burst out, 'But my father would have *hated* the idea. Elmslee has been in the family for generations, and he wouldn't have dreamt of parting with it. He loved the old place.'

'I take it you do too?'

'Yes.' She sighed. 'But there's nothing I can do. He willed it to Helen.'

'I see. So you have plenty of grounds for disliking her?'

'I *don't* dislike her. At the very least, she made Dad happy.'

'Your loyalty is admirable. If a trifle misplaced.'

Rebecca shook her head. 'I owe her a lot. After my mother ran away with another man, my father grew morose and started to drink heavily. I don't know what might have happened if he hadn't met Helen. They helped each other.

'She was in despair too. Her boyfriend had taken what little money they had and disappeared, abandoning her and the child, and leaving nothing but a pile of unpaid bills.

'A bare six weeks after she and Dad met they were married quietly, and he brought her to live at Elmslee. A year later he adopted Lisa.'

'Did you dislike having a new stepmother?'

'No. Though I'd loved my own mother very much she had never cared about me, and Dad seemed more settled than he'd been for years.'

'You weren't jealous of your stepsister?'

'No.'

Only once had she shown any sign of jealousy, and then Helen had sent her to her room in disgrace. It had been a salutary lesson, and she had never allowed herself to be jealous again.

'I've always been fond of Lisa.' Firmly, she added, 'I still am.'

'Even though she stole your fiancé?'

'You make it sound deliberate.'

'Wasn't it?'

As she hesitated, he said, 'So you think it was.' Adding curiously, 'Didn't you fight for him?'

'No.'

After she'd seen them together it had never occurred to her to even try. Her pride wouldn't have allowed her to.

'You just let her take him?'

When she stayed silent, he said thoughtfully, 'Though perhaps you were sensible. Someone as fickle as Jason isn't worth fighting for.'

'How can you be so disloyal?' she cried. 'You're supposed to be his friend.'

'It happens to be the truth,' Gray observed, his voice dispassionate.

'A fine friend you are!'

'I've always had his best interests at heart.'

As he reached to pour more wine it occurred to her vaguely that, though he was keeping her glass topped up, he was drinking little himself.

As though reading her thoughts, he explained, 'I'll be driving back to London later.'

So he wasn't a house guest. Which was odd, if he'd travelled all the way from the States...

'Speaking of hearts,' he pursued after a moment, 'when did Jason manage to lose his to your stepsister and break yours?'

'Last Easter.'

Any other time she wouldn't have answered such an ironically phrased question, but the amount of champagne she had drunk was succeeding in undermining her natural reticence.

'How did it happen?'

'Helen said they would like to meet Jason and see my ring.'

'Had you been engaged for long?'

Rebecca swallowed hard. 'Two months.'

'I didn't see your engagement announced in any of the papers.'

'It was never put in.'

'Why not? I would have thought your stepmother was the kind to fly to the social pages and spread the good news.'

'Unless she was cherishing fond hopes, even then, of her own daughter supplanting you.'

'It wasn't like that at all,' Rebecca denied. 'As a matter of fact it was Jason himself who wasn't keen to have it put in the papers. He preferred our engagement to be...unofficial.'

Slipping the ring onto her finger, he had said with charming insouciance, 'You can break the news to your own family if you want to, but I'll need time to talk Uncle Pip round, and I'd like the pair of you to meet before we tell the world.'

'Any particular reason for wanting it kept under wraps?' Gray asked.

'I think he was concerned that his ogre of an uncle might

not approve of him getting engaged to his PA. But if you and Jason are quite close I'm surprised you don't already know all this.'

'I'm afraid he isn't very good at keeping in touch,' Gray said smoothly. 'And, apart from the odd flying visit to London, I've been over in the States for a couple of years.'

Making the connection, she asked, 'You work for Finance International?'

'That's right.'

She wondered why he hadn't said so earlier, when he went on, 'Knowing what company gossip's like, I would have expected the news of your engagement to have filtered through. Especially if you wore your ring at the office.'

'I didn't. Jason asked me not to, so I wore it on a chain round my neck.'

'The whole thing sounds a bit hole-and-corner,' Gray observed sardonically, and watched as her cheeks turned pink.

'It was simply that he wanted time to talk his Uncle Pip round, and for the two of us to meet, before the engagement became public knowledge.'

But as far as she was aware, Jason had never even mentioned the engagement to Philip Lorne, much less arranged a meeting.

Seeing the look on Gray's face, she began defensively, 'I know the whole thing must sound ridiculous when Jason's twenty-three—'

'It does, rather.'

'But he was just six when his father was killed in an accident, and his mother died when he was barely fifteen. His uncle was made his guardian, and has been virtually running his life since then.

'Apparently Philip Lorne can be quite formidable, that's why Jason likes to keep on the right side of him and not rock the boat.'

Seeing the faint expression of contempt on Gray's face,

she said sharply, 'Don't think for a minute that it's cowardice—'

Pouring more champagne into her glass, he queried, 'So what would you call it? Expediency?'

Ignoring the blatant mockery, she hurried to defend her ex-fiancé. 'As well as Finance International, Philip Lorne controls all his late sister's business interests. Although Jason has a generous allowance, his uncle holds the purse strings, apparently for as long as he sees fit.'

'I'm well aware of the facts and the family history, of course,' Gray said, his voice dry. 'Though I hadn't appreciated that his uncle was quite such an ogre.'

'As Philip Lorne is based in New York, you know him, presumably?'

'Yes, I know him.'

'What kind of man is he?' she asked curiously.

'He has a reputation for being a tough, but fair, businessman. I believe he's well-respected—'

'No, I mean what do you *personally* know about him?'

'I know he works very long hours, doesn't suffer fools gladly, cares about the environment and gives to charity.'

'What about his private life?'

'He likes to keep his private life just that.'

'I take it he's a very wealthy man?'

'You could say that. Though on the whole he lives fairly quietly, prefers to go about without being recognised, and hates publicity.'

'Would you say he was a violent man?'

'No, I wouldn't. What makes you ask?'

'It seems he once threatened to turn his young wife over his knee. What made it worse was that she was pregnant at the time.'

'Who told you that?'

'Jason. It happened quite a few years ago when he was just a teenager, but he still remembers it.'

Rebecca shivered. 'I thought Philip Lorne sounded an absolute brute. I was glad to know he wasn't coming to the wedding.'

'Was he invited?'

She shook her head. 'Jason said he wouldn't approve, and he'd prefer to face him when the whole thing was a *fait accompli*…'

Realising belatedly that her tongue was running away with her, she pulled herself up. 'I'm sorry. I really shouldn't be telling you all this.'

His voice without expression, Gray said, 'I'm finding it most interesting. Just for the record, do you happen to know *why* Lorne threatened his wife?'

'It was something to do with a family heirloom, a ring, she was wearing without his permission.'

'If that was all, I would most certainly agree with your assessment.'

Putting a hand on his arm, she gave him a pleading glance. 'For Jason's sake, I wouldn't like any of this to get back to Philip Lorne.'

'I promise I won't say a word.' Then casually, 'By the way, what happened to *your* ring when the engagement ended?'

'I gave it back to Jason, of course.'

'He didn't say you could keep it?'

'I wouldn't have kept it. Who wants a bitter reminder like that?'

Proving that he knew a great deal about Jason's affairs, Gray responded ironically, 'Apparently his previous fiancées did.'

## CHAPTER TWO

'OR PERHAPS you didn't know he'd had any?'

Lifting her chin with an air of defiance, Rebecca said, 'Yes, I knew he'd been engaged twice before.'

She had heard it through the office grapevine the very same day she had accepted Jason's ring and his proposal of marriage.

'And it didn't worry you?' Gray asked.

'Not particularly.'

That wasn't strictly true. It had worried her enough to turn down Jason's plea that they should move in together.

Learning the reason for her refusal, he had first been angry, and then apologetic, saying, 'I suppose I should have told you myself. But as far as I was concerned it was of no great importance, and I was scared of losing you.'

She had been too much in love to want to doubt him.

'I must say I'm surprised,' Gray remarked, after a moment. 'If it was a stable, long-lasting relationship you were hoping for...?'

'Of course it was.'

'Surely a series of short-lived engagements couldn't be described as a good omen?'

'Hardly *a series*,' she said coldly. 'And Jason explained how they had both been...well...in the nature of experiments.'

Gray raised a sardonic brow. 'Really?'

'I believe his exact words were, "Youthful ventures intended more to test the waters of matrimony than with any serious intention of swimming."'

'And how did you interpret that?'

'I'm sorry?'

'I'm sure you don't lack intelligence, so it must be true that love makes people blind.'

'I don't know what you're getting at.'

'Didn't it sound as though he lacked commitment? As though he regarded those previous engagements as just another fling?'

'It did cross my mind,' she admitted.

Swallowing more champagne, she added unsteadily, 'But he assured me that I was quite different. He said he wanted to marry me so we could spend the rest of our lives together.'

But after a few short weeks, all that had changed.

To Rebecca's chagrin, her eyes filled with tears.

She tried desperately not to blink, but a single fat teardrop spilt over, rolled down her cheek and plopped into her hand as it lay, palm uppermost, in her lap.

Picking up her hand, Gray raised it to his lips and, delicately, with the tip of his tongue, collected the tear.

The intimacy of the gesture shook her, and she sat as though turned to stone, her amber eyes fixed on his lean, attractive face.

After a long moment, strangely breathless, she withdrew her hand, and looked anywhere but at him.

'Of course he'd have to *say* that,' Gray observed cynically. 'But in my opinion, when it came to marriage, Jason was in no hurry to let any woman pin him down.'

'He married Lisa,' Rebecca pointed out.

'Yes. It seems he more than met his match when it came to your stepsister…

'Incidentally, though you mentioned the change of heart came at Easter, you still haven't told me exactly how it happened.'

Once again he refilled her glass.

Reluctant to talk about it, but unhappily aware that she'd gone too far not to, Rebecca took another drink and began, 'Helen had arranged to have a small house party at Elmslee.

She asked me to come down and join them, and bring Jason.'

Neither of them had particularly wanted to go, but Helen had been so pressing that it had been almost impossible to say no.

'So you don't live here?' Gray asked curiously.

'I left home when I went to college.'

'And you didn't come back?'

'No.'

'Why not, if you all got on so well? Living in the country too quiet?'

'Not at all, I love the country, I always have. But as I was working in London, it made more sense to rent a small flat there.'

Her father had urged her to come back and live at Elmslee, suggesting eagerly that she could travel to and from the office with him. At first she had been sorely tempted, but Helen's cool reception of the idea had made her turn it down and plump for complete independence.

'So that's what you did?'

'Yes.'

'So when you and Jason were invited to Elmslee for Easter, you weren't living together?'

'No.'

'I can only presume you were holding out for a wedding ring first?'

Watching her expressive face, he smiled with quiet triumph. 'Whang in the gold, I see…'

Rebecca sighed. As soon as Jason's engagement ring was on her finger he had redoubled his efforts to get her to live with him.

Truth to tell, she had desperately wanted to. It was the recollection of his previous short-lived engagements that had made her cautious. Fearing that if she gave in too easily she might lose him, she had held back.

But she had still lost him.

If only she had agreed to at least sleep with him, things might have been different, she thought sadly.

Or, then again, they might not.

From first meeting Lisa, he had only too clearly been bowled over by her blonde beauty and her curvaceous figure.

'She's an absolute stunner,' he had said admiringly, 'a real pocket-Venus. You and she are total opposites.'

Then, realising too late how that must have sounded, he'd tacked on hastily, 'Though of course you're equally gorgeous, but in a different way.'

Rebecca had never, to the best of her knowledge, been described as pretty, let alone gorgeous.

Tall and slender, she'd been blessed with good bone-structure, almond eyes, even white teeth and a flawless skin. Even so, she knew herself to be no beauty. Her nose was too strong, her mouth too wide, her chin too firm.

Attractive, was most people's description. It was a description she was getting fed up with hearing...

Gray's voice broke into her thoughts, saying something she didn't catch.

Looking up fuzzily, she said, 'I beg your pardon?'

'I imagine Jason wasn't too pleased when you refused to move in with him. He likes his pleasure on tap, so to speak. He doesn't enjoy having to work for it, or having it doled out in small amounts.'

When she said nothing, he added thoughtfully, 'I take it your stepmother knew that you weren't actually living together?'

'Yes.'

'So she gave you separate rooms?'

'Yes.'

'Didn't you make any objection?'

'No.'

'I see...'

She was about to frame a protest, when he added, 'And

it might even have worked if you'd had the sense to keep him well away from your stepsister.'

Oddly enough, she hadn't seen that meeting as a threat. In retrospect, she knew how naïve and foolish she had been.

But they would have been bound to meet sooner or later, and she couldn't have coped with a marriage where she had to worry about every beautiful woman that crossed Jason's path.

As though reading her thoughts, Gray said satirically, 'Lock up your husband, and all that.'

'I wouldn't want...' She broke off.

'A husband you couldn't trust?' he hazarded.

'Yes.'

'Then, my dear Rebecca, you're better off out of it. As you know only too well, Jason isn't exactly renowned for his fidelity.'

Caught on the raw, she hit back. 'Jealous of his success with women?'

'What do you think?'

Though he was nowhere near as handsome as Jason, she felt oddly convinced that he would have no need to be jealous of him, or any man.

Unwilling to admit it, she said, 'Presumably you're here on your own today.'

'Don't you agree that's fortunate?' He smiled at her. A curiously intimate smile.

She put the little *frisson* that ran through her down to the fact that the air was appreciably cooler now the sun had set and dusk was creeping in.

'But I'm afraid we've strayed away from the point again,' he said, topping up her glass once more.

As she took a sip and looked at him a shade owlishly, he reminded her, 'You were about to tell me what happened at Easter.'

While he listened attentively, making an effort to dispel the tiredness that was creeping over her, she found herself telling this virtual stranger things she wouldn't have told her best friend.

'It was obvious from the start that Jason thought Lisa was stunning. In fact, he said as much. She seemed to like him, and several times—both the mornings we went riding, one evening at cards, and again when we played Murder—I found myself paired off with her current boyfriend, while they joined forces.'

Helen too had made quite a fuss of him, and clearly enjoying himself, Jason had remarked how pleased he was that they had decided to come.

Stupidly, Rebecca saw now, she had been glad that things were going so well.

'Go on,' Gray said.

'We had been planning to go back to London on Easter Monday, but because the rest of the party were staying until the following day Helen asked us to stay too, and Jason agreed.

'After dinner that evening we were in the middle of playing Charades when the strap on my watch broke. Jason said he would try to fix it for me later, and slipped it into his pocket.

'By the time we went upstairs to bed, we'd both forgotten about it. Jason kissed me goodnight at my bedroom door as usual, then went to his own room across the landing.

'It wasn't until I was about to take off my watch to shower that I remembered Jason still had it.

'The room Helen had given me had no clock, and because I always wear a watch I felt lost without one. After I'd showered and got ready for bed I pulled on a dressing gown and went to Jason's room to fetch it.'

She emptied her glass, and he took it from her and set it down on the bench.

'Go on,' he said again.

She took a deep breath. 'I tapped at his door. There was no answer, so I tapped again, but quietly, in case I disturbed anyone else. When there was still no answer, thinking he must be in the shower, I walked in…'

The words tailed off and she looked down at her lap, where her hands were clenched into fists.

'I take it your stepsister was there with him.'

'Yes,' she whispered.

They had been together on the bed, in a flurry of naked limbs and hoarse breathing. As she'd stood rooted to the spot, both of them had glanced up, their faces blind with passion.

She could still clearly recall how their expressions had altered. Jason's flushed, handsome face had looked startled and guilty, while Lisa's expression had changed to one of quiet triumph.

Without a word, Rebecca had turned and blundered away, stumbling in her haste to escape from the ugly little scene.

But she had carried it in her mind's eye like a video recording. One that she was unable to switch off; one that had replayed itself continuously until she thought she would go mad.

Peering at his companion in the gathering gloom, Gray asked, 'What did you do?'

'I went back to my room, but I couldn't sleep. Railton, the nearest town, has a twenty-four-hour taxi service, so at two o'clock in the morning, I packed my things and called a taxi.

'The following day I made myself go into the office to hand in my notice and give Jason his ring back. The rest you know.'

Gray frowned. 'I'm curious about one thing. How did you and your stepsister manage to stay friends?'

'Lisa was living in town—'

'With Jason presumably.'

'Yes. One day she called at my flat. She said she was sorry, she had only knocked at Jason's door to say good-night, and somehow it had just happened.'

'But you didn't believe her?'

She shook her head.

'Tell me, what made you agree to be a bridesmaid?'

The sun had long since set, and with dusk pressing against the windows she was starting to feel distinctly cool in the short-sleeved silk dress.

Repressing a shiver, she answered, 'I didn't at first. In fact I'd booked a holiday in the Caribbean so I could avoid the wedding.'

'Why didn't you go on it?'

'When Helen found out, she was furious. She said that if I wasn't chief bridesmaid everyone would think there'd been a family split.'

'Would it have mattered what people thought?'

'That's what I asked.'

'And what did she say?'

Rebecca rubbed her hands up and down her bare arms while she made an effort to sort out the jumble of thoughts in her head.

'She said something like, ''Jason's a well-to-do, titled man from a wealthy background. After Lisa and he are married we'll no doubt be moving in top society, and it might spoil everything if there was unkind talk.'''

'I see,' Gray murmured, his voice sardonic. 'Well if your stepmother has those kind of expectations, perhaps her daughter should have set her cap at the organ-grinder.'

'The organ-grinder?' Rebecca echoed blankly.

'I'll explain it some time.' Seeing that she was beginning to shiver, he rose, adding decidedly, 'Time we were moving. It's starting to get cooler in here.'

She got to her feet and, as her head began to whirl, sat down again with a bump. 'You'd better go. The reception will be over now. They'll be wondering where you've got to.'

He laughed mirthlessly. 'I very much doubt it. Come on,

now, let's have you up and moving before you catch a chill in that dress.'

'I'll come in a minute or so. You go on.'

'No chance. I'll see you back to the house. You must be getting hungry.'

She shook her head.

'After so much champagne you probably need to eat, and before too long.'

'I don't want to eat. At least not *here*.' She was aware that she sounded panicky.

'Then what *do* you want?'

'I want to go back to London.'

'How did you get to Elmslee?'

Focusing with an effort, she told him, 'I came down with some family friends, but they'll be staying until tomorrow.'

'Shouldn't you do the same?'

'No,' she cried vehemently. 'I couldn't bear to. Not after what Helen said.'

Desperate now to be left on her own so she could gather herself, she added, 'You really ought to go. I'll be all right... Honestly, I will.'

Unconvinced, he said, 'Let me see you stand up.'

'I'm not sure I can just at the moment,' she admitted. 'When I stand, I go dizzy.'

'When did you last eat?'

'I can't remember.'

'Lunch?'

Shivering in earnest now, she said, 'I didn't have any lunch.'

'Breakfast?'

'Only coffee.'

'Hell!' he exclaimed softly. 'I'm not surprised it's gone to your head. And it's no wonder you're feeling cold.'

'I just wish you'd go and leave me.'

'You're in no fit state to be left.'

Enunciating every word with care, she said, 'When I've

sat for a little while longer I'll be quite capable of walking back to the house.'

'Then what will you do?'

'As soon as I've got back to my room and changed, I'll ring for a taxi.'

'Do you seriously think you'll be able to cope on your own?'

She *had* to. Haughtily, she said, 'Of course I will.' The effect was spoiled by the fact that, in spite of all her efforts, she was having a job to stay upright.

Smoothly, he said, 'I think it would be better if I saw you safely back home.' Putting an arm around her, he urged her to her feet.

Angry with herself, knowing she should have had more sense than to drink so much champagne, she tried to pull free. 'Thank you, but I don't need any help.'

'Don't be foolish, of course you need help,' he said curtly.

'I can manage,' she insisted, and clenched her teeth to stop them chattering.

'Very well.' He removed his arm.

She made a valiant attempt to stand unaided, but was forced to clutch at him.

'Still convinced you can manage?' he asked.

Her legs buckling under her ignominiously, she sank back onto the bench.

With an air of I-told-you-so, he took off his jacket, put it around her shoulders, slipped her arms into the sleeves and fastened the buttons to keep it in place.

It half buried her and the sleeves hung over her hands, but it still held his body heat, and she found the warmth curiously comforting. Leaning her head back against the wooden wall, she closed her eyes.

'Don't go to sleep.' He tapped her cheek with a none-too-gentle finger. 'We need to be moving.'

When the heavy lids lifted, he helped her to her feet once more.

'Please, I—'

'No more arguments.' Putting an arm around her, he began to steer her towards the door. 'It's high time I got you back to the house.'

'I'm not your res...res...' She made another attempt. 'Your responsibility.'

Flatly, he said, 'It's my fault you're tipsy.'

But, while she was undeniably tipsy, one small part of her mind remained stone-cold sober, and, standing aloof, watched and judged with critical detachment.

She had been stupid to let her stepmother's comments throw her. If only she had ignored them, stayed cool and aloof, kept her dignity...

But she hadn't. And now it was too late. If anyone saw her obviously the worse for drink, she would look like a complete loser. Spineless and pathetic.

She felt ashamed, totally humiliated in a way that even Helen's spiteful remarks had been unable to make her feel.

As, one arm supporting her, Gray reached for the latch, she begged, 'Please stop...'

'Feeling sick?' he enquired.

'No.'

'Thank the lord for that.'

'But I don't—'

'If necessary I'll carry you.'

He opened the door and, holding it with his foot, said firmly, 'Let's go.'

'Oh, please, can't we wait? I don't want to risk meeting anyone.'

'There's no point in waiting any longer. If we go now, there's a chance that most of the guests will still be congregating in the marquee.'

Even in her panic-stricken state it made sense, and she let herself be chivvied outside and helped down the steps.

The air was cool and fresh, the clear, dark-blue sky pricked with stars. A faint breeze carried the scent of honeysuckle.

Thankfully that part of the garden appeared to be deserted, and only the faint sound of music drifted their way.

'All ready?' he asked.

'Yes.'

But when she tried to walk her sense of balance had totally deserted her, and even with Gray taking most of her weight her rubbery legs refused to work.

'I can't see us getting far at this rate,' he remarked calmly, 'so you'd better put your arms round my neck.'

Lurching a little, she obeyed, linking her hands inside the sleeves of his jacket.

A moment later he was lifting her effortlessly. His strength was as comforting as his warmth, and, her head against his shoulder, she gave up the struggle and let him take control.

She couldn't remember ever being carried before, and the feel of the powerful male body she was being held against, and the solid bone and muscle beneath her cheek, stirred her senses in a way she had simply never envisaged.

Dimly she realised that it must be the champagne that was lowering her inhibitions and making her feel this way.

His step brisk and his breathing even, carrying her as easily as if she were a child, he said, 'I propose that we head for the rear of the house. If we go in the back way there should be less chance of us being seen.'

Avoiding the floodlit areas, Gray skirted the old walled garden, and as they got nearer to the main lawn he began to move with even greater care.

Though the sound of the orchestra playing and a buzz of conversation was still coming from the brightly lit marquee, thanks to the space-heaters and the beauty of the evening, some guests had elected to sit outside.

As they got closer the pungent scent of cigar smoke, mingled with coffee, wafted towards them.

They were just drawing level with the entrance to the marquee, when two couples came out and, laughing and talking, headed in their direction.

Gray muttered something beneath his breath, and in one fluid movement set her down, her back against the nearest tree trunk, and, shielding her from the possibility of prying eyes, bent to kiss her.

Rebecca hadn't been kissed since the night her engagement had ended so disastrously, and, though it was a chaste kiss, meant merely for show, the feel of his mouth on hers had the strangest effect.

She was vaguely aware that the little group were quite close, but, as her lips parted beneath the slight pressure of his, somehow it no longer seemed to matter.

As she clung to him, dizzy and helpless, he continued to kiss her while the foursome passed by, still talking. Only when their voices had faded into the distance did he raise his head.

Glancing around, he said softly, 'The coast seems to be clear momentarily, so we'd better make tracks. If we keep to the far side of this yew hedge, we should be out of sight for most of the way.'

Lifted high in his arms once more, she was carried through an archway of yew to another expanse of lawn.

His footsteps made no sound on the grass, and with the faint scent of his aftershave in her nostrils, and the feel of his silk shirt beneath her cheek, she found herself experiencing a kind of drifting unreality, as if the whole thing was just a dream.

'I take it there's a way through near the house?'

His question made her open her eyes, and rousing herself, she answered, 'Yes, there's another archway just before you get to the orangery.'

'That's useful. I've parked by the orangery.'

As they approached the house, even through the shelter-ing yew, they could see it was ablaze with lights. 'Where exactly is your room?' he queried. 'Is it easy to get to?'

Struggling against an overwhelming desire to let go and sink into sleep, she made herself concentrate. 'It's the first door on the right at the top of the main staircase.'

'Sounds comparatively simple.'

As they reached the archway, he added wryly, 'The only thing is, we appear to have left it a bit late for getting in and out unseen.'

To Rebecca's consternation she saw that the place was alive with people coming and going in ones and twos and small groups.

'Which leaves our present situation open to all kinds of misinterpretation,' he added grimly.

'Whatever are we going to do?' she moaned.

'Would you prefer to simply get in the car and go?'

'Yes… No…'

'Which?'

'I can't. The key to my flat is in my handbag.'

'Then perhaps you'd better wait in the car while I go and fetch it.'

'Oh, thank you,' she said fervently.

'Luckily, what with arriving late, I'm parked a fair way from the house.'

Moving with caution, he kept beyond the range of the lights until they reached the end of the line of parked cars.

'Here we are.' Setting her down carefully beside a silver Jaguar, he unlocked it and helped her into the front passen-ger seat.

'Just in case anyone walks past, it might be as well to take off your headdress. Being light-coloured, it tends to be noticeable.'

For a moment or two she fumbled ineffectually, hampered by nerveless fingers and the over-long jacket sleeves.

'Let me.' Stooping, he felt for the pins that held it in place and began to remove them one by one.

'There.' He lifted the circlet of fresh flowers free, letting the long, silky hair tumble around her shoulders. 'Presumably you don't want to keep it?'

'No,' she said emphatically.

'If we were in Hawaii you could give it to Pele. As we're not…' He sent the circlet skimming like a Frisbee into the night.

Though the whole thing seemed completely surreal, somehow the gesture lifted her spirits and made her giggle like a schoolgirl.

Dropping the pins into the door pocket, he queried, 'I imagine you have an overnight case or something I can put your things into?'

The alcohol was taking even more of a hold, making her thoughts as sluggish as wasps in treacle, and it was a moment or two before she was able to say, 'Yes… But if you can bring my bag I don't mind if you leave everything else. I mean, if someone sees you, won't it look a bit odd if you come down carrying a case?'

'Not half as odd as it'll look if I come down carrying a lady's handbag. But if I put everything into a case, I could simply be a guest who's decided not to stay after all.'

Her voice slurred, she asked, 'What will you do if there are still a lot of people about?'

'Walk in as if I owned the place,' he answered cheerfully. 'There must be plenty of house guests who won't necessarily know one another, so I'm unlikely to be challenged unless I'm unlucky enough to run into your stepmother.

'Now, are you warm enough? Or shall I leave the engine running?'

'I'm warm enough, thank you.'

He slammed the car door quietly, and she watched him walk away, only his white shirt visible until he got within range of the lights.

This wedding couldn't have been much fun for *him*, she thought. Not only had he missed the reception, but he was also going to drive back to London without even speaking to his friend.

He was a strange, complex man, sardonic and abrasive, bordering on cruel at times, yet he'd gone out of his way to help and care for her…

Resting her head against the leather upholstery, she closed her eyes with a sigh.

A movement beside her, and the muted roar of the engine springing into life, made her lift her head and open bleary eyes.

Reaching across to fasten her seat belt, Gray answered her unspoken question. 'Everything's fine. All your belongings are in the boot.'

'Thank you…' Almost before the words were out, she was fast asleep again.

'Wake up, sleeping beauty.'

Eyes still closed, she tried to brush away the intrusive fingers that were stroking her cheek.

'We're home.' He'd found her address amongst her things and driven straight there.

She didn't care. All she wanted was to be left in peace. She tried to say so, but the voice was insisting, 'Come on, wake up,' and the fingers were no longer stroking, but slapping lightly.

Feeling aggrieved, she opened heavy lids and realised dazedly that they were parked in front of Prince Albert's Court, and that Gray was standing by her side with the car door open.

'That's better,' he murmured. 'Now, let's see how you are on your feet.'

He hauled her out, and, finding she was like a rag doll,

half carried her across the pavement and through the main entrance into a bare hallway with doors on either side.

It was an unprepossessing block in a drab neighbourhood, and, presumably in a half-hearted attempt to brighten the place, all the doors had been painted different colours.

As her head began to droop, he said sharply, 'Don't go to sleep again until I know which is your flat.'

'That one.' She pointed an unsteady finger at a mustard-coloured door on their right.

'Nice and close, which is just as well.'

'The key…' she began.

'It's all right, I've already found it.' Supporting her with one arm, he unlocked the door.

Having helped her inside, he lowered her onto the couch and, leaving the door a little ajar, went out again to bring in her belongings.

When he returned her eyes flickered open momentarily, then closed once more.

Coming to give her a little shake, he reminded her, 'You really ought to have something to eat.'

'Couldn't eat…'

'What about some coffee?'

She shook her head.

'In that case the best place for you is bed, and the sooner you're tucked in the better.'

He helped her into the bedroom and sat her down on the edge of the double bed.

Catching a blurred glimpse of herself in the mirror, she felt a sudden revulsion at the sight of the gleaming necklace of cultured pearls that had been the bridegroom's gift to the bridesmaids.

*Pearls for tears.*

Having tried, and failed, to unfasten it, desperate to be rid of the thing, she began to tug at it.

'Whoa there,' Gray cautioned. 'Let me.'

He unfastened the necklace and tossed it onto the dressing

table, then, crouching to slip off her shoes, asked, 'What about your clothes?'

Gathering her dignity, she said, 'I can manage.'

Watching her struggle ineffectually with the small covered buttons that fastened the bodice of her dress, he suggested, 'It might be a whole lot easier to sleep in it.'

'No.'

'Then you'd best let me help you.'

He unfastened the buttons, and, easing the dress from beneath her, lifted it over her head. 'There, you can always sleep in the rest.'

'No. I couldn't bear to.' She wanted to be rid of all her wedding things right now, this minute.

While she swam in and out of consciousness, he helped her off with the remainder of her clothes and settled her head on the pillow.

Pulling up the duvet, he remarked, 'It's been a long day.'

A long day... Lisa's and Jason's wedding day... The worst day of her life...

And the worst night. Their wedding night and the start of their honeymoon.

Would they be going to Paris? Jason had promised to take *her* to Paris. They had been going to do so much. But now she was all alone, with nothing and no one in her life.

Unsure whether or not she'd spoken the words aloud or merely thought them, she found slow tears rolling down her face.

'And it's obviously been too much for you.' Sitting on the edge of the bed, he brushed a strand of hair away from her wet cheek.

His tenderness was her undoing, and she began to cry even harder.

'Don't cry, little one.'

'Why not?' she asked bitterly.

'Because if you cry I'll have to comfort you, and one thing can lead to another.'

Big eyes on his face, she sniffed dolefully.

'Don't cry any more now. By tomorrow things may not seem quite so bad.'

He sounded kind and caring, and, knowing that Jason didn't care a fig about her, she was pathetically grateful that someone did.

As his dark face swam in and out of focus, she caught hold of his hand. 'Thank you.'

'Goodnight and sweet dreams.' He rose to his feet.

Still clinging to his hand, she begged hoarsely, 'Don't leave me. Please don't leave me. I don't want to be on my own tonight…'

# CHAPTER THREE

WHEN Rebecca first stirred and began to slowly surface, her mind was a complete and utter blank. She hadn't the faintest idea how she had got to bed, or what had happened the previous day.

After a while, insubstantial images began to swirl and eddy in her consciousness, appearing and disappearing like wraiths in a mist.

Lisa and Jason standing in church together and being declared man and wife.

Helen, wearing a peacock-blue hat trimmed with iridescent feathers, saying, so everyone could hear, 'Of course poor Rebecca's terribly disappointed…'

Herself fleeing to her childhood sanctuary to lick her wounds in private.

Then a tall dark-haired stranger appearing with a bottle of champagne and saying drily, 'I've been told that women always cry at weddings, but don't you think this is overdoing it a bit?'

Squeezing her eyes tightly closed, as if that would stop the images appearing, she groaned as she remembered how, the champagne loosening her tongue, she had told him things she wouldn't normally have told a living soul.

Oh, how could she have been stupid enough to get tipsy? She had made a complete fool of herself, and if it hadn't been for…Gray Gallagher…yes, that was his name, *everyone* would have known it.

Though it was like looking through a glass darkly, she half remembered him carrying her back up the garden…kissing her…helping her into his car…then taking off her headdress and sending it skimming into the night, before going back to the house to fetch her things.

She could recall nothing after that.

But he must have seen her safely home, as she was in her own bed and her overnight case and bag were on the chest.

There was a lot to thank him for.

If she ever saw him again.

Knowing what he must think of her, she found herself hoping fervently that she *wouldn't* see him again. Such a meeting was bound to be desperately uncomfortable, to say the least.

But there should be no problem, she realised belatedly. He lived and worked in the States, so presumably, having flown in especially for the wedding, he'd go back now it was over.

Her thoughts growing muzzy, she closed her eyes again and lay drifting on the edge of sleep, until the sound of breakfast television from the next-door flat roused her.

What time was it? she wondered.

Peering blearily at her watch, she found it was gone eight o'clock.

Normally she was up and about well before seven. But, as though the past weeks of eating little and sleeping less had finally caught up with her, she felt mentally and physically exhausted, all her normal drive and energy missing.

Even so, she should make a move.

But what was there to get up for? It wasn't as though she had a job to go to.

In that case she should be out looking for one, her conscience responded promptly. It wouldn't be too long before she ran out of money.

The grim reality of the thought shocked her into action, and, her ash-brown hair tumbling round her shoulders, she struggled to sit up.

It wasn't until her head stopped spinning that she realised

she was naked. She had no recollection of taking off her clothes, but her bridesmaid's dress and undies were folded over a chair.

If she had been *compos mentis* enough to fold her things so neatly, why hadn't she put on a nightie? She always wore a nightie...

Her head throbbing dully and her mouth desert-dry, she gave up the puzzle and, throwing back the duvet, swung her feet to the floor.

She was heading for the bathroom, when she noticed something that stopped her in her tracks.

A creature of habit, she invariably slept with a single pillow, and on the right-hand side of the bed. Now the left-hand side was rumpled, and there was an extra pillow.

As she stared at it stupidly, she realised two things. It was the spare pillow that normally lived in the top of the wardrobe, and it bore the imprint of a head.

Feeling as though she had been kicked in the solar plexus, she sank down on the nearest chair. It *couldn't* be what it looked like, she thought, even as she understood that it *could*, and undoubtedly *was*.

She began to shake like a leaf.

No, surely he wouldn't have done such a thing?

Or would he?

What did she know of the man? Very little except that he lived in the States, worked for Philip Lorne, and was a friend of Jason's.

Of his morals she knew less than nothing.

But the mere fact that he'd taken advantage of her drunken state and then cleared out spoke volumes.

As the full horror of the situation sank in, she whispered, 'Oh, dear God.'

It was savage retribution for being stupid enough to get drunk, and trust a perfect stranger.

Several minutes passed before she was able to get up and,

stomach churning, knees like jelly, make her way to the bathroom.

Drops of water were still clinging to the patterned glass of the shower-stall, while the fresh scent of some masculine shower gel hung on the air. A damp towel had been draped over the laundry basket, and a disposable toothbrush discarded in the bin.

He'd obviously made himself thoroughly at home before leaving, she thought bleakly.

Disliking the idea of standing where he had stood, but desperate to feel clean again, she forced herself to ignore the sense of shock and outrage, and step into the shower.

Watching water and bubbles of peach-blossom shampoo cascade down her slender body, she noted—in an oddly detached way, as though this creamy flesh wasn't really hers—that it bore not the slightest sign of marks or bruises.

But presumably she had been either too far gone to struggle, or already unconscious when he stripped off her clothes.

Despite the steamy heat she went cold, every nerve in her body screaming a protest. It took a moment or two to gather herself enough to carry on.

When she had dried her hair she pulled on a towelling robe and, sinking onto a stool to clean her teeth, caught sight of herself in the mirror.

Staring abstractedly at the white-faced woman who stared mutely back at her, she wondered, what was she to do?

But there was nothing she could do.

So, rather than sit here brooding, she decided, she would go out and make a fresh effort to find another job. At least that would be a positive step. It should help to take her mind off what had happened.

Feeling a fraction more cheerful, she brushed her hair and coiled it into a neat chignon, before making up with care.

Then, her legs still feeling shaky, she forced herself to go back to the bedroom.

Averting her eyes from the bed, she found a silky top in

mint-green and a stone-coloured trouser suit, and, suddenly desperate to get out of the flat, dressed with all speed.

Common sense told her that she ought to have some breakfast before she went, but the thought of food made her stomach churn even more.

Though she *was* in need of a drink.

Going through to the kitchen, she put on the kettle and with unsteady hands made a pot of coffee and poured herself a mug of the fragrant brew.

She had just added milk and a spoonful of sugar and sat down at the table to drink it, when she heard the sound of the front door opening and closing.

A moment later the tall, broad-shouldered figure of Gray Gallagher filled the kitchen doorway.

The formal garb of yesterday, with its matching shirt and tie was gone. Wearing smart casuals and a short car coat unbuttoned and swinging loose, he looked completely at his ease.

'Mmm…' He sniffed appreciatively. 'Thought I could smell coffee.'

While she sat speechless, he strolled over and helped himself to a mugful, as though he lived here and had every right.

'I wondered if you'd be up. You were still asleep when I left.'

As he spoke he studied her, surprised afresh by her beauty. A beauty he had only fully appreciated that morning when he had stood looking down at her sleeping face.

Yesterday he had seen her as attractive, with a lovely, passionate mouth and fascinating amber eyes. Now he noticed the shape of her face, her delicate ears, her pure bone structure.

Dropping into a chair opposite, he began to drink his coffee, his eyes still appraising her.

Her heart racing suffocatingly fast, Rebecca found her voice and demanded, 'How did you get in?'

'I borrowed your key in case you were still asleep when I got back.'

'I didn't expect you back.'

He lifted a dark brow. 'Why not?'

'After what happened...' Her words tailed off.

With a wry smile, he observed, 'I'm rather surprised you remember what happened.'

'I don't,' she admitted. 'But it's quite obvious.'

Picking up her agitation, he asked mildly, 'What's quite obvious?'

'You must have undressed me!'

When he failed to deny it, she burst out angrily, 'You took advantage of me.'

His good-looking face the picture of innocence, he enquired, 'In what way?'

'You know perfectly well!'

'If you mean we slept together...'

'Are you trying to pretend we didn't?'

'No.'

'You're a swine.' Her voice shook.

Smoothly, he enquired, 'What makes you think I'm solely to blame?'

Pushing away the awful thought that she might have invited it, she said raggedly, 'If you'd had a shred of decency, you'd have gone. Left me alone.'

'I was about to, but you pleaded with me to stay.'

'No! I don't believe it.'

'Your exact words were, "Please don't leave me. I don't want to be on my own tonight."' For good measure, he added, 'You took hold of my hand and clung to me.'

Somewhere deep down it struck a chord, and, though she wanted to dismiss it all as lies, she couldn't doubt that he was telling the truth.

Unable to repudiate it, she retorted, 'You must have realised that I was still too drunk to know what I was doing or saying.'

'Drunk or sober, it was clear that you were in need of some…company.'

'If you knew what kind of woman I am,' she cried bitterly, 'you'd know perfectly well that I don't go in for that kind of *company*, or one-night stands.'

'As I don't know what kind of woman you are, I'm afraid I wasn't able to judge.'

'So you went ahead and slept with me!'

'Are you using the words ''slept with'' as a euphemism for ''had sex with''?'

'Yes, I am.'

'Then the answer's no, I didn't.'

'You didn't?' she echoed blankly.

'If you knew what kind of man I are, you'd know perfectly well that I don't go in for one-night stands either.'

Coldly, he went on, 'Nor do I enjoy ''sleeping with'' unconscious women. And believe me, a second or two after asking me to stay you were out for the count.'

With the beginnings of relief, but still needing some additional reassurance, she said, 'So you *didn't* sleep with me?'

'I could just say *no* again, but in the interests of accuracy it's a fact that I slept beside you in the same bed. That's all. Nothing more, nothing less.'

Remembering her naked state, she said, 'If that really is all, I don't understand why you went to the trouble of undressing me.'

Straight-faced, he said, 'It was no trouble.'

Watching her blush, he continued, 'But before you start accusing me of getting my kicks that way, it had been a long day for me too, and I was more than ready for some sleep versus hanky-panky.'

Flustered, she pointed out, 'I could have slept in my clothes.'

'After I'd unfastened your pearls I suggested that, but you

were desperate to get rid of all your wedding finery, so I helped you.'

Once again some faint recollection told her he spoke the truth.

'Apart from that, I never laid so much as a finger on you. Happy now?'

Crossly, she accused, 'At first you deliberately led me to believe the worst.'

When he merely looked at her, she demanded, 'Why?'

'It seemed to be what you *wanted* to believe.'

'I didn't want to believe anything of the kind,' she cried indignantly. 'I was absolutely *horrified*.'

Pulling a face, he complained, 'You said that in such a heartfelt way, I could quite easily end up with a complex. Or at the very least a severely dented ego...'

Against all expectations, she found herself laughing. Not only did it ease the tension, but it made her realise that she had barely smiled, let alone laughed, in many weeks.

'More coffee?' he queried, rising to his feet.

She nodded.

'Milk and sugar?'

'Milk and one sugar, please.'

It was the first time she had been calm enough to look at him objectively, and while he poured their coffee she studied him, covertly weighing him up.

He was even more attractive than she had realised, with a lean, strong-boned face and handsome eyes beneath dark, level brows.

His teeth were white and even, and his long, flexible mouth, with its austere upper lip and sensuous lower, aesthetically pleasing.

But apart from Gray Gallagher's looks and his physique there was something about him, something charismatic—a maturity, a quiet confidence—that gave him an air of authority and power. An air that, she felt sure, would turn most women on.

He glanced up suddenly, and, annoyed that she had been caught staring at him, she looked hastily away, a tinge of betraying pink rising in her cheeks.

When he just waited, leaving the ball in her court, she went back to one point that was still niggling. 'I don't understand why you stayed here last night.'

He passed her the replenished mug and sat down again, crossing his legs the way men did, one ankle resting casually on the opposite knee. 'You mean, if it wasn't simply to have my wicked way with you?'

Her colour deepening, she said crisply, 'As you weren't an overnight guest at Elmslee Manor, I presume you had a hotel booked.'

'I didn't, as a matter of fact.'

'Oh.'

'No, I wasn't in need of a free night's lodging.'

'I wasn't thinking any such thing...' she began, then stopped, realising by the gleam in his eye that he was angling for a rise.

'I have my own place.'

Startled, she said, 'Well, if you have your own place I really can't imagine why you stayed here. It's hardly the height of luxury.'

'You seemed to want me to stay and, as I felt guilty about the state you were in, I thought it best to keep an eye on you.'

Seeing how pale she still was beneath the make-up, he queried, 'How are you feeling this morning?'

'A bit rough, but probably better than I deserve.'

Noting, with an odd little flutter, that his handsome, heavily lashed eyes, which she had expected to be grey or light blue, were green flecked with gold, she took a deep breath and went on, 'I owe you an abject apology.'

He half shook his head, but she ploughed on determinedly, 'Firstly, for misjudging you, and secondly, for yesterday. You must have come over from the States especially for the wedding, and because of me you even missed the reception.'

'That was my choice,' he pointed out.

'But it means your journey has been a complete waste of time.'

A twinkle in his eye, he drawled, 'Oh, I wouldn't say that.'

She swallowed. 'Unless, of course, you have business in London?'

'Not at this precise moment.' An edge to his voice, he added, 'Though I will have in a couple of weeks.'

'So when do you go back to the States?'

'This morning.'

'Oh.' In spite of having earlier wished him gone, she felt a strange sense of disappointment. Doing her best to hide it, she said, 'Well, I hope you have a good flight back to New York.'

'I'm not going back to New York. At least, not at the moment.'

'I thought you lived there.'

'Yes, I do. But first I have a one-night stop-over in Boston for an urgent business meeting, then a trip to California.'

'Business or pleasure?'

'A bit of each. Finance International have just acquired a rundown vineyard in the Napa Valley, so I'm going over there to take a look at it and try to work out the potential.

'Mainly, however, I'm looking forward to a break. I haven't had a holiday since I've been in the States, so I'm hoping to take it easy and enjoy the sun for a couple of weeks before flying back to London.'

Then with no change of tone, so that at first she scarcely took in what he was saying, 'Why not come with me?'

'Come with you?' she echoed after a moment. 'You mean to California?'

'Why not?'

'I—I just couldn't,' she stammered.

'Have you ever been to California?'

'No.' The furthest she'd ever managed to get was to the Italian Alps on a cheap skiing break with some college friends.

'But you like travelling. You told me you'd booked a Caribbean holiday.'

'Yes, but I—'

'They both start with the letter C,' he pointed out quizzically, 'and if you go you might find you like California better.'

It had been one of her childhood dreams to someday see the west coast of America...

Snapping off the thought, she told herself not to be a fool. The mere idea of going to California with Gray Gallagher, a man she had thought of as rude and abrasive, was ridiculous.

But his attitude had changed, she realised. He no longer seemed so scathing, so deliberately cruel. In fact he'd been positively kind.

Even so...

She shook her head. 'I couldn't possibly go.'

'What is there to keep you in London? You've given up your job, so there's nothing to fill your days. Unless you *want* to sit and think of Lisa and Jason enjoying their honeymoon?'

Seeing the look on her face, he regretted his cruelty. It was like slapping a child.

His tone kinder, he observed, 'Now the marriage is a *fait accompli*, it's time you cut free, left the past behind you. Though this trip is no big deal, a complete change of scenery might be just what you need to take your mind off things.'

He sounded so down-to-earth that, from being unthinkable, it began to seem feasible.

When, trying to cope with the rush of excitement that threatened to overrule common sense, she said nothing, he urged, 'Go on, give me one good reason why you shouldn't come.'

Pulling herself together, she asked, 'You mean apart from the obvious one?'

He grinned appreciatively. 'The obvious one being that you're a "nice girl", and nice girls don't go away on holiday with strange men?'

'Exactly.'

'A somewhat dated outlook, yet in my book a commendable one. But apart from that?'

As she had absolutely no intention of going, it was absurd to have to give a reason. All the same she found herself doing it.

'For one thing I couldn't afford the air fare.'

'You wouldn't need to—I'm using the company jet.'

'And for another I must stay in London and keep looking for a job.' Unguardedly, she added, 'If I don't get one before too long I'll be in a mess.'

'You mean financially?'

Reluctantly, she answered, 'Yes.'

'Well, I have plenty of contacts both here and in the States, so don't worry about getting a job. I'll see you're fixed up as soon as we get back.

'And as far as this holiday is concerned you won't need to pay a penny.'

Seeing her expression, he said wryly, 'There are no strings attached, I assure you. I'm not asking you to share my bed.' A gleam of laughter in his green eyes, he added, 'Unless, of course, you want to—'

'I *don't* want to.'

'There you go,' he complained, 'denting my ego again. But seriously, there's a house that goes with the vineyard, so you can have your own room and simply come as my guest. At the end of the fortnight I'll bring you back to London.'

Letting go of one obstacle, she cited another. 'It might be more than your job's worth.'

'No one questions what I do. I have a completely free hand.'

And he must be fairly high up the ladder to have been given the use of the company jet. Still, she protested, 'But if Philip Lorne found out...'

'So long as I'm getting the work done, he wouldn't concern himself. And I think at the very least Finance International owe you a holiday.

'Because of Jason you've lost out quite badly, and I know Lorne well enough to be sure that if he heard what had happened he wouldn't be at all pleased with his nephew.'

'You won't tell him?' she asked quickly.

'It all depends.'

'On what?'

'On whether or not you decide to take up my offer.'

'That's blackmail.'

'Call it friendly persuasion.'

'If there are no strings attached, why do you want me to come?'

'Apart from the reasons I've already stated, when I'm not working I like to have a companion, someone to share things with.'

Frowning, she wondered why a man with his kind of looks and charisma would need to use blackmail to get himself a companion.

'If you wanted companionship, why didn't you bring a girlfriend?' she asked.

'I don't happen to have one at the moment. So it occurred to me that, as we're in the same boat, a spot of joint companionship wouldn't come amiss.'

Though she had her doubts about Gray Gallagher being a *comfortable* companion, perhaps she should take this unexpected opportunity. A trip to California might be just what she needed to enable her to kick-start her life again.

After weeks of being alone and in despair, trapped in a kind of vacuum, it was time she at least made an effort to pick up the pieces and face the future.

As though following her train of thought, Gray pressed, 'Short-term at least, we could each fill a gap in the other's life.'

It sounded good, except that the gap in her life was too big to fill, Rebecca thought bleakly.

His green eyes on her face, Gray asked sardonically, 'Or perhaps no one else could *possibly* fill the gap Jason has left?'

Ruffled by the blatant mockery, she answered shortly, 'No, they couldn't. But there must be plenty of women in California who'd be only too happy to fill the gap in *your* life. Taking me would be like taking coals to Newcastle.'

'I agree that there are probably plenty of women out there, but I don't want to spend half my holiday looking for one. I just want to take it easy with someone I already know.'

'But we haven't got to know one another yet,' she pointed out.

A devilish gleam in his eye, he said, 'Considering we only met yesterday, I know quite a lot about you.'

Deciding it was safest to let that go, she went on tartly, 'And if we did get to know one another, we might find we weren't at all compatible.'

Leering at her, he suggested, 'Alternatively, we might discover that we were strongly attracted... Suppose we couldn't keep our hands off each other?'

Realising that he was teasing her, she made herself say matter-of-factly, 'If it's all the same to you, I'd rather suppose we *could*.'

He grinned appreciatively.

Thinking how attractive he looked when he smiled, she added firmly, 'In all probability, we'd dislike each other.'

'I don't see how you come to that conclusion,' he objected. 'However, if we did happen to discover that we couldn't stand the sight of one another there's no great harm done. It should be relatively easy to behave in a civilised manner for a couple of weeks. Don't you agree?'

She nodded. 'I suppose so.'

'In that case, what do you say?'

Wavering, she asked seriously, 'But won't it affect your arrangements in Boston?'

'Not in the slightest. All I'll have to do is phone ahead and book another room.'

'And you're sure it won't get you into trouble with Philip Lorne?'

'Quite sure.'

Wondering if she could trust him, she hesitated.

'Don't I look harmless enough?'

With that gleam in his eye he looked anything but. Unwilling, for a variety of reasons, to say so, she retorted, 'Crippen *looked* harmless.'

'Well, judged by that yardstick, you'll be quite safe so long as you don't marry me.

'So what do you say?'

'All right.'

'Great.'

He rose and glanced at his watch. 'We haven't a lot of spare time. We'll need to be at the airport in a little under two hours. How long will it take you to pack and find your passport?'

On her feet now, she answered dazedly, 'No more than fifteen minutes.'

'Excellent! Don't forget to put in something warm for the evenings, just in case. Though it will most likely be hot and sunny, northern California isn't exactly the Caribbean.'

When she just continued to stand there, her expression dazed, he queried, 'Is there a problem?'

'I just can't believe I'm actually going to see the west coast.'

Ironically, he said, 'After losing out in the marriage stakes, look on it as a consolation prize. Off you go, now.'

Moving like some automaton, she went into the bedroom, and took a medium-sized suitcase from her cupboard. Her being naturally tidy and organised made it a simple matter to select and pack a small but versatile wardrobe, and she was ready in less than fifteen minutes.

A light woollen coat over her arm, she picked up her bag and case and went through to the living-room to find Gray was standing by the window looking out, his broad back to the room.

She noticed how neatly his ears were set against his well-shaped head, and the way his thick, dark hair, albeit cut short, tried to curl into the nape of his neck.

Though her feet made no sound on the carpet, he turned at her approach.

'Full marks,' he applauded. Then in surprise, 'Is this all the luggage you're taking?'

'Yes.'

Relieving her of the case, and heading for the door, he observed, 'I'm beginning to realise you're a very unusual woman. My ex-girlfriend would have needed at least three suitcases as well as loads of hand luggage.'

'I don't have all that many clothes,' she said.

'Is that from choice or necessity?'

Unwilling to admit that it was from necessity, she said quickly, 'I must just drop my key next door and ask Joanne to do the washing and clear the fridge.'

'What a practical woman you are,' he teased.

'That's why I make a good PA.'

The key delivered, and a hasty promise given to explain everything on her return, Rebecca followed Gray out to the waiting car.

After the previous warm, sunny spell, the weather had turned appreciably cooler. A brisk wind drove a flock of ragged grey clouds across the sky like unruly sheep, and it was beginning to spit with rain.

He put her case in the boot, and, with a courtesy that seemed to come naturally to him, opened the door for her and helped her into the front passenger seat of what she now realised was a sumptuous car.

She should have been high on excitement, she thought as he slid behind the wheel, but instead her mind lay curiously still and empty.

It was as though she had suddenly let go of all her worries about the past and future; as though she had given up trying to control her life, and had simply accepted what was happening to her.

# CHAPTER FOUR

THE drive to the airport proved to be a silent one. Gray appeared to be busy with his thoughts, while Rebecca sat staring at the passing scenery without any of it really registering.

On arrival they were met by a nice-looking, efficient young man wearing a smart suit and carrying a clipboard.

'Kevin, how are you?' Gray asked cordially.

'Fine, thank you, Mr Gallagher.'

The two men shook hands.

'This is Miss Ferris, who's been working at our London branch.'

'Nice to meet you, Miss Ferris.'

'Everything under control?' Gray queried, retrieving a laptop from the boot.

'Absolutely. Most of the formalities have been attended to, and take-off should be in forty-five minutes' time. If you'd like to go ahead, I'll see that the rest of your luggage is put on board and the car taken care of.'

Leaving the noise and bustle of the main concourse, they went through to a private lounge, the door of which was guarded by a member of the uniformed security staff.

Squaring his shoulders, the man said respectfully, 'Good morning, Mr Gallagher.'

'Morning...Peters, isn't it?'

'That's right, sir.' He looked gratified, as if remembering his name was a compliment. Then, opening the door, 'Hope you have a good flight, sir, madam.'

'Thanks,' Gray said easily.

Her conviction that Gray Gallagher must be high up in

the company reinforced, she allowed herself to be escorted into an opulent lounge, obviously set apart for VIPs.

A female member of the airport staff, smartly dressed and not a blonde hair out of place, was waiting to welcome them.

'Everything's nicely on schedule, Mr Gallagher. You'll be able to go on board shortly.' Including Rebecca in her smile, she added, 'It should be a nice, smooth flight.'

Having been shown to a blue suede settee, they were served with excellent coffee and petits fours.

Accepting the coffee, Rebecca shook her head at the array of small fancy cakes and biscuits.

'I take it you haven't eaten yet?' Gray queried.

'No. I didn't want anything earlier.'

'You must be starving. If you'd prefer, I'll ask for something plainer. A sandwich perhaps?'

Touched by his concern, she said, 'No, thank you. I'm fine.' Oddly enough, she still wasn't feeling at all hungry.

'Well, if you prefer to wait, we'll have an early lunch on the plane.'

Through the smoked-glass panels of the outer wall she could see a sleek executive jet drawn up quite close by. She thought how tiny it looked in comparison to the huge passenger jets that were coming and going in the distance.

They had just finished their second cup of coffee when the blonde returned to tell them they could board as soon as they were ready.

A hand at her waist, Rebecca found herself escorted across the tarmac and up the steps to the plane, where a steward was waiting to greet them and take their coats. Once they were safely on board, the steps were wheeled away, and the door was closed and locked into place.

As soon as they were seated in the small cabin and their belts fastened, the jet began to taxi to the head of the runway, where, Gray told her, the pilot would go through the last-minute safety checks while he waited for clearance.

'We're off,' he said with satisfaction, when after a few minutes they began to move.

It wasn't until they had started to accelerate that Rebecca lost colour and began to tremble.

Perhaps it was a backlash from her previous, unnatural calm, combined with a lack of food, that conspired to produce a feeling of nausea, followed by a rising panic that threatened to overwhelm her.

She was sitting absolutely still, staring straight ahead, when Gray took her icy cold hand in a warm, comforting clasp.

'It's all right,' he assured her. 'I've taken off and landed countless times and lived to tell the tale. Our pilot, Captain John Connelly, is very experienced. He was flying jumbo jets for one of the top airlines before joining Finance International…'

Holding her hand, he kept talking quietly, reassuring, until they were safely airborne and had levelled out.

'All right now?' he queried.

'Yes… Thank you… I—I'm sorry…'

'There's absolutely no need to be. Feel up to making a move?'

'Yes, of course.'

'Then let me show you around before we eat.'

He lifted her hand and touched his lips to the delicate blue-veined skin on the inside of her wrist, before releasing it.

Her heart gave a queer lurch, and she felt suddenly breathless. Telling herself that it was all part of her previous panic, she unbuckled her seat belt and rose to her feet.

A hand at her waist, he escorted her into an attractive lounge. It was furnished with a bookcase, a businesslike desk and swivel chair, a console incorporating a TV and a music centre, a soft leather couch, two matching armchairs and a coffee-table.

There was a Persian carpet on the floor, and on one

bulkhead a fine modern painting she recognised as a Jonathan Cass.

Putting the laptop on the desk, and following the direction of her gaze, Gray asked, 'Do you like modern art?'

'Some,' she answered cautiously.

'What do you think of Cass?'

'I thought his last exhibition was wonderful. He can get so much *feeling* into his work.'

'Do you have a favourite?'

'*Images.*'

Nodding, as if he was satisfied with her answer, Gray led the way through to the rear of the plane, where there was a shower-room and toilet, and a small, but sumptuous, bedroom.

She had never been inside a privately owned jet before and was staggered by the quiet luxury that surrounded her.

Returning to the lounge, he settled her on the couch and took a seat beside her.

Almost at once there was a discreet knock, and a white-coated steward appeared, and queried, 'Would you care for a pre-lunch drink, sir, madam?'

Turning to Rebecca, Gray raised an enquiring brow.

Repressing a shudder, she shook her head. 'I don't think so, thank you.'

'Just lunch, please, Malcolm.'

'No wine, sir?'

'No wine.'

The steward, small and wiry, with thinning grey hair, returned promptly wheeling a luncheon trolley set with silver cutlery and delicate china.

Having positioned it by the port windows, he drew up a couple of dining chairs.

'We'll serve ourselves,' Gray told him. 'I'll ring when we're ready for coffee.'

'Chef asked me to mention he's made blackcurrant cheesecake, not too sweet, just as you like it.'

'Perhaps you'll thank him, and bring some in with the coffee?'

'Certainly, sir.'

When he had pulled out Rebecca's chair, still standing, Gray lifted the silver lids from the various dishes and told her, 'There are savoury pancakes, asparagus tips, stuffed baby aubergine, baked artichoke hearts and herb dumplings. What would you like?'

Still feeling hollow and queasy, rather than hungry, she began, 'I'm not sure if I—'

'You must eat something,' he broke in firmly. 'You're much too thin as it is…'

When she began to shake her head, he pointed out, 'I've seen you without any clothes, remember, so don't try to tell that's not the case.'

As he watched her blush furiously, he reflected that it was refreshing to find a woman who could still blush. These days a lot of women were far too worldly to be embarrassed by the thought of a strange man seeing them naked.

Finding it a sweet amusement to tease her, he added, 'Though for the sake of *your* ego, I should mention that no man in his right senses would have been disappointed.'

Amber eyes sparkling with anger, she retorted smartly, 'How very kind of you tell me.'

So in spite of the battering she'd taken recently she still had spirit, he decided admiringly.

'Though it really wasn't necessary,' she went on, '*my* ego's fine.' And thought, *if only that were true.*

'I must say I'm glad to hear it,' he said smoothly. Then with genuine regret, 'Sorry if I sounded patronising. It wasn't intentional.'

Stony-faced, she muttered, 'I bet.'

'Truly.'

She found it hard to believe that this man would do or say anything that wasn't intentional. He had too much *awareness*, too much self-control.

Looking at her from beneath absurdly long lashes, he coaxed, 'Pax?'

Suddenly finding him extremely likeable, she smiled and answered, 'Pax.'

Rocked by the radiance of that smile, and wondering how he could ever have thought her less than beautiful, he stooped and touched his lips to hers.

Taken completely by surprise, the shock of that lightest of kisses sent her heart racing and stopped her breath. After a moment she asked huskily, 'What did you do that for?'

His face innocent, as if he had no idea of the havoc that brief meeting of mouths had caused, he said, 'It seemed appropriate. Surely pax is the kiss of peace?'

Then prosaically, 'Now, suppose I give you a pancake and some asparagus? You should enjoy them both. Henri is an excellent chef.'

After she had forced down the first mouthful or two, her empty stomach settled and she began to eat with an appetite.

'That's more like it,' Gray approved, and helped her to another pancake before tucking into his own.

She hadn't expected to eat it all, but somehow she did, and even managed a piece of cheesecake.

When the steward tapped and came in to wheel away the lunch trolley, they moved to the couch to drink their second cup of coffee.

'How do you feel now you've eaten?' Gray queried.

'Much better, thank you.'

'You've got a bit more colour. It's my guess that for a long time now you haven't been either eating or sleeping properly. Jason has a lot to answer for.'

Rebecca shook her head. 'It's not fair to blame Jason. It isn't his fault.'

'Then who would you blame?'

'Nobody, really.'

'Not even Lisa?'

'She couldn't have taken him if he hadn't wanted to go,' Rebecca said evenly.

'How very philosophical.'

'Nor could she have made him marry her if he hadn't wanted to.'

'That's not necessarily true. Believe me, there are ways and means. Though at his age, Jason should have known better than to fall for any of them.'

His voice exasperated, Gray added, 'He can be a complete and utter fool at times.'

'I suppose he couldn't help the way he felt about Lisa, any more than he could help the way I felt about him.'

'Are you trying to tell me that as far as you were concerned he didn't make the first move? That *you* made all the running?'

'No, of course not, but—'

'So *he* did?'

'Well, yes…'

'Which means he wanted you?'

'I thought he did,' she said hesitantly.

'I'm *sure* he did. At least physically. But from what you've told me, he wasn't getting very far.

'Whereas most women would have been only too happy to move in with him, he'd been unable to persuade you to. Which must have aggravated him enormously.'

When she remained silent, Gray went on, 'Despite his charm, Jason can be surprisingly ruthless. He'll go to almost any lengths to get what he wants, as was made evident by his previous engagements.'

'I don't understand.'

Patiently, he explained, 'Apart from the two he admitted to, I happen to know that if some bit of fluff he particularly lusted after was holding out on him, he'd produce an engagement ring.

'Then when he got tired of her, or someone new came

along, he'd tell ''his fiancée'' regretfully that it had been a mistake.

'If she showed any signs of playing up, he'd offer to let her keep the ring. When it comes to the crunch, most women will settle for what they can get,' Gray added cynically.

Angrily, she asked, 'Are you saying that Jason regarded me as just another bit of fluff?'

'You don't believe he did?'

'No, I don't!' She didn't *want* to believe it. She *wouldn't* believe it.

'Well, whether you believe it or not, Jason's behaviour leaves a lot to be desired. He's obviously caused you a lot of heartache and brought you down.'

'Jason isn't to blame,' she said again. 'My father's sudden death had come as a shock, and I was feeling very low when we met.

'That's what made meeting him so special and wonder-ful—' She stopped speaking abruptly.

Gray's mouth tightened, but all he said was, 'You must have missed your father a good deal.'

'I loved him dearly, and he was the only person who had ever really cared about me,' she said simply.

'He couldn't have been all that old; what did he die of?'

'A series of heart attacks.' Her voice shook a little. 'He was only forty-nine. But things hadn't been going well for some time. He'd had a great deal of stress. A lot of financial problems to cope with.

'The company's profits had been falling steadily over a number of years. Then when one big deal went disastrously wrong, Bowman Ferris lost a huge amount of money.

'In order to survive, Dad was forced to mortgage Elmslee. From then on things went from bad to worse. He did his best to hide it, but I knew he was having a desperate strug-gle.'

'So that's why you refused an allowance?'

'I didn't want an allowance.'

'Which I suppose, in the circumstances, was just as well,' Gray commented, frowning.

Suspecting a hint of censure, she hurried to her father's defence. 'Elmslee has never been cheap to maintain, Lisa was at an expensive boarding-school, and Helen too used to a life of luxury to cut down on her spending—'

'While you went out to work.'

'I *wanted* to,' she insisted. 'If we'd still been well off, I would have done the same…'

Gray said nothing, but she could sense his anger.

'None of it was my father's fault. He did his very best. Though Bowman Ferris was on the verge of bankruptcy when Dad died and Finance International took over, he'd made a deal to ensure there was enough money to continue to pay the mortgage on Elmslee, and also to provide Helen with a modest personal allowance.'

'A bit hand-to-mouth when someone's used to spending freely,' Gray commented. 'Which is no doubt why she decided to sell the manor.'

'Dad did his utmost to protect his family and Elmslee,' Rebecca said again.

'But while Helen would presumably take care of Lisa, he'd made no provision for you.'

'You knew how things were?'

'Yes, I knew.'

*Being one of Finance International's top executives, of course he would know.*

Her voice hoarse, she said, 'And that was why you suspected me of trying to marry Jason for his money!'

He made no attempt to refute the charge. 'I must admit that I did at first, but it—'

'I hate you!' she burst out.

Taking her hand, which was clenched into a tight fist, he said with infuriating calmness, 'There's no reason to get upset.'

'I think there's every reason.'

She tried to pull her hand free, but, refusing to release it, he began to straighten her fingers one at a time, kissing each one as he did so. 'If you let me finish what I was saying...'

Knowing it was childish, but unable to prevent herself, she turned her head away.

'Are you listening?' he enquired silkily.

When she didn't answer he put the tip of her index finger in his mouth and sucked.

Shivers running up and down her spine, she croaked, 'I'm listening.'

'I was about to say that it didn't take me long to realise I was mistaken.' Then, gently, 'If you look at me, I might even apologise.'

Turning to look at him, she met his gaze and held it, even though she could feel her colour rising. 'Go ahead,' she invited, 'apologise.'

'I'm sorry.'

'You don't look a bit sorry.'

He laughed. *'Touché.'*

Then, his eyes fixed on her mouth in a way that made butterflies dance in her stomach, he asked, 'Now what would you like to do?'

'Do?' she echoed.

'For entertainment, I mean. There's a good selection of music, plenty of books, and a wide range of films.'

His eyes gleaming green as any cat's between dense lashes, he added hopefully, 'Or perhaps you'd like to join the—'

'No, I wouldn't!' she broke in sharply, remembering the luxurious bedroom, with its double bed and the coverlet turned down ready.

Face straight, eyes dancing with suppressed laughter, he asked, 'Sure?'

'Quite sure.'

He sighed. 'Oh, well, if you don't fancy the idea... But I thought you might find it interesting to join Captain

Connelly in the cockpit for a while. Enjoy a bird's-eye view of flying.'

'Oh…'

Stroking a fingertip down her hot cheek, he asked, 'Or did you think I meant something else?'

'No, of course not,' she denied hurriedly.

He clicked his tongue in reproof. 'How can you lie like that? You thought I meant the Mile-High Club.'

'That's what you *intended* me to think,' she burst out indignantly. 'And don't bother to deny it!'

'I promise I won't even try.'

'I wish you'd promise to stop teasing me!'

'I'm afraid I can't. I find it almost irresistible. You rise to the bait so nicely…

'By the way, if you want to change your mind…'

'About what?' she asked cautiously.

'Going into the cockpit…'

Knowing it might be the only chance she would ever get, she said, 'I would like to take a look.'

Captain John Connelly, a nice-looking, middle-aged man with iron-grey hair and bushy eyebrows, greeted their entrance with equanimity.

'Good to see you, Mr Gallagher.'

'Nice to see you, John.'

Leaning negligently against the cockpit door, he made the introduction. 'This is Miss Ferris, who has been working at our London branch.'

'Pleased to meet you, Miss Ferris.' Indicating the co-pilot's seat, he added, 'Take a pew.'

'Thank you.' Feeling a little strange, she eased herself into the seat, and looked through the cockpit window. All she could see ahead was clear, uninterrupted blue, while beneath them a few white cotton-wool clouds floated serenely.

'How's it going?' Gray asked.

Captain Connelly made an O with his thumb and index

finger. 'Flying conditions are excellent. We should be in Boston well on time. Would you like to take over for a while?'

So Gray was a pilot too, Rebecca thought. Then wondered why she was surprised. Already she felt sure that he was the kind of man who could do or be anything he chose.

'No, thanks, I've some work to catch up on,' he answered easily. 'But first I thought Miss Ferris might like some idea of how you fly a jet.'

'To be absolutely honest, this thing virtually flies itself...'

While Rebecca listened with unfeigned interest, Captain Connelly explained how the aircraft's controls worked and what the various instruments and gauges were for.

'Piloting a plane must be stimulating,' she remarked at length.

'Admittedly it's never dull, but like any other job it becomes routine after a time.'

When they had chatted for a while, in spite of finding it all fascinating, Rebecca was forced to smother a yawn.

Gray, who seemed to miss nothing, asked, 'About ready to make a move?'

'Yes.'

'Thanks, John,' he addressed the pilot. 'We'll leave you to it.'

Rising to her feet, Rebecca added her thanks to Gray's before following him from the cockpit.

'You look tired,' he remarked as they made their way aft.

'I am tired,' she admitted, feeling as though she could sleep for a week.

'Well, as you know there's a perfectly good bed, and it will be several hours yet before we land at Boston. In fact having a nap might not be a bad idea. It'll certainly help with the time difference.'

'Then I will, if you don't mind.'

'Not at all. When I've caught up on some work, I might even...' He paused.

When, remembering his remark about her rising to the bait, she studiously ignored his attempt to tease her, he went on, 'Take a short nap myself. But don't worry, the couch is quite comfortable.'

He gave her a come-hither look. 'Unless you should change your mind about joining a fairly exclusive club. If you do, just let me know.'

Smiling, she answered serenely, 'Thanks, but I won't change my mind.'

'You're learning.' He sounded regretful.

In the bedroom, finding the blinds were already pulled down over the windows to keep out the light, Rebecca stripped off to her undies, and, stretching out on the bed, pulled up the lightweight cover.

She barely had time to register that the bed and the pillows were the essence of comfort, before she was fast asleep.

Something touching her cheek made her stir. She put up a hand to brush it away, and, encountering another hand, opened her eyes.

Gray was standing by the bed, smiling down at her.

'Feeling better?'

Her sleep had been sweet and dreamless, and for the first time in weeks she felt completely refreshed.

'Much better, thank you.' Peering at her watch, she exclaimed, 'No wonder! I've slept for hours.'

'You must have needed to. Now, how about a nice cup of tea?'

On the bedside table was a tray set with fine china tea things and a plate of biscuits.

'Sounds wonderful.' Pushing herself into a sitting position, she dragged the coverlet up with her and trapped it under her arms.

Appearing amused by her modesty, he reached for the teapot. 'Milk and sugar?'

'Just milk, please.'

Noticing there were two cups and saucers, she asked, 'Are you joining me?'

'Are you inviting me to?'

'What if I say no?'

'Then I'll take mine in the lounge,' he answered cheerfully, and, filling two cups, handed her one.

'Thank you.'

He waited.

She held her breath while she counted to ten.

Picking up his own cup, he was about to turn away, when she asked demurely, 'Please won't you join me?'

His green eyes gleaming, he sat down on the edge of the bed and turned to face her.

Suddenly he was much too close for comfort. She could feel his muscular thigh pressing against her leg through the thin coverlet.

Heat rose in her body, and her heart began to race in the most disconcerting manner.

She was trying to ease her leg away a fraction without making it obvious, when he queried silkily, 'I'm not crowding you, I trust?'

Realising too late that she couldn't hope to win, and wishing she hadn't deliberately set out to tease him, she fought back, 'No, not at all.'

His ironic little salute acknowledged a worthy opponent, before he observed, 'We'll be landing at Logan Airport in about twenty minutes, so I'm afraid there's no time to continue our game.'

With a feeling of relief, she said, 'Then we'll call it a draw, shall we?'

'Not at all,' he disagreed, and, taking her hand, kissed the palm.

Her stomach plunged as though she'd stepped off a very high building.

'I've found it most entertaining,' he added, 'and I look forward to resuming later.'

She could only hope that either he didn't mean it, or when 'later' came he would have forgotten all about it.

Logan International Airport was only three miles from the centre of Boston, and, coming in to land in fine, sunny weather, they had an excellent view of the city built on the peninsula formed by the Charles river and Fort Point Channel.

'It looks fantastic,' Rebecca exclaimed.

'You've never been to Boston before?'

She shook her head.

'Do you know much about it?' he queried.

'Only what every schoolgirl remembers, that the seaport was founded by the Puritans in 1630 and outpaced its rivals to become the largest British settlement. Apart from that one bit of history, very little. I suppose you know it well?'

'Fairly well.'

'And you like it?'

'Yes, it's a fascinating mixture of colonial and cosmopolitan, history and high-tech.

'On one hand, up-to-the-minute expressways carry endless streams of traffic, while on the other, the narrow, cobblestoned streets of Beacon Hill have a picturesque, turn-of-the-last-century look and feel.'

'It sounds charming. I'd love to see it.'

'When we've checked into our hotel and got rid of the luggage, I'll be happy to show you around.'

Peering from the plane window, she asked, 'Whereabouts are we staying?'

'At the Faneuil, which is in downtown Boston,' Gray told her. Adding humorously, 'The streets there are a driver's nightmare. Rather than following the usual grid system, they appear to have been laid out by the colonial cattle…'

When their taxi drew up outside the Faneuil—a period hotel with a handsome façade—a short, dapper man with dark hair and glasses appeared.

'Mr Gallagher, how nice to have you back.'

'Thanks, Benson. Nice to be back.'

'If you'll come this way, sir, madam.'

A single snap of his fingers summoned a bellboy, smartly uniformed in red and gold, who collected their luggage and followed the little party at a respectful distance.

They took the lift up to the second floor, where, having crossed an inner lobby, the manager opened one of the doors with a flourish.

'As you requested, you have a suite of rooms overlooking the garden—a central sitting-room with a bedroom and bathroom either side…'

Correctly interpreting Rebecca's quick glance, Gray whispered in her ear, 'Don't worry, you can always keep yours locked at night.'

When he'd shown them round, murmuring, 'I hope your stay, short as it is, will be a pleasant one,' Benson bowed himself out.

After the bellboy had deposited their luggage, pocketed a handsome tip and departed, Gray turned to Rebecca and suggested, 'If you want to freshen up, I'll give you a knock in about ten minutes, shall I?'

She nodded. 'Please.'

He disappeared into his own bedroom, closing the communicating door quietly behind him.

Rebecca followed suit, and, glancing around at the understated but evident luxury, wondered uneasily how much all this was costing and who would be picking up the bill.

Finance International presumably. She only hoped Philip Lorne never got to hear about it.

She had just washed her face and hands and unpacked what she thought she might need for the night, when the knock came.

'How are you doing?' Gray's voice enquired.

She opened the door. 'All ready.'

'In that case, let's go.' He sounded so full of *joie de vivre* that she felt her spirits rise.

He had changed his short coat for a well-cut leather jacket and looked both elegant and sexy.

'There's a bistro just round the corner, so I suggest we have a bite to eat first.'

Suddenly finding she was hungry, she agreed, 'That sounds great.'

'Like French food?'

'Love it. Apart from snails and oysters, that is.'

'I can agree as far as snails go, and I admit to preferring my oysters smoked.'

La Renaissance looked fairly ordinary, with narrow, high-backed booths and an unpretentious decor. But Rebecca soon found that the food, though simple, was out of this world.

As, sitting side by side, they ate bowls of thick garbure blanche, he asked, 'So what would you like to see, apart from Beacon Hill?'

'Will we have time for anything else? I thought you had a business appointment?'

'It's a business dinner, to be precise, scheduled for eight o'clock at the Faneuil.' He stopped speaking as the waiter came to take away their bowls, and serve iced glasses of coupe martuxa.

The raspberry sundaes were delicious, and Rebecca had almost finished hers, when she noticed that Gray's eyes were fixed on her mouth in a way that made her toes curl.

His intention was clear, but before she could do anything to deflect it, he leaned towards her and licked the corner of her mouth.

Though it was over in a split-second, the erotic little gesture transfixed her. It was as openly sexy as if he'd reached across and unbuttoned her blouse.

As she sat quite still, her spoon poised in mid-air, he explained, 'A tiny flake of raspberry.'

Then, as though nothing untoward had happened, he ordered coffee and calmly turned the conversation back to sightseeing.

'When we've had a look at Beacon Hill, if you're up to walking four kilometres, we could follow the Freedom Trail.'

Still struggling to regain her equilibrium, she asked huskily, 'The Freedom Trail?'

'It's marked by a red line that runs along the city's sidewalks and links sixteen important sites in the history of Boston and America. One of the best known is Paul Revere's house, the oldest in the city. There's also a statue—the Ride of Paul Revere.'

'Of course! We were taught about his famous midnight ride to warn his fellow revolutionaries of the approach of British troops from Boston.'

He smiled at her, a slow smile that started in his eyes before it reached his lips. 'There you are, that's another piece of history you remember.'

Gray, she soon discovered, was an interesting and stimulating companion, and the afternoon proved to be most pleasurable. She loved the old-world charm and atmosphere of Beacon Hill, and the narrow, cobblestoned streets, gas-lit at night, that ran down to the river.

When they had stopped for a rest and a pot of tea in a very English-looking tearoom, they joined the Freedom Trail at Boston Common.

From there they walked to the harbour, where they went on board the frigate *U.S.S. Constitution*, known affectionately as 'Old Ironsides', after British cannon-balls bounced off her heavily planked sides.

When they reached the Bunker Hill Monument, which was the end of the trail, seeing she was getting weary, Gray suggested a taxi back.

It had turned seven when they reached the hotel, and Rebecca, who was starting to think longingly of bed, thanked her lucky stars that she had had such a good sleep on the plane.

They had just reached their suite when, watching her stifle a yawn, Gray asked, 'Tired?'

'I won't be sorry when it's bedtime,' she admitted.

'Well, we shouldn't be too late. Our man's a stickler for punctuality, so with a bit of luck dinner will be over by nine-thirty.'

He sounded as if he was expecting her to join him.

Carefully, she said, 'As you have an appointment, I'd be quite happy to skip dinner and go straight to bed now.'

Gray shook his head decidedly. 'I'd like you to be there too.'

'But surely if it's business...'

'The man I'm meeting prefers his business dealings to take place in a social atmosphere. And as he gets on better with women than with men—most men hate his guts, but women seem to go for his kind of macho charm—he invariably brings a female companion along and expects his opposite number to do the same.'

She recalled one of Jason's business contacts who had worked in much the same way.

'If you hadn't been here I would have had to go to an agency and hire a dinner companion. Which is far from ideal when business is being discussed and things may get heated.'

'You seem to be expecting problems.'

'I am,' Gray admitted ruefully. 'Considering everything, our last meeting went very smoothly. This one, however, promises to be a rough ride.

'Though he's one of the richest men in America he hates to lose money. Over the past six months he's lost quite a lot, and stands to lose more, but somehow I have to convince him that the only way to go is forward.

'If he decides to pull out of the project at this stage, and we can't meet the shortfall, the whole thing will come tumbling round our ears. It'll cost PLFI hundreds of millions of dollars.'

'It won't…?'

'No, it won't bring the company down, but it will be quite a serious blow, and affect several other big investment schemes.'

She was just about to ask him what the project was, when, glancing at his watch, he said, 'We'd better get moving. Can you be ready by a quarter to eight?'

'Yes, of course.'

He grinned. 'Then I'd better go get my spurs buckled on.'

# CHAPTER FIVE

SHOWERED and made-up with care, her ash-brown hair swirled into a sleek chignon, Rebecca put on a pair of strappy sandals and a simple, sleeveless sheath, as yet unworn.

Cut with an uneven hemline, its silk chiffon was a swirl of subtle colours over a plain underslip with a built-in bra. Thin slivers of each colour made up the spaghetti shoulder straps.

It was a romantic dress, bought especially for a gala concert Jason had been going to take her to.

She waited for the thought to hurt, but somehow it didn't. Perhaps she had suffered so much pain that she'd grown too numb to feel?

A last quick check in the long mirror, and she was ready with five minutes to spare. Even so, Gray was already in the lounge, sitting at the small desk, his laptop open in front of him.

Glancing up at her approach, he switched off the computer and rose to greet her. His gaze swept over her from head to toe, taking in the glossy hair, the pretty dress and the long, slender legs.

'Will I do?' she asked a shade nervously.

'You look absolutely delightful.' He came over and took her hand.

At five feet eight inches she was tall for a woman, but even though she was wearing high heels Gray was a good six inches taller.

Wearing an evening jacket and a black bow tie, he looked so powerfully attractive that she found herself absurdly breathless.

'It's a great pity we're not free to go out and paint the town,' he said with a rueful smile. 'If this meeting wasn't so important…'

Feeling an odd little flutter, she withdrew her hand and said quickly, 'But it is.'

He sighed. 'I'm afraid so. Right, let's go.'

The hotel restaurant was fairly busy and there was a buzz of talk and laughter as the *maître d'* showed them to one of the more secluded tables.

As soon as they were seated a wine waiter appeared with an ice bucket containing a bottle of vintage champagne, and four long-stemmed glasses.

'Would you like me to open it now, sir?'

'No, thanks, leave it until our guests arrive.'

'Very good, sir.'

A few moments later, glancing up, Gray said softly, 'There they are.'

In the entrance was a tall, heavily built man with grizzled hair that, brushed straight back from his forehead, lay close to his head in tight waves.

By his side was a voluptuous blonde, perhaps half his age. She was wearing a glittering blue dress that left very little to the imagination.

'Just as I expected,' Gray murmured softly. 'A real Barbie doll.'

Rebecca scarcely heard. Her startled gaze was fixed on the man, rather than his companion. But surely it couldn't be…? Though hadn't Jason mentioned that Andrew Scrivener lived in Boston?

As the *maître d'* led them over, her worst fears were confirmed. Though it was a while since she had seen him, there was no mistaking that powerful face with its large, hooked nose and sensual mouth, those obsidian eyes set deep beneath almost black brows.

Gray rose to his feet to greet them, and the two men

shook hands with a show of civility rather than any great cordiality.

To Rebecca's relief, Gray introduced her simply as Miss Ferris, without naming any connection with Finance International.

Hoping for the best, she held her breath.

Andrew Scrivener acknowledged her courteously, but, though his hooded eyes lingered on her face for longer than was necessary, he made no mention of them having met before.

For which she was truly thankful.

When the introductions had been completed, Gray suggested, 'Perhaps you'd like to eat first and discuss business later?'

'Fine by me,' Scrivener agreed.

Gray signalled the waiter and, apart from Rebecca, who asked for mineral water, they drank champagne while they looked at the menu and gave their order.

That done, while the blonde, whose name was Marianne Midler, stared around her, Gray chose a safe topic of conversation and made a determined effort to break the ice.

He was getting very little response from Scrivener, when, remembering something she had learnt from Jason, Rebecca mentioned the arts.

'I understand that Symphony Hall houses both the Boston Symphony and the Boston Pops Orchestras?'

His heavy face suddenly becoming animated, Scrivener asked, 'Indeed it does. You like music, Miss Ferris?'

'Yes, very much.'

'Have you ever been to Symphony Hall?'

'No, I haven't. This is my first trip to Boston.'

'How long are you here for?'

'Just one night.'

'Pity.'

With a glance at Gray, he asked, 'I can't persuade you to stay on?'

'I'm afraid not. We're due to fly out to California tomorrow afternoon.'

'I'm heading that way myself in a week or so to see how my new house is progressing. Then I'll be visiting my younger sister in San Francisco. She's just given birth to her second child, so we've cause to celebrate.'

The blonde shuddered. 'I'd *hate* to be pregnant.'

Scrivener gave her a cold look.

'I just bet you feel the same.' She appealed to Rebecca for help.

'I'm afraid not,' Rebecca said evenly. 'If I ever get married I'd like a family.'

'But think what having a baby does to your figure!'

'It's just as well all women aren't like you,' Scrivener observed, frowning.

Putting a hand on his sleeve, the nails painted a shimmering blue to match her dress, she protested, 'But Andy, darling—'

'Stow it, Marianne,' he said curtly.

As, pouting prettily, she withdrew her hand he turned his attention back to Gray. 'It's a business trip, I take it?'

'Partly. Finance International have acquired the Santa Rosa vineyard in the Napa Valley, so I'm going to take a look at the prospects.'

'Ought to be good. We're practically neighbours. A few years back I bought Hillsden Wineries and put in an experienced manager.

'Though Collins is only young he certainly knows his stuff, and since then it's been going from strength to strength. Choose the right manager, and yours should do the same.'

Turning to Rebecca and sounding almost jovial, Scrivener said, 'Well, if you can't stay right now, you must certainly come to Boston again. During the summer there are open-air concerts down by the river.

'Marianne likes music…don't you, babe?'

Basking in the renewed warmth of his attention, the blonde changed her pout to a smile, and from then on the atmosphere became more relaxed and the conversation flowed easily.

Andrew Scrivener, as Rebecca recalled, had a certain charm when he chose to use it, and during an excellent meal he showed a side of himself that could only be described as charismatic.

Coffee and liqueurs had been served and drunk before business was mentioned. Then the atmosphere abruptly changed for the worse as the two men embarked on a low-toned discussion that, on Scrivener's part at least, sounded distinctly irate.

Apparently bored by business matters, Marianne claimed Rebecca's attention and launched into a monologue on her last cosmetic surgery, and what she was planning to 'improve' next. 'I thought I might have my bottom lip made fuller...'

While Rebecca did her best to look like an interested listener, more than half her attention was focused on what the men were saying.

But with Marianne's strident voice tending to drown out the other conversation, all she could pick out were odd, disjointed phrases.

It seemed to be a battle royal. But while Gray stayed cool and firm, but restrained, Scrivener got even more heated and hostile.

After a while it became obvious that Gray was fighting a losing battle, as the other man refused to listen to him.

'You're wasting your time, Gallagher. I'm pulling out as of now.'

When Marianne paused for breath, Rebecca heard him add angrily, 'I was a fool to get involved in the first place. If I'd played my hunch and taken notice of Miss Ferris instead of young Beaumont...'

She froze. So he *did* remember her!

Gray looked up sharply. 'I wasn't aware that you and Miss Ferris had met.'

'Beaumont brought her along to that first meeting in London and introduced her as his PA. If I remember rightly, you were in the Middle East at the time; that's why he was standing in for you.

'He's a bit of a lightweight, and still wet behind the ears in some ways. It's a pity I ever agreed to meet him. His review of the situation wasn't sound.'

Coolly, Gray suggested, 'Perhaps you'd like to tell me exactly what was said?'

'He said that the then current backers of the Archangel Project had gone broke and it was a good chance to get in on the ground floor.

'I pointed out that the complex had so far failed dismally to attract customers.

'He argued that, though it had got off to a bad start, it was still a sound financial bet, and being able to buy into it at such a late stage was an opportunity not to be missed.

'I ought to have waited and talked to you,' he added in disgust.

'If you had, I would have told you exactly the same. When the whole project is really up and running it will be worth billions.'

'In my opinion it'll never be up and running. It's just one big white elephant. When you think about it, who the hell would want to holiday in a series of huge plastic domes in the middle of a desert?'

'With the facilities they'll offer when completed, my guess would be quite a lot of people.'

Scrivener shook his head. 'Wishful thinking. My gut says the whole complex will probably just sit there and rot.

'When I'm doing business, I tend to follow my hunches. At that meeting in London, though I had a hunch Miss Ferris was right, I didn't follow it.'

Gray frowned. 'I don't quite see how Miss Ferris comes into this.'

'I asked her what she honestly thought of the Archangel Project.

'When, obviously unwilling to follow Beaumont's lead, she tried to sidestep the question, I asked if she would invest any of her own money in the project.

'She said no, she couldn't help but feel it was too big a risk.

'I've always been impressed by a woman's ability to use her intuition, especially when that intuition goes hand in hand with a sound grasp of business and a good brain. I believe Miss Ferris has both. I also admire her integrity.'

Turning to Rebecca, he went on, 'My hunch told me you were right, and I should have listened.'

She took a deep breath, and said firmly, 'I'm extremely glad you didn't, Mr Scrivener, because now I'm convinced I made a mistake.'

His black eyes boring into her, he sneered, 'So this time, instead of being totally honest, you're saying what Gallagher's instructed you to say.'

'I'm doing nothing of the kind. Mr Gallagher never instructed me to say anything. I didn't even know who he was meeting until you came into the restaurant.'

Scrivener shook his head. 'Miss Ferris, I'm disappointed in you. Presumably you've moved up the ladder and are now Gallagher's PA, so—'

'But I'm not. I no longer work for PLFI.' Lifting her chin, she added, 'And if I did, I still wouldn't be prepared to say anything I didn't believe.'

Watching him weigh up her words, she added, 'When I said I personally wouldn't put money into the Archangel Project, it was because at that point I thought it had been built in the wrong place at the wrong time.

'Since then I've revised that opinion. After all, Las Vegas

started out in the middle of a desert. And on that showing, Archangel could be the holiday place of the future.'

'*Could* be?'

'I was being cautious. I'm sure it *will* be.'

'So are you saying I should go on?' His harsh voice held a challenge.

'It's not my place to say any such thing, but I certainly believe it's the best option by far.

'For one thing, if you pull out now you must stand to lose everything you've already put into it, which would be a terrible waste.'

'If I go on, I could lose a whole lot more.'

'You *could*,' Gray took up the baton, 'but the last report I saw made me believe that most of the teething troubles are over and that things are starting to run more smoothly.

'I'm not suggesting that there won't be some ups and downs, and maybe it won't start to make money for a year or two yet, but all the signs are there that when it does take off, it'll take off big.'

'And you agree?' Scrivener asked Rebecca.

'I'm convinced it will become a millionaire's playground.' She smiled at him mischievously. 'You may even want to holiday there yourself.'

For a moment he appeared amused by her audacity, then, his eyes glittering like a snake's, he asked, 'If you're no longer working for PLFI, what are you doing here in Boston with Gallagher?'

Ambushed by the question, and aware that if she looked at Gray for guidance Andrew Scrivener would think the worst, she hesitated. Then after a moment, seeing nothing else for it, she answered with as much sang-froid as she could muster, 'As it happens I'm with Mr Gallagher for purely personal reasons.'

Those hooded eyes pinned her. 'Personal reasons?'

'Miss Ferris is taking a holiday in California as my guest,' Gray told him levelly.

'I see…' Scrivener's sensual lips twisted. 'Well, I must say I envy you, having such a charming and *loyal* companion.'

Before Gray could make any answer, Rebecca said crisply, 'If you think my loyalty stretches to lying, then you're quite wrong.'

Sounding unimpressed, Scrivener remarked, 'I believe that most women would lie for a man they're in love with.'

'You may be right, but—'

'Are you trying to tell me you're different?'

'No. I'm trying to tell you that it isn't what you seem to imagine. The relationship between myself and Mr Gallagher is quite platonic. I'm certainly *not* in love with him.'

His powerful head tilted a little to one side, he surveyed her. 'You have the look of a woman in love.'

When, suddenly rattled, she failed to deny it, he said, 'Is it because of young Beaumont?'

'How did you know?'

'I remember the way you looked at him. I must admit I quite envied him. So perhaps you're toeing the company line to keep *him* in a job?'

'Did I toe it last time?'

'No, and, judging by the look on his face, he wasn't at all pleased.'

'No, he wasn't.'

In fact Jason had been furious with her for speaking her mind, and later they had had their one and only row.

'Why the devil didn't you back me up,' he had demanded angrily, 'instead of nearly scuppering the whole deal? You must surely have realised that PLFI couldn't afford to go it alone, that we need Scrivener's cooperation.'

'I'm sorry Mr Scrivener asked for my opinion. I wish he hadn't. But I wasn't prepared to lie to him and tell him I thought the Archangel was a good bet when I don't believe it is.

'The last lot of investors to pull out were the third, and

most of them have ended up bankrupt. That project just swallows money, and so many things have gone wrong that it seems to me to be jinxed.'

'Well, it's a damned good job he listened to me and not to you, or I'd have had Uncle Pip down on me like a ton of bricks.'

After a few days he had ostensibly forgiven her, but he never again suggested she accompany him to any business meetings.

'But presumably he forgave you?' Scrivener's voice broke into her thoughts.

'Yes, of course,' she answered evenly.

'Who could do anything else?' he remarked with ponderous gallantry. Then pointedly, 'So if all's well, why are you going on holiday with Gallagher, rather than Beaumont?'

Wanting to say, *mind your own business*, but unwilling to lose any advantage they might have gained, she told him flatly, 'Because yesterday Jason married my sister, and today they're off on their honeymoon. That's the reason I felt forced to leave Finance International.'

Hearing the catch in her voice, Gray jumped in. 'We were sorry to lose Miss Ferris, who, as you remarked earlier, has both a sound grasp of business and a good brain. I felt that at the very least the company owed her a holiday.'

'I see.'

From his expression it was impossible to tell whether or not he believed what he had been told.

Glancing at Marianne, who hadn't said a word while the little drama was being played out, Scrivener stood up. 'Well, it's time we were going. Thanks for the meal, Gallagher.'

Gray rose to his feet and, having pulled out the blonde's chair, wished her a pleasant, 'Goodnight, Miss Midler.'

As the two men shook hands, Scrivener said, 'I'll let you know my final decision some time tomorrow.'

'We'll be starting for California mid-afternoon.'

'I'll catch you on your mobile. I have the number.' Then to Rebecca, 'It was nice meeting you again, Miss Ferris. I hope you have an enjoyable holiday.'

'Thank you.'

Watching the two walk away, she felt suddenly cold and wrung out, on the point of exhaustion.

Resuming his seat, Gray said exultantly, 'You were absolutely wonderful, and the company is very much in your debt.'

Rebecca felt a glow of returning warmth at his unstinting praise. She had wondered a little uneasily if he might have been annoyed by her involvement.

Watching her cheeks take on a tinge of colour, he queried, 'I presume Jason has been keeping tabs on the Archangel Project?'

'Not as far as I know. I just happened to see a well-informed article by James Berringer, the *Globe*'s financial correspondent.

'He presented the facts, then went on to look ahead and compare Archangel with other futuristic projects that in the end proved wildly successful. After a lot of thought, I revised my earlier opinion.'

'Thank the lord you did. If I *had* primed you, I think Scrivener would have known. But as it was, you came over as totally convinced and convincing, the only combination that could have tipped the scales in our favour.'

He leaned forward and, taking her face between his palms, kissed her on the mouth.

A jubilant kiss that held both relief and satisfaction; an ardent kiss that had her trembling and confused.

For the briefest of kisses in a public place it sent out shockwaves that rocked her very being, and triggered a sudden and overwhelming hunger.

She knew without a shadow of doubt that not even Jason's kisses had affected her so powerfully. If they had, she would never have found the strength to hold out against him.

Drawing back, Gray went on, 'Scrivener came absolutely determined to withdraw from the project, and you managed to achieve what I would have found impossible had I been on my own.'

Noticing that his voice had roughened somewhat and his face looked taut, as though the skin had been stretched too tightly over the bones, she said breathlessly, 'He may still withdraw.'

'I very much doubt it. I know him well enough to be sure that if he'd still been determined to pull out, he would have said so at once.'

Then, as though making an effort to return to normal, 'Now, shall we relax for a little while? You didn't have a brandy earlier, and you've more than earned one.'

She shook her head. 'I don't really care for brandy. But I would like some more coffee.'

'Sure it won't keep you awake?'

'I doubt if anything could do that.'

'Yes, you must be shattered. I'm afraid we're somewhat later than I'd expected. It'll be the early hours of the morning in London.'

'Well, at least I had some sleep on the plane.'

'Even so, you look about all in.'

They were making polite conversation like two strangers, while beneath the surface a silent and much deeper communication was going on, telling of need and hunger, of excitement and anticipation.

Reaching across the table, he took hold of her wrist. Her pulse beneath the light pressure of his thumb was rapid and uneven, and as she looked up he saw that her golden eyes appeared slightly dazed, their pupils large and dark.

Moving his thumb to stroke her palm, he suggested, 'It might make more sense to go straight up to our suite and have coffee served there.'

When she made no objection he rose to pull out her chair, and a hand at her waist escorted her out of the restaurant.

She was acutely conscious of his height, the length of his stride, the sexual tension between them.

The lift had just gone up to the top floor, and by tacit consent they used the stairs. They climbed in silence, without looking at one another, but from time to time her elbow touched his, or their thighs brushed lightly.

Outwardly they must have looked like any ordinary couple, but she was so aware of him that she found it difficult to breathe, and her heart was beating in great heavy thuds, so that she felt sure he must be able to hear it pounding.

When they reached their suite he opened the door with no sign of haste, and, having followed her inside, set his back to the panels.

He hadn't bothered to switch on the light, and in the glow of the city's not-quite-darkness she turned towards him.

Without a single word being spoken, he took her in his arms and began to kiss her as no one had ever kissed her before, or ever would again.

Kisses that went on and on, blowing her mind, sweeping her away, promising her the kind of delight she had always longed for and never yet experienced.

But, though his kisses were hungry and passionate, apparently holding himself in check, he made no move to take things further.

Knowing he was as aroused as she was, and bewildered by his restraint, her whole body crying out for more, she pressed herself against him.

As though he had been waiting for a signal, he ran a single finger up and down her spine. The caress was unexpected and thrilling, and she quivered like a violin being played.

Then while one hand cradled the back of her head, the other began to move over her, following the slender curve of waist and hip and buttock. At the same time his mouth left hers to stray down to the warm hollow at the base of her throat, where his tongue-tip proceeded to cause havoc.

She gave a little murmur of pleasure, convinced that there could be nothing more erotic—until he touched her breast, cupping the soft weight and brushing his thumb over the nipple, which instantly grew firm.

By the time he slid the straps of her dress off her shoulders to expose her small, beautifully shaped breasts, she was prey to the kind of sexual excitement she hadn't known existed.

When he bent his head and put his mouth to her breast the needle-sharp sensations his suckling caused were so exquisite that, unable at that moment to stand any more, she gave a little incoherent exclamation and made to push him away.

Straightening up at once, he adjusted the bodice of her dress with care, and eased the straps back into place, before saying coolly, 'I'm sorry if I'm not coming up to Jason's standard...'

Feeling like someone who had been enjoying a thrilling roller-coaster ride and was suddenly thrown off to land half-stunned and dazed, she just stared at him.

'I'd better say goodnight and let you get some sleep,' he added. 'We've a longish journey ahead of us tomorrow.'

He turned on his heel in the semi-darkness and walked away. A moment later his bedroom door closed quietly behind him.

It was clear that he had completely misunderstood her instinctive withdrawal. Shocked by the swift and totally unexpected ending to his lovemaking, she began to tremble violently.

He had talked about not coming up to Jason's standard, but he had far outstripped it.

Jason, always very self-orientated, wasn't in the same class for sensitivity and skill. Because he was always focused entirely on his own needs rather than on his partner's, interested only in reaching his objective rather than in the journey there, his lovemaking had been both cursory and clumsy.

It seemed dreadfully disloyal to even think such a thing, but it didn't make it any less true, and she found herself marvelling that she had never realised it before.

After a few kisses, if Jason decided he wasn't getting anywhere, regarding it as a waste of time, he would give up and sulk.

Whereas Gray had set out to give her pleasure, and had succeeded beyond her wildest dreams.

Her body still quivering with unappeased desire, her legs unsteady, her mind in a turmoil, she went through to her room and, switching on the light, sank down on the bed.

Where earlier in the evening she had felt dog-tired and only too eager to get some sleep, now she was wide awake and restless, frustration gnawing at her.

Perhaps a shower would help her to relax?

In desperation she seized on the stray thought, and, having stripped off her clothes, went through to the bathroom and cleaned her teeth before stepping into the glass cubicle.

She stood beneath the flow of hot water until her skin tingled, but it made no difference to how she felt inside.

When she had dried herself, rubbing the fine skin with unnecessary vigour, she took the pins from her hair and, her movements jerky, picked up her brush.

While she brushed out the thick, silky mass she tried to tell herself that it was just as well things had ended as they had. There was no way *she* could have called a halt, and if Gray hadn't backed off when he did it would have been too late.

She ought to be grateful.

But she wasn't.

Still aching with frustration and misery, she longed to be in his arms, yearned to have him satisfy the hunger he had so effortlessly aroused.

Fool! she berated herself angrily. How could she be thinking that way? No matter how skilful his lovemaking, all he wanted was a holiday fling, and she had never gone in for casual flings or affairs. It just wasn't in her nature.

Though as far as *she* was concerned, this wouldn't have been just a casual fling, soon over and easily forgotten. Something deep inside, something she couldn't put a name to, responded to Gray in a way she had never responded to anyone else.

Until now, she had regarded sex and love as going hand in hand, with love the more important of the two. But perhaps because of her childhood she had been afraid of strong feelings, wary of falling in love, knowing that love made one vulnerable.

Only Jason had come anywhere near to breaking through her defences. But in the end she had even held back with him, a man she had loved.

So where did that leave her? Was she going to remain a virgin all her life? Die without ever becoming a wife and mother? Or at the very least without knowing what it was like to be made love to by a man she wanted.

And she *did* want Gray Gallagher.

Pulling on a white towelling robe that hung behind the door, she returned to the bedroom as tense as when she had left it.

Her cotton nightdress lay limply across the double bed like the heroine of some Victorian melodrama. But *she* was no Victorian heroine. Perhaps by today's standards she was old-fashioned, with outmoded principles, but she was still a modern woman, able to choose her own path through life.

Gray was the only man who had ever made her long to throw her bonnet over the windmill. But from now on, having mistaken her reaction for rejection, she felt oddly certain that he would make no further move.

If she did want him as a lover, it was up to her to go to him and tell him so.

Giving herself no more time to think, barefoot, her hair tumbled in loose curls around her shoulders, she padded across the semi-dark living-room to his door.

She had raised her hand to knock when she realised she couldn't possibly do it. He might look at her with cool surprise.

That would be all it would take to make her want to curl up and die. She had none of the confidence of the truly liberated woman. In sexual matters she might follow, but she could never lead. Never take the initiative.

She was turning away when the door opened with a suddenness that made her give a startled gasp.

Gray stood in the doorway, his back to the light, wearing a short, navy-blue silk dressing gown.

'Something wrong?' he queried levelly.

'N-no... Yes...'

'Which?'

'I—I'd like to talk to you.'

'I was just about to fetch my laptop and catch up on some work.'

Boldly, she said, 'I couldn't sleep either.'

'Frustration's hell,' he agreed. 'Or are you going to tell me you're not frustrated?'

'If I told you that it wouldn't be true.' She looked at him pleadingly.

'Sorry, but on the earlier showing I wouldn't make a good stand-in for Jason, and I should hate to be found wanting.'

Gritting her teeth, she said, 'I don't want you to be a stand-in for Jason.'

'So what do you want?'

It was clear that he was going to give her no help. Swallowing, she said, 'I just want to make it clear that when I pushed you away it was because I... I...'

When he simply waited, she finished desperately, 'It was absolutely nothing to do with Jason.'

'You just couldn't stand me.'

'If I couldn't stand you, would I be here now? Wouldn't I be in my own bed, breathing a sigh of relief that I'd managed to escape your clutches?'

Though she couldn't see his face clearly, she was aware that he had relaxed.

'Well, it's nice to know that my sex appeal isn't quite on a par with Count Dracula's.'

'There's nothing wrong with your sex appeal, it's...' She hesitated.

'Appealing?' he suggested, tongue-in-cheek.

Unwilling to be laughed at in such trying circumstances, she retorted, 'At any rate it's better than your comprehension. You totally misinterpreted my reaction.'

'It seemed pretty clear at the time. You didn't exactly clutch me to your bosom.'

Her face burning with heat, she said crossly, 'Have you never heard of sensual overload?'

'Are you trying to tell me it was sensual overload that caused your reaction?'

'I'm not *trying* to tell you. I *am* telling you.'

'I see. Does it happen often?'

'It's never happened to me before,' she said, and immediately regretted her honesty.

'Well, well, well...' he murmured derisively, 'and here I was, jealous of Jason.'

Hating his mockery, she burst out, 'If you think it was easy for me to come...' Then, suddenly close to tears, she stopped speaking abruptly and turned away.

He caught her wrist. 'Don't rush off.'

She tried to jerk free. 'I'm not staying here to be made fun of.'

'My little love, I'm not making fun of you.'

Flustered by the casual endearment, she stopped trying to pull away, and, using the wrist he was still holding, he drew her unresisting into the bedroom and closed the door behind them.

# CHAPTER SIX

'I *WASN'T* making fun of you,' he repeated. 'If anything I was mocking myself.'

'Why should you be doing that?'

'For taking myself far too seriously. However, I'll do my best to make it up to you.'

He waited, one eyebrow raised expectantly.

When she said nothing, he suggested, 'Aren't you going to ask me how?'

Warily, convinced he was teasing her, she went along with it. 'All right, how?'

'I thought I might teach you how to cope with sensual overload.'

Finding herself suddenly breathless, she asked, 'How would you do that?'

His eyes gleaming, he answered, 'By giving you plenty of practice.'

She began to tremble.

'But we'll take it slowly, shall we?'

He slid his hands into the wide sleeves of her robe to hold her elbows and draw her to him. When their faces were only inches apart, he stopped and smiled down at her.

Their bodies weren't touching, but she was very aware of how close they were and the warmth of his hands cupping her elbows.

Lifting her face to his, like a flower to the sun, she was waiting for his kiss when he surprised her by suggesting softly, 'Why don't *you* kiss *me*?'

Her eyes flying to his mouth, a mouth that sent shivers up and down her spine, she hesitated for an instant, *wanting* to kiss him, but oddly shy. Then, gathering her courage, she stood on tiptoe and touched her lips to his.

For a moment he remained quite still, making no effort to kiss her back, and, disconcerted, she was about to draw away when his lips moved in response, returning the slight pressure.

At first his kiss was chaste, but soon it changed to teasing and sensual as his mouth coaxed hers to part and he ran the tip of his tongue delicately along the silky inner skin of her upper lip.

While his kisses became ever more tantalising and erotic, he withdrew his hands from her sleeves and, unfastening her robe, slipped it off her shoulders and lifted her onto the bed.

Lying in a pool of golden light cast by the bedside lamp, she gazed up at him, her whole body waiting, anticipating, responsive to a trustworthy lover.

He sat down beside her and his hands began to travel lightly over her, stroking and caressing as they went, seeking out every erogenous zone.

Feeling the shudders that ran through her, he drew back a little and asked, 'Going too fast for you?'

'No.'

'That's my girl.'

While one hand lingered on her breast to tease a pink nipple between finger and thumb, the other moved down to her stomach. When his exploring fingers found the warm, satiny skin of her inner thighs and the nest of silky brown curls, she couldn't repress a gasp.

'Get ready for it,' he warned softly, and, nuzzling his face against her breast, laved the other erect nipple before taking it into his mouth.

Everything she had so far experienced paled into insignificance, and, turning her head from side to side on the pillow, she began to make little mewling sounds deep in her throat.

The exquisite sensations he was creating were growing, tightening, escalating, until her entire being was concentrated on the release of that spiralling pleasure.

When it happened, her eyes closed, her whole body rigid now, helpless in the grip of such intense delight, she cried out.

For a while she lay quivering, before becoming quiet and still, utterly relaxed, lapped in a bliss as sensual and satisfying as warm, scented bath water.

She felt a gentle kiss on the tip of her nose, and opened her eyes to find Gray looking down at her, his expression oddly tender.

'Thank you,' she said simply.

'Has anyone told you you're an absolute delight to make love to?'

She shook her head.

'Not even Jason?'

Jason had never touched her so intimately.

When, haltingly, she said so, Gray looked staggered. 'I know you were holding back from total commitment, but surely you must have done some heavy petting occasionally? Just to keep him interested. To remind him what he was missing.'

'No, we didn't.'

'You mean your relationship went no further than a few kisses?'

'Yes.' Her voice wry, she added, 'Considering he's now my brother-in-law, it's just as well.'

A look of relief on his face, Gray murmured, 'Well, I'll be damned! Unless he was getting his kicks elsewhere, he must have been hellish frustrated.'

A thought struck her, and she asked a shade anxiously, 'What about you?'

Instantly on her wavelength, he smiled. 'I didn't miss out. Your body's so responsive I believe I enjoyed it even more than you did.'

A little embarrassed now, she was wondering why he'd chosen that way to pleasure her, when he added, 'And it served to release a little of your tension. Now we can take things slowly, make our lovemaking even more enjoyable, so that you'll never want the night to end.'

She found it hard to believe that anything could be *more* enjoyable. In any case, as far as she was concerned her previous hunger had been well and truly appeased. She was sated.

Watching her expressive face, he grinned. 'Don't you believe it. That was merely the hors d'oeuvre.'

He rose to his feet and, untying the belt, stripped off his dressing gown.

Watching him, she caught her breath and her throat went dry. Oh, but he was beautiful…virile…magnificent… Adjectives rushed into her mind, but none of them did him justice.

He was every woman's dream lover.

Narrow-hipped and broad across the shoulders, his whole body as well-proportioned as any Greek statue, he carried not an ounce of spare flesh, and in the lamplight his smooth skin gleamed like oiled silk.

Slipping in beside her, he added, 'But before we start the feast, I suggest we experiment a little first to see what you enjoy the most.'

'I really don't think…' she began. Then stopped abruptly as, with just the slightest pressure of a single finger, he brought the desire she had thought dead back to glorious life.

When she awoke and opened her eyes, daylight was filling the room. A glance at her watch told her it was late morning. She was alone in the big bed, but she could hear the shower running.

Remembering the previous night, she wondered what on earth had got into her. She could scarcely believe she had acted so completely out of character, abandoning herself so wantonly and passionately to a man she had only just met. A man she knew virtually nothing about.

Yet she had. And though it went against all her principles to indulge in a short holiday affair, she found that for perhaps the first time in her adult life she felt like a real woman, glowingly alive and supremely confident.

There was no way she could regret what had happened. It had been utter bliss. Gray had proved to be a fantastic lover. Generous and sensitive, he had known exactly what to do with his body and hers.

She had heard lovemaking described as skyrockets and fireworks; a soaring flight to the stars; stepping out of a plane at ten thousand feet; and, most poetic of all, a little death.

It had been all of those and more. A lifetime's experience crammed into one night.

Freshly awakened, and new to such pleasures, her body had welcomed his without restraint. In return he had been gentle and considerate, careful not to leave her bruised or tender.

Afterwards, as she lay contentedly in his arms, he had said, 'So I really am the first!'

Feeling her face grow warm, she'd answered, 'I'm afraid so. Do you mind?'

'Far from it. However, I must admit to being surprised. Though you tried to make it clear you were a nice, old-fashioned girl, I wasn't sure such a thing existed these days.'

'If I really *were* a nice, old-fashioned girl I wouldn't be in your bed now.'

'But when you accepted my offer of a holiday, you didn't intend this to happen, did you?'

'No.'

'So why *are* you in my bed? No, don't bother to answer that question. I know why, of course.'

Looking up at him through long curly lashes, she teased, 'You consider yourself irresistible?'

'Hardly.'

'Then why *do* you think I'm here?'

'A backlash from Jason,' he said. 'After losing out on that score—'

'This has absolutely nothing to do with Jason,' she denied hardly.

Gray was unconvinced. 'Surely it must have. After years of celibacy, why let your hair down now?'

'Perhaps I'd grown tired of being a virgin.'

'You mean when you found you couldn't swop that virginity for a wedding ring you decided to have some fun instead?'

'No, that's not what I mean.'

'Then why *me*?'

'I found you…attractive.'

'You're twenty-three. You must have found plenty of other men attractive.'

'Very few. I suppose I'm just hard to please.'

'Well, I hope you're not disappointed. You've ended up with a holiday instead of a honeymoon and a lover instead of a bridegroom. It must seem a poor consolation prize.'

Somehow the thought of what she had lost no longer had the power to hurt, and, refusing to be rattled, she said lightly, 'As consolation prizes go, I think it's a pretty good one.'

She felt him relax, and the hand that had been lying on her ribcage moved up to caress her breast. 'For that, you deserve a reward.'

A little smile hovering on her lips, she was reliving that 'reward' when the bathroom door opened and Gray appeared, wearing a short robe, a towel slung round his neck.

Newly shaved, his black hair plastered seal-like to his well-shaped head and his green eyes gleaming between thick, sooty lashes, he looked so appealing and virile that her heart turned over.

'Good morning,' he greeted her cheerfully, and, crossing to the bed, dropped a light kiss on her lips.

He smelt of shower gel and aftershave, and tasted of minty toothpaste. She found that healthy freshness a powerful aphrodisiac.

Lifting the towel to vigorously rub his hair, he told her, 'Breakfast, or, rather, brunch, should be here in a minute or so. Would you like it in bed?'

Feeling unwashed and tangly-haired, and needing to clean her teeth, she pushed herself into a sitting position and hastily refused. 'No, I'd like a shower first, so I'll get up. How much time have we got?'

Discarding the towel, he said, 'Plenty. We don't need to leave for the airport until early afternoon.' His eyes were on her breasts and, as though he'd touched them, her nipples grew firm under his appreciative gaze.

Trying desperately to appear casual, she pulled up the duvet to cover her nakedness, and looked around for her robe. It was well out of reach.

In spite of, or perhaps *because* of all that had happened the previous night, she felt suddenly shy, reluctant to get out of bed in front of him.

'Please could you pass my robe?'

Straight-faced, he said, 'Of course. Though it's so warm I doubt if you'll need it.'

He reached for the robe, but instead of handing it to her he held it ready, leaving her no alternative but to push back the duvet and climb out.

Knowing she was blushing, Rebecca was glad he couldn't see her face as she slid into it.

Folding his arms round her, he drew her back against him and, proving he missed very little, leaned forward to blow on her hot cheek, making her blush even harder.

Then, sounding remorseful, 'My love, it's a shame to tease you.'

'If you really think that, why do you keep doing it?' she demanded.

'You look so enchanting when you blush, I can't resist it.'

'Try.'

His cheek against hers, his crossed hands busy inside her robe, he suggested, 'If you want any help with that shower...?'

Her breath coming quickly, and afraid that at any moment she might weaken, she said repressively, 'No, thank you,' and, pulling herself free, fled, followed by his soft laughter.

Used to having a slice of morning toast and a cup of coffee, standing alone in her small kitchen, it was strange and exciting to be sitting opposite Gray while they drank fresh orange juice and tucked into crisp curls of bacon, maple syrup and pancakes.

His disturbing sexuality leashed, he was a pleasant companion, quietly good-humoured, happy to talk or simply eat in companionable silence.

Dressed in well-cut cords and a casual shirt, he still contrived to look like a man of authority.

Her eyes lingering on his lean, suntanned face with its fine, straight nose and those extraordinary eyes beneath level black brows, she wondered how she could ever have thought him less handsome than Jason.

He had a bone structure that would keep him looking good even when he was old, whereas Jason had the kind of matinée-idol looks that by middle-age would start to grow slack and pouchy.

When the feeling of betrayal that should have followed this disloyal thought failed to arrive, she was surprised.

'You're looking very serious,' Gray remarked, reaching to pour her coffee. 'What's on your mind?'

'I was thinking about Jason.'

His face darkening with a sudden anger, Gray burst out, 'Damn the man!' Then more quietly, 'Love's the very devil…'

But did she still love Jason?

Even as her mind started to frame the question, she knew she didn't.

The spell he had undoubtedly cast had faded and died, and so had her love. Otherwise she could never have given herself so completely to another man.

'But if you can put your feelings for Jason aside, I hope you'll find that coming with me is preferable to sitting at home alone.'

She was about to tell him that she no longer had any feelings for Jason, when he went on, 'Neither of us want any new emotional entanglements. Which means we'll be free to simply enjoy ourselves with no danger of getting involved or asking more than the other person is willing to give.

'It could work pretty well. Wouldn't you agree?'

It was only common sense, but somehow it sounded so cold-blooded that she felt chilled.

As she hesitated he asked sharply, 'You're not having second thoughts about last night?'

'No,' she answered, her golden eyes meeting his.

His faint sigh of relief was audible, before he pursued, 'About the holiday?'

'No.'

'That's good.' He smiled his slow smile at her.

She thought wonderingly that it was less than forty-eight hours since they had met, but in some strange way it was as if she had always known him, as if he'd become part of her life, necessary to her.

No, she mustn't let herself think that way. He was her first, and would probably be her only lover, so he would always be very special to her. But she couldn't let him become *necessary*.

After this holiday they would be going their separate ways and he would probably never give her another thought.

All she had was the coming two weeks, so instead of repining she would enjoy every moment of them to the full and then, grateful for what fate had bestowed on her, let go...

They were in a taxi on their way to the airport, when Gray's mobile rang.

Having excused himself, he lifted the phone to his ear and spoke crisply. 'Gallagher... Yes... Yes... Excellent... Even better... Yes, we're quite prepared to match that... Yes, straight away... Thanks for letting me know...' With a glance at Rebecca, he added, 'I will, certainly.'

Dropping the small instrument back into his pocket, he told her calmly, 'That was Scrivener.'

'Has he come to a decision?' she asked eagerly.

'Yes. He's carrying on, as I thought he would.'

As she breathed a sigh of relief, Gray continued, 'The really good news is that, instead of putting a limit on further injections of cash, he's going all out. The sky's the limit. Whatever it takes to really get the complex up and running.'

'Oh, that's great!'

'It's better than I'd dared hope,' he admitted. 'And it's all due to you.'

When she began to demur, he shook his head. 'We both know it's the truth. Scrivener said so too.'

With a slight frown, as if the idea displeased him, Gray added, 'He also said that if you were looking for a new post and had no objection to working in Boston, he would be delighted to offer you a job as his PA.'

Surprise kept her silent for a moment, then she demurred, 'But Jason told me he always has a male secretary and PA.'

'That was because his last wife didn't trust him. In

the end, apparently tired of her endless jealousy, he divorced her.

'But in spite of three previous marriages he's still childless, so, needing a son and heir, he's apparently looking around for wife number four.'

'Marianne?' she suggested.

'I very much doubt it. Scrivener's no fool. Marianne and the others like her fulfil a need, but they're not wife material. When it comes to marriage he always chooses a woman with brains and character, as well as beauty.

'*You* seem to have made a distinct hit with our Andrew, so if you *were* looking for a wealthy husband it's my opinion you'd be in there with a chance.'

Rebecca shuddered inwardly. There was no way she would want to marry a man like Scrivener.

But Gray was going on, 'You could do a lot worse. Apparently where his women are concerned he's quite generous. It could be a marvellous opportunity for any woman who was willing to close her eyes to his extramarital activities, and simply enjoy the kind of lifestyle he can offer.'

His cynical words hurt.

Unwilling, however, to show it, she remarked lightly, 'I'll bear that in mind,' and saw by his expression that for some reason her answer had ruffled him.

Perhaps, still not fully convinced that she *hadn't* been after Jason's money, he'd been testing her?

Gray, for his part, was wishing he'd never brought up the subject of Scrivener remarrying. He'd been expecting Rebecca to protest vehemently that she *wasn't* looking for a wealthy husband, and could *never* bring herself to marry anyone like Scrivener. Instead she appeared to be considering the possibility.

He tried to tell himself that it didn't matter a jot if she *was*.

But somehow it did.

Scowling, he wondered if she would contact Scrivener

about the job offer, and take it from there. If she did, he only had himself to blame for putting the idea into her head.

Unhappy with the situation, Rebecca was about to try and retrieve it when, noticing that scowl, she chickened out, and the journey to Logan Airport was completed in a not altogether comfortable silence.

Gray's black mood persisted until they had boarded the small plane and were taxiing down the runway ready for take-off.

Then, having thought it through a dozen times, and coming to believe he had almost certainly misjudged her reaction, he turned to Rebecca and, giving her a smile, took her hand.

Catching her surprised expression, he said, 'You don't look scared this time, but it's a good excuse to hold your hand and apologise for my bad temper.'

Her happiness restored, she smiled back.

'Does that smile mean I'm forgiven?'

'It would if there was anything to forgive.'

'Generous woman.'

He lowered their clasped hands, and his knuckles grazed her thigh, making her jump. 'If you're in agreement, I thought that in a while we might resume our game.'

His eyes on her face, he waited, a slight smile tugging at his lips.

After a moment she recalled how, on the plane, he'd brought her tea in bed and deliberately sat too close. Then his comment, 'I've found it most entertaining, and I look forward to resuming later.'

Demurely, she said, 'Oh, *that* game. Well, perhaps this time, before we start, we should lay down some ground rules?'

He raised a dark, level brow. 'What had you in mind? Clothes on and hands off?'

Boldly, she asked, 'Where's the fun in that?'

'Well, provided you promise not to seduce me...'

She pretended to think about it. 'OK, I'll go along with that, so long as I don't have to stop you if you try to seduce me.'

'That's my girl.'

'After all,' she added seriously, 'it might be my only chance to join the Mile-High Club.'

Then, finding the idea gave her no pleasure, 'I presume you're a fully fledged member by now?'

'As a matter of fact I haven't yet joined.'

Though it shouldn't have made any difference, it did, and his answer brought a swift rush of mingled relief and gladness.

It had been cool and grey when they left Boston, but they landed at San Francisco International Airport in dazzling sunshine and, on Rebecca's part at least, a cloud of euphoria.

Because of the time difference it was still afternoon, and the Californian sun beat down fiercely. As soon as they left the air-conditioned terminal building, the heat struck through the thin soles of her sandals and seemed to envelope her in a sticky embrace.

She was pleased she'd decided on a sleeveless cotton dress, and taken her ash-brown hair up into a smooth coil.

A sleek white car, its hood down, was waiting for them, and as soon as the driver had handed over the keys they set off north for what Gray told her was a longish drive to the Napa Valley.

Though the air was hot and sticky with humidity, the open-topped car was pleasantly cool as they joined the endless flow of traffic on the freeway.

Rebecca's first impression of the west coast was of continuous traffic, a straggle of unprepossessing glass and concrete skyscrapers, and towering advertisement hoardings lining the roadside.

All the same, with so much to look back on and so much to look forward to, she felt as excited as a child on Christmas morning.

After a while Gray raised his voice above the wind and the engine noise and the soft phut of insects hitting the windscreen, to enquire, 'Do you want to press on, or stop for a bite to eat *en route*?'

Not at all hungry, and finding the smell of gasoline and onions from the roadside pull-ins distinctly unappealing, she said, 'Press on, if it's all the same to you.'

His look of relief seemed to suggest that he shared her feelings. But then, she was starting to discover, they were more often than not in tune.

While she enjoyed the sun on her face and listened to the soothing shush of the tyres, her mind went back to earlier that afternoon.

Recalling Gray's skilful lovemaking, she shivered deliciously, the mere remembrance making her heart race until it was difficult to breathe.

Saying, 'If we're going to join the club we might as well do it in style,' he had made love to her time and time again, with a kind of sweet ruthlessness that had left her quivering with pleasure, and emotionally exhausted.

She would have slept, but the hours had flown by and there had been no time for sleep...

Glancing sideways at her, Gray saw that, though her eyes were closed, a little smile still played around her lips.

Resisting a sudden mad urge to stop the car and kiss those smiling lips, he admitted to himself that he couldn't get enough of this woman.

She was like no one else he had ever met.

He had discovered that she was vulnerable in some ways, tough in others, shy and uncertain, yet remarkably self-controlled.

At first, in spite of her declared love for Jason, she had struck him as cool, sexually. Now he knew that coolness was only on the surface. A façade to hide behind. Underneath she was fiery and passionate, as hot-blooded as he himself.

He was well aware that Jason, though weak in many ways, was a charming and ruthless predator with a powerful sex appeal. How in heaven's name had a passionate woman, who was also in love with him, managed to hold out against his blandishments?

It was a question Gray couldn't really answer, but he found himself absurdly pleased that she *had*. She was too good for Jason.

Even if he had been on the level about marrying her—and in view of his past record that was unlikely—within weeks he would have been unfaithful, and she would have found herself saddled with a husband she could neither trust nor respect.

During the drive, while Gray was busy with his thoughts, Rebecca dozed intermittently, half waking from time to time, before drifting off again.

When she awoke fully and opened her eyes, they were in what she guessed was the Napa Valley. Sitting up straighter, she looked around her.

On either side the ground was rolling and fertile, its brilliant green just beginning to take on a slightly parched look that suggested a long spell of dry weather.

Slanting her a glance, Gray said, 'The road we're on now is the St Helena Highway, known as the vineyard road.'

'Have we far to go?'

'It shouldn't be too far. According to the directions I was given, the Santa Rosa spread is about fourteen or fifteen miles from Napa itself, and we drove through the town just a few minutes ago.'

After a while they skirted a small outcrop of hills and the wide, flat valley began to close in. Soon there were steepish slopes on either side, and they were in the vineyards.

'This should be our turning,' Gray said, and took a narrow road to the left.

At the bottom of the road a pair of tall iron gates were standing open. Across an archway above them, black wrought-iron letters bore the legend 'Santa Rosa Wineries'.

They drove through the gates and up a long drive, finally stopping in front of a white, one-storey, Spanish-style hacienda. Its tiled veranda had a series of archways and was festooned with climbing plants and bright with tubs of flowers.

A small, battered pick-up truck was parked close by. As they climbed out of the car, a woman appeared in the nearest archway dressed in red cotton trousers and a loose yellow top. A red and yellow spotted bandanna was tied around her head, and her bare feet were pushed into a pair of ancient sneakers.

'You must be Mr Gallagher.' Coming down the steps, she thrust out a thin brown hand.

'That's right.' Having shaken her hand, Gray drew Rebecca forward. 'And this is Miss Ferris.'

Again the hand shot out. 'Hi! I'm Gloria Redford. Ben and I have been taking care of the place since Manuel's daughter helped him move out.

'Stubborn old fool,' she added fondly. 'Instead of trying to manage, he should have sold Santa Rosa and gone to live with his daughter five years ago when his son died.

'Well, now you're here, I'd best be getting back.'

'Have you far to go?' Rebecca asked politely.

'I live in Yountville, so it's not far, but Ben and the others will be wanting their supper.'

Turning to Gray, she added, 'Oh, and speaking of supper, there's a trolley in the larder laid all ready for you, and you'll find enough food in the fridge to last for the time being.

'I'll pop back in a day or so to see if there's any items I've missed. If you need anything in the meantime, or you want me to pop in to change the beds or tidy the place, just give me a ring. My number's on the board in the kitchen.'

'Thanks.'

With a cheery grin, she bounded off to the pick-up. The engine roared into life, and a second or two later she was driving away, a cloud of dust billowing after her.

While Gray retrieved their luggage from the boot, Rebecca stood staring at the house that was to be their holiday home for the next two weeks, and thought that never in the whole of her life had she felt so blissfully happy.

# CHAPTER SEVEN

GLANCING at Rebecca, and struck by the glow on her face, Gray commented, 'You're looking very happy.'

'I *am* happy,' she said simply.

'Then let's hope we can keep it that way. Ready to take a look at the house?'

'You bet!'

She followed him up the veranda steps and through the door Gloria Redford had left open.

Putting their cases down, Gray suggested, 'Let's explore, shall we?'

The main living area ran from the front of the house through to the back. It was cool and spacious, with white walls, terrazzo flooring, lots of plants and the minimum of furniture.

There was a huge open fireplace of unplastered stone, and, to either side of the flower-filled hearth, tier upon tier of built-in bookcases, all of which were empty.

After a moment or two, Rebecca realised that it was the complete absence of any personal things that made it seem like the ideal summer layout for the cover of a glossy magazine.

At the far end, sliding glass panels led out to a paved patio. There was a brick-built barbecue and several comfortable-looking chairs and loungers grouped around a table. Beyond the patio was a swimming pool, the late-evening sun sparkling on its blue water.

On one side of the living area was a sizable kitchen with a cool larder, and beyond that two bedrooms and a bathroom.

At the opposite end of the house, two large, airy, *en suite* bedrooms led into each other. They seemed to be guest rooms, and identical apart from the fact that in one the duvet and rugs were thundercloud-blue, and in the other mulberry.

Both had a double bed, and were lined on one wall with white tongue-and-groove wardrobes. Light muslin curtains screened the long windows.

'As you're the guest,' Gray said, 'you get first choice. Which room would you like?'

Taken aback, because she had presumed he would want them to share, she stammered, 'I—I don't really mind. You choose.'

He grinned. 'I'd prefer whichever one *you're* in. But, having promised you a room of your own...'

She took a deep breath and asked, 'What if I said I didn't want a room of my own?'

'I was rather hoping you *would* say that.' He waited expectantly, one eyebrow cocked.

'I don't want a room of my own,' she obliged.

He dropped a quick kiss on her lips. 'Then let's share this one. It has a bathroom on either side, so at least you can have a bathroom of your own.'

With a fast-beating heart she went into the mulberry room, while Gray fetched their cases. Putting them on the bed, he queried, 'Shall we be exemplary and unpack straight away?'

*If she were his wife, she would do it for him.*

'Then, as soon as I've freshened up, I'll find the ingredients for a long, cold drink.'

'Sounds good.' Her voice was husky.

While she emptied her case and put away her things, Gray unpacked with a speed and efficiency that spoke of long practice in looking after himself.

Watching him covertly, she wondered why he had never married. It seemed strange that a man of his age, a man who appeared to have everything, hadn't been snapped up long since.

Unless he was one of those males who hated the thought of being tied down, and wanted the freedom to love all and marry none?

Busy with her thoughts, she unconsciously slowed down, and he easily finished first.

His case stowed neatly in the bottom of one of the cupboards, he picked up a change of clothing and disappeared into the nearest bathroom.

A moment or two later she heard the shower running.

Feeling hot and sticky, she decided to follow suit. Taking fresh undies and a skimpy button-through dress—bought especially for the Caribbean—she went into the second bathroom.

When she had showered and changed she brushed out her long hair and pulled it back into a loose knot, then, cool and refreshed, went in search of Gray.

She found him lounging on the patio, a tray of drinks at his elbow.

He rose to his feet at her approach and smiled at her. Wearing light trousers and an olive-green shirt open at the neck to expose the tanned column of his throat, he looked devastatingly attractive, and her heart turned over.

'What's it to be?' he asked.

'Fruit juice, please.'

Pulling forward a cushioned chair, he settled her into it, before lifting a glass jug and pouring two tall tumblers of juice chinking with ice.

'Thank you.' Accepting the tumbler he handed her, she leaned back and sipped appreciatively.

It was a lovely evening; the air was warm and as clear as glass, fragrant with the scent of flowering shrubs and full of the shrill sound of cicadas.

The sun had gone and a blue dusk was stealthily creeping in. Through the screen of vegetation, she could see lights beginning to twinkle on the opposite slope and along the valley floor.

Somewhere in the distance a dog barked, and closer at hand she could hear the faint sound of music and smell burning charcoal, as if the neighbours were having a barbecue.

When their drinks were finished, he rose to his feet and held out his hand. 'Shall we stretch our legs before we eat?'

She put her hand in his and, as always when he touched her, felt her skin tingle in response.

Fingers entwined, they made their way past the swimming pool, and descended a short flight of stone steps into a nicely kept garden.

As they strolled along the winding paths Rebecca watched a pale moon rise and hang low on the horizon, while the clear blue colour over the hills changed to a velvety purple and the stars above them grew bigger and brighter.

Unconsciously, she sighed.

'Why the sigh?' he asked.

'I was just thinking how beautiful it all is.'

'Then you're not sorry you decided to come?'

'Surprised, but not sorry,' she answered.

'Surprised?'

'It just wasn't like me. I mean…it's so completely out of character.'

He squeezed her hand. 'Well, I'm very glad you managed to step out of character for once.'

'Tell me something. If I'd refused to come, would you have carried out your threat to tell Philip Lorne what had happened between Jason and me?'

'What do you think?'

'I've no idea,' she admitted. 'I know so little about you.'

'Yet you trusted me.'

'I suppose I must have done.'

'Do you still?'

'Yes.'

'In spite of the fact that we're now lovers?'

'It was as much my doing as yours.'

'And you don't regret it?'

'No.'

'What if I told you I have a live-in lover stashed away at home?'

Just for an instant shock scattered her wits, then, collecting herself, she asked evenly, 'Have you?'

'No. A couple of months ago my live-in lover left me for someone else.'

'How long had you been together?'

'Just over a year.'

Though his face gave no clue as to how upset he was, she said, 'I'm sorry.'

'There's no need to be. Any feeling I had for her died a long time ago.

'Though Cleo is one of the most beautiful women I've ever set eyes on, I soon discovered that her nature didn't match.

'Our sleeping together gradually became just a matter of habit and convenience, and, as she was hardly ever at home when I was, companionship ceased to exist. We might have drifted on for a while longer if she hadn't met a retired oil-man with more millions than he could spend. Tex, she assured me, was prepared to give her everything she wanted, and quite happy to indulge her every whim.

'I wished her luck.'

As they rounded the corner of the house and found themselves back on the patio, Rebecca said, 'Even so, it's bound to be sad, breaking up with someone you once loved.'

Seeing the glow had gone from her face, and cursing himself for a fool, he changed the subject. 'Now, where would you like to eat? Inside or out?'

'Outside, if that suits you? It's much too nice to be indoors.'

Nodding his approval, he suggested, 'Then pull up a lounger while I go and fetch our supper.'

He was back quite quickly, wheeling a trolley covered with butter muslin. A white linen napkin was draped over his arm.

She was surprised to see that his hair was parted in the middle and slicked down smoothly with water.

He whipped off the muslin to display a simple meal of ham, soft cheese, green salad and fat, rosy peaches. Then, shoulders rounded, head bobbing, he said unctuously, 'At your service, madam. What can I help you to?'

She could never have imagined him playing the fool, and, struggling to keep a straight face, she said, 'Thank you, James. I'd like some cheese and salad.' He filled a plate, then looked up to ask, 'And will madam have a glass of wine? I understand it's the produce of Santa Rosa.'

His crossed eyes were her undoing, and she burst out laughing. When she could control her mirth sufficiently, she warned, 'If the wind changes, you'll stay like that.'

He came to lean over her, leering. 'If I do, will you still like me?'

'Oh, certainly,' she said and lifted her hand to ruffle his damp hair, while helpless laughter bubbled up inside her.

'You're not taking this seriously,' he complained, and stopped her laughter with a series of kisses.

Kisses that went on and on, growing more fervent, blowing her mind, while he dealt with the buttons of her dress.

He was easing down her dainty briefs when, snatching at the coat tails of sanity, she gasped, 'Don't! Someone might come.'

Grinning down at her, he whispered in her ear, 'Both of us, I hope.'

Then with a quick movement he flattened the lounger completely, and followed her down.

\*     \*     \*

It was some time before they got round to thinking about food, and when they did Gray opened the bottle of Santa Rosa Chenin Blanc.

When they had both tried the wine, he asked, 'What's your opinion?'

'I'm no expert,' Rebecca said.

'Nor are ninety per cent of the people who drink wine. Just tell me what you think of it.'

'I like it. It's nice and fresh and fruity.'

He switched on the patio lights, and, having held up his glass to judge the colour and clearness of the wine, he took another thoughtful sip.

'Mmm... If we decide to produce ordinary table wine for a year or two while we do some replanting, this could be a reasonable proposition.'

'Then the vineyard's still in production?'

'After a fashion. Though the vines have been taken care of and the grapes continually harvested, for several years now no wine has actually been produced on the premises.

'One of the big neighbouring concerns, who make and bottle huge volumes of both red and white table wine, have bought Santa Rosa's grapes to blend with their own.

'They'll probably do the same this year. But once we're up and running it will be different.'

'Will you be in competition?'

He shook his head. 'Rather than simply producing drinkable table wine, I'd prefer to concentrate on the production of fine wines. It's more challenging, and, if successful, extremely lucrative.'

'How soon could you start?'

'That would depend on the established grape varieties, and on what kind of plant there is. Tomorrow we can take a look at the winery building, if you're at all interested?'

'Oh, yes, I am,' she said eagerly. 'It sounds absolutely fascinating.'

Stretched side by side on loungers, they talked for a while

about wine and the vineyard's prospects, then gradually fell silent.

It was very late, but, euphoric and enjoying the magic of the night, they continued to sit there.

After a while Gray reached out and, taking her hand, held it, his thumb gently massaging her palm.

She shivered.

It was so romantic that she thought with a strange kind of longing, *this could be our honeymoon...*

Only of course it wasn't.

As far as she and Gray were concerned this was a mere holiday fling, a short-term affair with no commitment on either side.

It was Lisa and Jason who were on honeymoon, enjoying a romantic start to their new life together as man and wife.

Sighing, she wondered, what if the fairy godmother she had believed in as a child could wave a magic wand and give her the chance to swop places with Lisa? Would she take it?

No, she wouldn't.

Looking back, she could see that she had been falling out of love with Jason for a long time without realising it.

Freed from that emotional burden, she could now accept that he belonged in the past, and rejoice because his defection was no longer an ever-present regret lying like a dark shadow on her mind...

As though her thoughts had disturbed him, Gray turned his head to glance at her. 'You look very pensive,' he remarked.

'I was thinking about—' Suddenly recalling his angry reaction last time she had mentioned Jason, she stopped speaking abruptly, a spot of colour creeping into her cheeks.

His jaw tightened. 'Jason, presumably?'

Seeing by her expression that he'd hit the nail on the head, his voice curt, he said, 'You seem to do little else.

Did you think about him when we were in bed? Imagine it was him making love to you rather than me?'

'N-no, of course not,' she stammered. 'As a matter of fact, I...'

About to tell him that she no longer loved Jason, she hesitated. If she did, would he think she'd just been pretending all along? That she really *had* just been after Jason's money?

He obviously didn't totally trust her on that score, otherwise he wouldn't have taunted her about Andrew Scrivener.

And surely it couldn't matter to him what her feelings for Jason were? *He* had no interest in her, apart from a sexual one.

Hadn't he laid it on the line? 'Neither of us want any new emotional entanglements...'

She took a deep, steadying breath, and went on, 'As a matter of fact I was just thinking about Lisa and Jason enjoying their honeymoon.'

'You visualise a romantic one, no doubt?' Gray enquired sarcastically.

Refusing to be put down, she said quietly, 'I think honeymoons *should* be romantic.'

'Presumably you've never been on one.'

'No.' Almost to herself, she added, 'And I probably never will.'

'I'm sorry,' Gray said, his fingers tightening around hers. 'I'm being a brute to you. But I'm not in the mood for such sentimental claptrap.'

'You're a cynic,' she accused.

'Better a cynic than a romantic.'

'You really *do* hate the idea of romance.'

'I think of it as the old Chinese curse.'

'What Chinese curse?'

'May all your dreams come true.'

'Oh...'

'Believe me, honeymoons aren't necessarily either romantic or happy, and it's my guess that Lisa and Jason are unlikely to be enjoying theirs.'

Withdrawing her hand, Rebecca sat up straighter. 'What makes you say that?'

'All the signs indicate that it will very quickly develop into a battleground, so if you're thinking *happy ever after*, forget it.'

Shocked, she cried, 'I don't know how you can say such a thing!'

'Because it's the truth,' he said wearily.

'I don't believe it.'

'Think,' he urged her seriously. 'What kind of woman is Lisa?'

Without waiting for an answer, he went on, 'Beautiful undoubtedly, charming when she wants to be, but shallow and spoilt, selfish to the core, wilful, scheming and deceitful, wouldn't you say?'

Rebecca flinched. 'She may be all of those, but she's a lot of other things as well. She can be caring and thoughtful—'

But Gray was going on relentlessly, 'And what kind of man is Jason?'

Again he answered his own question. 'Handsome undoubtedly, charming when it suits him, but just as shallow and spoilt, as selfish and wilful, as scheming and deceitful as his new wife.

'Can you really see any hope for them…?'

Battered by words as though they were stones, she just wanted to crawl away.

'*I* can't,' Gray added. 'Especially when he discovers how she's lied to him.'

'Lied to him?'

'Then she didn't tell you?'

'Tell me what?'

'That she was pregnant.'

Rebecca's jaw dropped.

'No, I can see she didn't.' Gray's voice was grim.

'I don't believe it,' she said flatly.

Her stepsister had once confided that she had no intention of ever having children. That she had taken, and would always take, every precaution to make sure she never became pregnant.

'You must be mistaken,' she insisted. 'Lisa doesn't like babies. She would have taken care.'

Gray smiled grimly. 'I don't doubt it.'

Pulling herself together with an effort, she demanded, 'Then what makes you think she's pregnant?'

'Jason thinks so.'

'How do you know?'

'Let's say I heard it on the grapevine. I guess he must have confided in someone that that was why the wedding was taking place in such a hurry.

'I feel sure he was right, as far as it goes. But not for the obvious reason, that the blushing bride didn't want to appear pregnant.'

She frowned. 'What other reason could there be?'

'That your dear stepsister didn't want to chance being found out, and every month that passed increased the risk.'

'I don't know what you're getting at.'

As though speaking to a not-very-bright child, he explained, 'I don't believe for a moment that she's pregnant, and as she and Jason were living together he was bound to discover the truth sooner or later.'

'But why should she tell him she was pregnant if she wasn't?'

'It's one of the oldest tricks in the book. I'm only surprised Jason fell for it.'

Rebecca shook her head as if to clear it. 'I can't see why she would need to lie, when they were going to be married anyway.'

'I think you'll find that, having had his fun, he was trying to wriggle out of marrying her. That's why she, or possibly her mother, came up with the scheme.

'One thing I don't understand is why Jason took it so quietly.'

'Perhaps he was afraid of his uncle getting to know? From what he told me, Philip Lorne has always been very strait-laced.'

'Far from being strait-laced, Lorne has got his nephew out of quite a few scrapes in the past,' Gray said positively. 'So many in fact that he'd put his foot down and told Jason that if he got into any further trouble, his allowance would be stopped.

'It's ironic really that for once in his life Jason took the threat seriously. If he *had* told his uncle, I've no doubt Lorne would have helped him.'

'But what could he have done?'

'What he's done in the past when other women who were after Jason's money tried to trick him into marriage—paid her off.'

*Paid her off...*

But this time the woman in question was her stepsister. It was her own family Gray was taking about with such critical contempt.

Seeing her stricken face, he said, 'I'm sorry if that sounds brutal.'

Through a dry throat, she asked, 'What makes you so sure she was only after his money?'

'Oh, come on!'

'Have you ever thought that she might genuinely love him?'

Gray's white teeth flashed in a mirthless smile. 'It's my bet that she loves his money a lot more.'

'You're seriously warped,' Rebecca accused, her voice hoarse. 'You presumed *I* only wanted to marry him for his money.'

'At first, knowing how things stood, it seemed more than likely.'

'You mean I was part of the clan.'

'At the time I thought so. Can you blame me?'

'So to prove that I was just out for all I could get, you offered me a free holiday.'

'It wasn't like that at all.'

'Then why did you ask me to come with you?'

'Because I wanted your company.'

'The company of someone whose family you talk about so contemptuously?'

'You know perfectly well that isn't how I feel about you.'

'I don't know anything of the kind.'

'What can I say to ease your mind?'

'You could admit you might be wrong about Lisa.'

'Do you genuinely believe I am?' he challenged.

She wanted to say yes, but couldn't.

'No, I thought not. At least you're honest.'

'That's a laugh!' she cried bitterly. 'I just wish to God I'd had the sense to stay in London.'

'I'm sorry you feel like that, because—'

The heat of futile anger rising inside her, without waiting to hear any more, she scrambled to her feet and fled.

When she reached their bedroom it was pleasantly cool and dim. At the half-open window the muslin curtains billowed slightly in the night breeze.

Sinking down on the bed, she covered her face with trembling hands. If only she had never agreed to come to California, never been stupid enough to let herself be drawn into this ill-judged affair...

It would have been bad enough if they had been merely holiday companions. Being lovers made things so much worse.

But she didn't *have* to sleep with him. He had offered her a room of her own, so she would *have* one and take care to keep her distance.

She rose to her feet and switched on the light. Then, opening her wardrobe, she began to bundle her things together.

'Leave them,' Gray said.

Turning her head, she saw he was standing in the doorway, watching her. His dark face serious, he added, 'I'll move out, if you want me to.'

'Yes, I do.' Close to tears, she hurried into the bathroom and bolted the door behind her.

When she emerged some ten minutes later the room was empty and his clothes had gone.

After tossing and turning until the early hours of the morning, she finally dropped off to sleep, but it was a restless sleep that brought unhappy dreams, and she awoke with tears on her cheeks.

The room was full of light and heat, and there wasn't a breath of air. The curtains hung limply at the windows, while reflected sunbeams shimmered on the white ceiling.

For a moment or two she couldn't think where she was, then it all came flooding back. The drive to Napa, their arrival at Santa Rosa, Gray so unexpectedly acting the fool, his ardent lovemaking, the shared meal and, just when everything seemed so wonderful and romantic, their quarrel.

If it could be called a quarrel.

Rather, it had been understanding, for the first time, how Gray really felt. She had been shocked and saddened by the way he had sneered at romance, and his obvious contempt for her family.

But if it was true that Lisa had lied to get Jason to marry her, and she felt oddly sure that it was, perhaps she couldn't blame him for thinking so badly of them all.

And no matter what he said about *not* including her, he must firmly believe they were all tarred with the same brush. It was obvious that he hadn't invited her because he liked her, or for her company, as he'd said, but simply to fulfil a sexual need.

With a heavy heart she wished yet again that she hadn't been foolish enough to get involved with him.

However, she had, and now it was too late. She was stuck here with no means of getting back, which meant a fortnight spent in his company.

Shuddering at the thought, she wondered just how bad it would be. But that, of course, would depend on his reaction to what had happened. She still didn't know him well enough to be able to predict which way he'd jump.

Would he sulk? Be angry and vindictive? Try to get her to change her mind about sleeping with him, and make her life a misery when she didn't? Or would he be cold and distant?

The latter would be by far the easiest to cope with, and she could only hope he'd play it like that. If he was prepared to go his own way and let her go hers, they needn't see too much of each other.

On the other hand, if he chose to be really difficult and obnoxious, he could make the coming two weeks unbearable.

Pushing the far from pleasant thought away, she looked at her watch. It was almost lunchtime. He was bound to be up by now. So what should she do?

Common sense told her there was little choice. She couldn't stay in her room indefinitely, so she might as well go out and face him, see what kind of devil she had to cope with.

Just the previous day her heart would have leapt at the thought of seeing him, but now it lay unmoved. It seemed that the powerful sexual attraction she'd felt was over as quickly as it had begun.

When she had showered, deciding it was too hot to wear a bra, she pulled on a pair of briefs and a loose cotton shift that tied on the shoulders. Then, fastening her hair into a single thick plait, she took a deep breath and followed the aroma of fresh coffee through to the kitchen.

Looking fresh and vital in stone-coloured jeans and a dark blue T-shirt, a tea towel draped around his lean hips, Gray was standing at one of the work surfaces, breaking eggs into a bowl and beating them.

His manner was relaxed, almost laid-back, and no horns were visible.

Glancing up at her approach, he said equably, 'Good morning. I hope you slept well?'

Taken aback by his friendly tone, it was a moment or two before she lied, 'Very well, thank you.'

Pouring the eggs into a pan and beginning to draw them into the centre, he told her, 'I was just about to give you a call. I thought we might have lunch by the pool. Omelette and salad suit you?'

So he'd decided to act as though nothing had happened. It was the one thing she hadn't thought of, but, willing to follow his lead and keep things on a civil footing, she answered politely, 'Yes, fine, thank you.'

'I do like a woman who's easy to please.'

If there was a *double entendre* there she let it go. Adding the large, golden omelette to a trolley containing a green salad, a crusty loaf, some smooth curls of butter, a bowl of oranges and a pot of coffee, he whipped off the tea towel and invited, 'Lead on, MacFerris.'

Without thinking, she asked, 'Shouldn't that be "Lay on"?'

Striking an attitude, he declaimed, 'Methinks that Shakespeare is oft misquoted.'

Only the previous day she would have laughed. As it was, his clowning failed to amuse her, and, barely managing a smile, she led the way out to the pool.

It was a lovely morning, the sun high over the eastern rim of the valley, and the bees busy amongst the flowers.

They sat in the shade of a fringed umbrella and ate in

what might, to an onlooker, have been mistaken for a comfortable silence.

In truth it was an uncomfortable one, on Rebecca's side at least, and she tried hard to think of something to say.

But, inhibited by the knowledge of how he felt about her, she could think of nothing. All the pleasure had gone out of being with him, and she would much sooner have been left alone.

She was aware that Gray looked at her from time to time, as though trying to correctly judge what her mood was, but, apparently wary of putting a foot wrong, he let the silence reign.

After a while, relaxing her guard a little, she found her gaze straying in his direction. He was peeling an orange, the rind sliding in an unbroken coil through his lean brown hands.

As he pulled the flesh into segments he glanced up and, seeing she was watching him, offered her a piece.

She shook her head mutely and looked away.

When they had done eating and finished drinking their second cup of coffee, he suggested casually, 'I thought we might take a look at the winery, if you're still interested?'

She toyed briefly with the idea of refusing, of quietly making it clear that she no longer wanted his company. But it might mean the onset of fresh hostilities, and she didn't want to risk that.

'Yes… Yes, I am,' she said at last.

'But you were thinking of saying no?'

She met his enquiring glance with a guilty one of her own.

'There's no need to answer, I can see you were.

'Look, I'm sorry you were so upset last night. It must have been very unpleasant to hear your family criticised in that way.

'But if you want me to retract what I said about your

stepsister, I'm afraid I can't. I believe it's the truth, and I'm sure you do.

'I'm convinced that both she and her mother are quite unscrupulous and will use any dirty trick in the book to get what they want.

'That doesn't mean I think *you* are like that. In fact I'm certain you're not. I firmly believe that you've been the innocent victim in all this.

'Jason, on the other hand, is very much to blame. If he was more discerning and less licentious, he would save everyone, including himself, a great deal of trouble.'

Gray finished speaking and waited for Rebecca to say something. When she didn't, he sighed. 'I had hoped speaking out would clear the air, and that we could get back to where we were.'

She looked at him, her face stony. If he thought that an apology and a facile assurance that he didn't include *her* in his condemnation would put everything right, he was very much mistaken.

'But it seems I was wrong…'

When she still said nothing, his manner becoming coolly brisk and determined, he said, 'So what if we go take a look at the winery?'

# CHAPTER EIGHT

RISING to his feet, he held out his hand, an unmistakable challenge in his green eyes.

Unwilling to engage in open warfare, she reluctantly put her hand in his and allowed him to pull her to her feet.

When she would have freed it, however, his grip tightened just enough to make it clear that he had no intention of letting it go.

Realising with a sinking heart that she was now facing a war of attrition, she gave in and, feeling rather like a prisoner, allowed herself to be escorted down the steps and into the garden.

The cloudless sky was the colour of lapis lazuli and the Californian sun poured down golden as honey. Beyond the circle of lawns and flowerbeds, as far as the eye could see, were row upon row of vines, green and lush, climbing the hillside in orderly ranks.

A crop-spraying helicopter clattered noisily along the valley, flying low over the vineyards, a trail of spray suspended behind it like fine mist.

Reaching the low wall that separated the garden from the rest of the property, they went down another flight of steps to the large stone building that housed the wine-making plant.

Ranged alongside were some enormous hoppers, and several enclosed conveyor belts. Noting her interest, Gray explained, 'They would have been used to carry the grapes from the harvesting lorries into the winery itself.'

Ignoring the big main doors, with their rusting locks and peeling green paint, he led her around the building to a side-door.

'This looks to be a better bet.'

Releasing her hand, he took a bunch of keys from his pocket and selected one.

It turned at the first attempt.

'More by good luck than good management,' he admitted with a grin as he pushed open the door to the accompaniment of creaking hinges.

Disused for a number of years, the winery stood empty apart from its existing plant, and the confines of the long, hangar-like building echoed to the sound of the heavy door swinging shut behind them, and their footsteps.

Not much light filtered through the high, dusty windows, and in the warm, musty dimness they walked until they reached a series of prefabricated buildings that Rebecca took to be offices.

A desk and chair, and a couple of old filing cabinets, proved her to be right on the first.

Opening the door of the second, Gray said, 'This is obviously the computer room, where all the information about every single vintage will have been stored. It's also where the machinery that controls the temperature of the fermentation vats is overseen.

'Then next door, I think you'll find, is the lab where, when we get into production, our chemist will do his stuff…'

Carrying on until they reached a flight of stone steps, they went down to the vaulted fermentation chambers that held the huge stainless-steel vats, with their various dials and levers.

Down here, Rebecca found, it was appreciably cooler, even dimmer, and oddly scary, like the setting for some horror movie.

'It all seems very dead at present, even a touch sinister,' Gray remarked, echoing her uneasy thought. 'But it'll come to life again when all these vats are full of wine and the dials are winking.'

She had no doubt he was correct, but right now, oppressed by the atmosphere, she couldn't wait to be outside in the sun again.

Perhaps that sense of urgency came through, because without another word Gray began to lead the way back to the stairs.

Hurrying after him, in her haste she caught the toe of her sandal against the rough edge of a flagstone and tripped.

Quick as a flash he turned and fielded her, taking her weight against his chest.

The breath momentarily knocked out of her, she lay against him, while all the attraction she had told herself was gone for good came flooding back.

But she mustn't allow herself to be attracted.

Regaining her balance, she attempted to pull free, but his arms closed around her, holding her there.

In a sudden panic, she braced her hands against his chest, and tried to push him away.

She might as well have tried to move a monolith.

Staring at the strong column of his throat, she ordered jerkily, 'Let me go.'

'Afraid to look at me?'

Lifting her chin, she met his eyes. 'No, I'm not.'

'Good.'

Before she could guess his intention, he bent his head to cover her mouth with his.

She began to struggle, but, pinning her arms to her sides, he held her easily while he kissed her long and leisurely.

When he finally drew back a little, she cried hoarsely, 'You're nothing but a brute. I hate you.'

His mouth swooped once more and, taking advantage of her parted lips, he deepened the kiss, exploring her mouth with a kind of insolent enjoyment that set every nerve in her body quivering.

It was punishment, she knew, but even so, her senses

reeling, she wanted to put her arms around his neck and kiss him back.

When he finally released her, dizzy and off balance, she staggered and he was forced to reach out and steady her.

'All right?' he queried after a moment.

Refusing to answer, she gathered the shreds of her dignity around her, and headed somewhat drunkenly for the stairs.

Walking beside her, he put a strong hand beneath her elbow.

She was mortified to find she was glad of it.

They were almost at the end of the winery, when Gray paused briefly to take a closer look at one of the pieces of equipment.

Anxious to get outside, Rebecca carried on and reached the door first. Noticing he had left the bunch of keys dangling in the lock, obeying a sudden wild impulse, she slammed the door and locked it.

Let him stew in his own juice for a while, she thought with a surge of heady triumph.

A moment later, the keys in her hand, she was hurrying away.

By the time she reached the house the feeling of triumph had started to fade, and apprehension was fast taking its place.

Her legs suddenly shaky and a hollow sensation in the pit of her stomach, she dropped the keys on the patio table, and sank into the nearest chair.

Why in heaven's name had she been so idiotic? she berated herself. He would be furious.

Still, after the way he had treated her, he deserved all he got.

But two wrongs didn't make a right, conscience pointed out, so it was no use attempting to justify her actions. It had been utterly stupid, and would do nothing to help the situation.

Already feeling bad, she felt even worse when she contemplated the fact that sooner or later she would have to let him out and face his wrath.

She had no doubt that the longer she was doing just that, the angrier he'd be. Perhaps if she went straight back now and apologised?

To hell with that! her fighting spirit answered. She might as well be hung for a sheep as a lamb. But, agitated and restless as she was, with nothing to do to pass the time, every minute was going to seem like an hour…

'Cooee!' a voice called. 'Anyone at home?'

A second or two later Gloria Redford appeared round the side of the house. She was wearing blue cotton trousers, a tie-dyed top and the same old sneakers.

'Hi!' she said cheerfully. 'I'm just off to Napa, so I thought I'd pop in to see if there was anything you needed. Mr Gallagher's working, I suppose?'

Without waiting for an answer, she carried on, 'You're not looking too happy… If you're feeling bored, do you want to have a run into town with me?'

To Rebecca the offer seemed to be the answer to her prayers. Carefully, she asked, 'How long are you likely to be there?'

'No more than an hour.'

'Well, if you're sure it's no trouble?'

'None at all. I'd appreciate the company.'

Rebecca hesitated for a moment, wrestling with her conscience. But Gray wouldn't come to any harm, and she'd let him out the moment she got back…

'In that case I'd love to come. I'll just get my bag and lock the door.'

'Do you need to lock up, if Mr Gallagher's home?'

'He's in the winery,' Rebecca said and, feeling her face grow hot, turned and hurried into the house to find her bag.

While the older woman did her shopping, Rebecca strolled around the pleasant town. Any other time she would have really enjoyed seeing Napa, but today it was simply a distraction, and her heart wasn't in it.

When the best part of an hour had passed, having agreed on one of the coffee shops as a meeting place, Rebecca found a table and sipped a cappuccino while she waited.

Gloria arrived some twenty minutes later. Saying shopping always made her hungry, she ordered a large coffee and a plate of cookies.

A good-natured, garrulous woman, when she found Rebecca had little to say she launched into an account of her family while she worked her way through the cookies.

She had, she announced with no trace of self-pity, three young sons, a husband—who was a labourer in the wine industry—an arthritic mother and her elderly father-in-law to look after. All of whom lived under the same roof.

'We could really do with a bigger house, but through no fault of his own Ben has just lost his job, so we'll be lucky to keep this one.

'Unless your Mr Gallagher would be willing to put in a good word for him? I mean, when the company starts re-staffing the Santa Rosa winery?'

'I'm afraid I can't answer that. But you could always try asking him,' Rebecca suggested.

'Thanks, I will. Ben's very experienced—he's done everything from picking to driving a lorry and working in the fermentation rooms.'

After a while, growing restive, Rebecca glanced furtively at her watch, and was horrified to see how quickly the time had flown by. 'I really ought to be getting back,' she said, and waved for the bill.

'That's fine by me,' Gloria agreed accommodatingly. 'Though I'll have to stop for gas first.'

By the time Rebecca had climbed out of the battered pick-up at the entrance to Santa Rosa, more than three hours had elapsed.

Gray was bound to be hot and thirsty, she thought anxiously, and no doubt he'd be absolutely *livid*. Her imagination provided her with a picture of him pacing like a caged tiger.

Oh, if only she'd had more sense. But it was much too late for regrets.

She thanked Gloria and, panic snapping at her heels, practically ran up the drive. By the time she reached the house she was hot and perspiring freely, and her hands were so unsteady it took several attempts before she could unlock the door.

Having finally managed to let herself in, she went straight through and opened the sliding glass panels that led onto the patio.

The bunch of keys had been lying in the sun, and the hot metal almost burnt her hand as she snatched them up and hurried towards the winery.

Her heart pounding, her breath coming uncomfortably fast, she found the right key after a couple of attempts, and, unlocking the door, pushed it open.

Apart from the creaking of the hinges, there wasn't a sound. Holding the heavy door, she looked along the length of the building. There was no sign of movement, and not a soul to be seen.

Reluctant to venture any further, she stood in the doorway and called his name.

When there was no answer, she called again several times, as loudly as possible, and stood listening to the echoes.

Perhaps he was in the office, or the lab, or the computer room? Thinking about it, Gray wasn't the sort of man to do nothing while he waited. He would almost certainly be using his enforced imprisonment to think and plan for when Santa Rosa became fully operational again.

She knew from her earlier visit that the door closed itself, but, unable to find a way to prop it open, she was forced to let it bang behind her.

Making her way down to the prefabricated buildings, she peered through each of their windows in turn.

All three were undoubtedly empty.

Her heart throwing itself against her ribcage, she thought, what if something had happened to him?

But what could possibly have happened to him?

Suppose he'd been going down to the fermentation chamber? He might have tripped on the stone steps and banged his head. He could be lying seriously injured, or even dead.

Oh, dear God, and it would be *her* fault.

Her footsteps loud in the silence, she forced herself to go to where she could see down the steps. There was no sprawling figure.

Well, he had to be *somewhere*.

The only place left where he could possibly be was the fermentation chamber itself. Advancing to the top of the steps, she called his name.

There wasn't a sound.

But he *must* be there.

She called again, despairingly.

Only silence greeted her.

Gritting her teeth, she marched down the steps and peered into the gloom.

It seemed to be deserted.

Dreading the thought of going any further into that eerie place, she turned to go back.

Then, knowing she couldn't just walk away without checking properly, she forced herself to walk the length of the chamber, peering to right and left as she went.

When she reached the end, she realised she'd been holding her breath and let it out in a long, shuddering sigh.

It just didn't make sense.

Unless he was playing some cruel game of hide-and-seek to get his own back?

Suppose he was lurking behind one of the vats, waiting to spring out on her? Or maybe creep up silently behind her?

Fighting down her over-active imagination, she told herself sharply not to be a fool. Apart from anything else, in such a vast, empty, echoing space, the lightest brush of a foot against the stone floor would make a noise she was bound to hear.

All the same, she couldn't prevent herself from hurrying and keeping glancing over her shoulder.

It was a great relief when she reached the stairs, and by the time she had climbed them her legs were starting to feel like chewed string.

She was almost at the end of the winery when a dark shape huddled beneath a wooden rack full of dusty bits and pieces caught her eye. The hairs prickling on the back of her neck, she forced herself to walk over and take a closer look.

It seemed to be a pile of old sacks. Stooping, she picked up the top one to make sure there was nothing underneath, and dropped it again hastily when a large spider ran out.

Backing away and straightening up unwarily, she found her hair was caught on a series of hooks that dangled from beneath the rack. In a sudden panic, she tried to pull free.

Realising it was only making matters worse, she forced herself to stand quietly for a few seconds before putting up her hands to feel for the hooks. By the time she managed to free the last strand, her hair had come unplaited, she was covered in dust, and half suffocated.

Hurrying to the door, she dragged it open and almost fell out into the fresh air and sunshine. Then, leaning against the wall, she took several deep breaths while the tension that had gripped her eased a little.

When she felt a bit better she re-locked the door and made her way back through the garden, wondering all the time where on earth Gray could have got to.

But one thing was certain, he couldn't have vanished into thin air, so somehow he must have found a way out of the place…

Busy with her thoughts, she had reached the pool before she realised that he was in the water, moving in a smooth, effortless crawl. His clothes had been tossed over one of the loungers.

She felt a rush of mingled emotions. Relief that he was quite safe, futile anger that she'd put herself through so much torment, and a mounting fear that soon she would have to answer for what she had done.

In the middle of a racing turn at the far end of the pool, he saw her. Levering himself out of the water in a single, lithe movement, he began to walk towards her.

Stark naked, with an all-over tan and the physique of an athlete, he looked superbly fit and virile, and she caught her breath.

His eyes never leaving her face, he advanced so purposefully that it took every ounce of courage not to turn and run.

It wasn't until he got closer that she noticed his shoulder was bruised and he had a nasty-looking cut on his upper arm.

Taking the bunch of keys from her hand, he tossed them onto one of the pool-side loungers, and, surveying her dusty, dishevelled state, enquired silkily, 'Enjoyed your second tour of the winery?'

His manner was quiet, almost pleasant, but beneath that calm veneer she could sense he was furious.

When apprehension kept her silent, he pursued, 'You've been a long time.'

'How do you…?'

'I was on my way down the hillside, after taking a look at the vines, and I watched you go in.'

Her jaw dropped. 'Why didn't you call out to me?'

'Why do you think?'

Watching her confusion, he said, 'When you left the keys in the lock, I was sorely tempted to get a bit of my own back.'

She shuddered, and, her mouth dry, asked, 'How did you get out?'

'Through one of the windows.'

'I thought they were too high.'

'So did I, until I eventually managed to find the remains of an old metal ladder.'

Seeing her gaze was fixed on the jagged cut on his upper arm, he added, 'It gave way just as I got the window open.'

'I—I'm sorry,' she stammered.

'I'm glad to hear it.'

'Not for locking you in.' The rebellious words were out before she could prevent them.

He raised a dark brow.

'If you hadn't kissed me like that... But I didn't want you to get hurt.'

'It's only a scratch,' he said dismissively.

But it was a lot worse than that, and she asked anxiously, 'Did you put some antiseptic on it?'

'No.'

'You should have done.'

'I couldn't get into the house.'

Watching her hand fly to her mouth, he said wryly, 'When I found everything locked up, I thought you might be anticipating a siege.'

'I went into Napa with Mrs Redford,' she admitted in a small voice.

'Yes, I saw the pick-up bring you back. Three hours is a long time to be left cooling one's heels.'

Biting her lip, she stayed silent.

'But no doubt you thought I deserved it. That it was fitting retribution.'

So far he hadn't so much as raised his voice, but he wasn't the kind of man to allow a woman to get the better of him, and she wondered when he would finally unleash his pent-up anger.

The waiting, in itself, was a form of punishment, building up the tension, fraying her nerves until they threatened to snap.

Longing to sit down and have a cool drink, she wiped a trickle of perspiration from her grimy forehead with the back of her hand.

'You look all hot and bothered,' he commented, moving towards her. 'Perhaps a swim might help?'

There was a hint of smooth menace in his voice that rattled her further, and, retreating a step, she shook her head. 'No, I don't—'

Still advancing, he urged, 'I can thoroughly recommend it. But you wouldn't want to go in with your clothes on, would you?'

In a single swift movement, he caught the hem of her dress and pulled it over her head.

She wasn't wearing a bra, and in spite of her protests it was the work of a moment to strip off her dainty briefs.

'That's better,' he said approvingly.

'Leave me alone,' she cried, backing away. 'I don't want to go in. I can't—'

The words ended in a strangled yelp and a splash, as she tumbled backwards into the deep end.

She came up gasping and choking, helplessly thrashing the water, before going under again.

A moment later, from behind, strong hands caught her under the arms, and with one swift kick Gray carried them both to the surface.

Held safely by him, she filled her lungs with air, and her first wild terror began to subside a little. Still she felt panicky, her breasts rising and falling with her laboured breathing.

'You're quite safe,' he assured her. 'I won't let you go.'

Turning onto his back, so that his body supported hers,

he settled her head on his chest and smoothed the long strands of wet hair away from her face.

After a minute or so, reassured by his strength and confidence, she began to relax and they floated easily together.

Feeling that change, he said quietly, 'Forgive me, I had no idea you couldn't swim.'

'When I was quite small I fell into one of the local ponds and almost drowned. It frightened me half to death, so I never did learn.'

'Don't you think it's time we remedied that?'

'It may be too late.'

'It's never too late. The first step is to stop being afraid, and learn to enjoy the water. Are you happy at the moment?'

'Yes,' she admitted.

The water was pleasantly warm. She could feel the brush of his taut thighs against hers, and the way the slight motion of his arms made little eddies.

Perhaps it was her reaction to being safe, but her limbs felt heavy and languid, and she was filled with an unaccountable happiness.

After a while, he said softly, 'Stretched out like this, anyone can float. Give it a try.'

A moment later she was floating without his help, just his hand cupping her head lightly, reassuringly. As he'd promised, the water supported her, bore her up, and with a feeling of gladness, of release, she let go of her fear.

Even when he removed his hand, it didn't return.

'Kick down,' he instructed.

She obeyed, and they were face to face, his hands circling her waist.

Looking down at her, he asked softly, 'Did I ever tell you how beautiful your breasts are?'

Her cheeks grew hot as she remembered her nakedness, but the expression on his face made her want to glory in it, rather than try to hide it.

As though sensing how she felt, he cupped the nape of

her neck with one hand, and used the other to lift her face
to his.

That gentle touch was command enough, and her lips
parted in response.

While he kissed her deeply, into the vacuum left by the
ebb of her previous fear a different sensation started to flow,
a passionate need that came in liquid waves, sweeping over
her, drowning everything in its path.

Responding to that need, he slid both hands down her
neck and shoulders, then, one hand spread across the small
of her back, he brought the other up under her breasts.

She made a little sound deep in her throat as he caressed
the wet, smooth skin and found the sensitive nipples, which
firmed instantly beneath his touch.

Then, with a shudder, she closed her eyes and gave herself up to the sheer pleasure his skilful fingers were evoking.

When both his arms slid around her, drawing her against
him, she went willingly, pressing even closer until her nipples were brushing the sprinkle of crisp dark hair on his
chest.

'Put your arms around my neck,' he whispered against
her lips, 'and we'll share a new experience.' When, feeling
his hard male need of her, she obeyed, he cradled the backs
of her thighs and guided them into place around his waist.

Her desire as strong as his own, she locked herself there,
her long hair floating around their shoulders like mermaid's
tresses.

His arms holding her, his legs moving just enough to keep
them afloat, he made love to her with tenderness and passion, filling her being with such intense delight that she gave
a little gasping cry at each long, slow thrust.

His eyes gleaming with a purely male triumph, he encouraged her, 'Yes, my love... Yes...' until she cried out
one last time and began to shudder helplessly against him.

When she became conscious once more of the water lapping around her shoulders and the warmth of the sun on her head, her inhibitions returning, she started to pull away.

'Don't,' he said urgently. 'I realise you're used to bottling up your emotions, hiding what you're thinking and feeling, but don't do that with me. Talk to me.

'You enjoyed what we just shared, didn't you?'

She nodded.

'Not good enough, I'm afraid. I want to hear you say it aloud. I want you to *tell* me what you were thinking and feeling.'

But she had stopped thinking, and she could find no words to express such extremes of feeling.

Looking up at him, she whispered, 'It was absolutely wonderful.'

'Is that all?' he teased.

Lifting her chin, she added wonderingly, 'I never knew physical pleasure could be so…*intense*…'

He kissed her gently. 'Some of it was due to the fact that you were so terrified previously. Extremes of sensation heighten one another.

'Now, feeling confident enough to make it to the side on your own?'

'I don't think so,' she admitted.

'Then come here.' Settling her cheek against his shoulder, he lay on his back once more, and paddled them lazily to the shallow end.

As soon as she found her feet he hauled himself out and, water pouring off him, turned to offer her his hands. A moment later she was standing dripping beside him.

His eyes running over her appreciatively, he bent to lick a drop of water from one of her pink nipples, before drawing it into his mouth.

The desire she had thought appeased came back with a rush, but, uneasy in the broad daylight, she gasped, 'Don't! Someone may see us.'

'Mmm...' he murmured, and continued to suckle with obvious enjoyment.

Her instinct was to hold his dark head to her breast, but, refusing to give way to it, she took a handful of wet hair, and tugged.

He retaliated, and, feeling the light pressure of his teeth, she let go of his hair and froze.

When, in his own good time, he released her and drew back, she turned and bolted into the house.

Gathering up her clothing and his own, he followed at a more leisurely pace.

Still partially entangled in a web of sensual pleasure, Rebecca had showered, shampooed her hair and was blow-drying it before it came home to her exactly how idiotic she had been.

With no intention of resuming their affair, she had done just that.

No, she hadn't, she corrected herself quickly. Certainly she'd behaved stupidly, but just because she had let him make love to her again, it didn't mean she was prepared to go on with the affair.

But it *did* mean that she was going to find it harder to convince him she really meant it when next time she said no.

Well, she would just have to make her position clear straight away, so he knew the score.

But she didn't relish the prospect.

If only she'd behaved more sensibly in the first place it wouldn't have been necessary. If she hadn't locked him in the winery, she wouldn't have ended up in the pool...

Still, some good had come of it. Apart from all the pleasure they had shared—which she didn't want to think about—he seemed to have forgotten his anger, and she had undoubtedly taken the first big step towards conquering her fear of water.

She finished drying her hair, and, wrapping herself in a

bathsheet, opened the door a crack and peeped into the bedroom.

When there was no sign of Gray, she went through to find some clothes.

Pulling on a cotton shirtwaister, and leaving her hair loose around her shoulders, she went outside. As she had expected, he was lounging on the patio. There was a tray of drinks at his elbow.

He looked coolly elegant in pale trousers and an olive-green shirt open at the neck. Rising to his feet at her approach, he settled her into a chair, enquiring, 'Are you getting hungry?'

'Not really.'

'Then I'll leave it a little while before I rustle up something to eat. In the meantime...' He poured two tall glasses of Pimm's, and handed her one.

'Thank you.' She drank thirstily.

When her glass was empty, taking a deep breath, she began, 'About what happened in the pool. I didn't mean to—'

'Behave so wantonly?' he mocked her gently.

Watching her cheeks grow warm, he said with satisfaction, 'You're beginning to lose some of those built-in inhibitions, and let go—'

'But that's just it,' she broke in desperately. 'I shouldn't have done. I didn't want to—'

'You'd be happier if all our lovemaking took place in bed at night, behind closed doors?'

'No, that's not what I mean. I don't intend there to *be* any more lovemaking. I didn't mean to go on with this...affair... I didn't *want* to...'

Immediately the air was thick with tension.

Stammering a little, her golden eyes pleading, she went on, 'W-we're in separate rooms now and I'd like it to stay that way.'

'I see,' he said slowly. 'So you still haven't forgiven me for what I said about your family?'

The noise of a motorbike coming up the drive practically drowned out his words. Almost immediately the engine note died, and they heard the faint peal of the front doorbell.

'It seems we have a visitor. Excuse me.' He rose to his feet and disappeared into the house.

# CHAPTER NINE

REBECCA sighed. The interruption was more than welcome. Having made her point, she didn't want to get involved in another diatribe on her family's lack of principles.

Gray had been gone only a short time when the motorbike engine spluttered into life once more and was vigorously revved up. A moment later it roared away down the drive.

Whoever it was hadn't stayed long. Perhaps it had been Mrs Redford's eldest boy bringing a message?

As though to confirm that, Gray reappeared with an opened envelope in his hand. His face giving no clue to what he was thinking, he tossed it on the table and resumed his seat.

Then, as though waiting for some question, he slanted her a glance. When she said nothing, he asked casually, 'Fancy going out?'

'Going out?'

'Having failed to reach us by phone, your admirer has sent a hand-delivered invitation to a barbecue party this evening.'

'My admirer? I don't know what you mean.'

'Andrew Scrivener.'

'Andrew Scrivener?'

'If you go on like this we shall have to change your name to Polly.'

She took a deep breath. 'Andrew Scrivener has invited us to a barbecue party this evening?'

'Got it.'

When she still looked blank, Gray said, 'If you remember, the night we had dinner in Boston he told us that he was coming out to California, and that he owned Hillsden

151

Wineries. Hillsden is only about eighteen miles away, which, as he observed, makes us practically neighbours.'

'Now you mention it, yes, I do remember. But it had gone clean out of my head.' Apologetically, she added, 'So much happened later…'

His smile slyly reminiscent, he murmured, 'Yes.'

Feeling her face grow warm, she objected, 'But didn't he say in a week or so?'

'That's what he said.'

'So presumably he's brought his visit forward for some reason.'

'Exactly.'

He put so much meaning into the word that she lifted her chin abruptly. 'You don't seriously think *I'm* the reason?'

'I don't doubt it. I saw the way he kept eyeing you that night in Boston. Like a cat looking at a saucer of cream.'

'Oh,' she said blankly.

'So you'd better get your best bib and tucker on.'

'Then you intend to go?'

'Unless you don't want to.'

She didn't but, unwilling to say so out of hand, she asked, 'Will it make any difference to your business deal?'

'I very much doubt it. So feel free to say so if you don't want to go.'

He had said a *barbecue party*… Wondering if some different company might ease the current situation between them, she hesitated.

Noting that hesitation, he gave her a challenging smile. 'On the other hand, if you want to make hay while the sun shines?'

Stung by his words, his inference that she wasn't so different from her family after all, she picked up the gauntlet and, returning his smile with a brilliant one of her own, agreed, 'I might just do that. What time do we need to start?'

Perhaps, even then, she was hoping he would back down, say he hadn't meant it, that it had been merely a joke.

But, his face devoid of expression, he said, 'Half an hour should do it.'

'Then I'll go and find my best bib and tucker.'

Her heart like lead, she left him sitting there and went back to her bedroom.

As a gesture of defiance she made up with care, before brushing out her hair and swirling it into a smooth coil on top of her head. Then, donning a silky, slim-fitting sheath in navy-blue, she slid her feet into dull-gold sandals and fastened gold hoops to her neat lobes.

She had just emerged when Gray appeared, and, noticing that he hadn't changed, she wondered if she was over-dressed for a barbecue. Well, if she was, she would just have to brazen it out.

He looked her over from head to foot, and, vexed by that arrogant appraisal, she twirled to give him a back view.

'Perfect,' he approved. 'Just the right combination of sex-iness and classiness to get Scrivener going.'

'I'm so pleased you think so.'

They walked out to the car in the golden light of a late evening. There was no sign of a breeze and the air seemed to be holding its breath.

'Do you want the top up or down? In other words, are you afraid of getting ruffled?' Gray asked, mockery in his voice.

'Down, please,' she said crisply.

With music playing softly, and the gentle flow of balmy air like velvet as it caressed her face, she should have en-joyed the drive.

But she didn't.

His dark face set, his manner withdrawn, as though deep in thought, Gray drove in silence and without a single glance in her direction.

Daylight was giving way to dusk when they drew into the driveway of Hillsden Wineries, and as they neared the sprawling ranch-style house they saw that the place was ablaze with lights.

To the right, a gravel parking area already boasted a string of prestigious cars.

Drawing up alongside them, Gray commented sardonically, 'This should give you a good idea of the company Scrivener attracts. Not an ordinary wagon in sight.

'By the way, before we go in, may I give you a word of warning? If you're not serious about becoming the fourth Mrs Scrivener, don't let him get you alone.'

'And if I am?'

'Do the same as you did with Jason—play hard to get. He'll respect you for that.'

She hadn't played hard to get with *him*, she thought, feeling a kind of despair. With Gray, there had never been any hesitation. Instinct alone had ruled her...

He slipped from behind the wheel and, with his usual courtesy, came round to cup her bare elbow and help her alight.

All the windows in the house had been thrown wide, and as they approached they could hear the sound of music and laughter. The music, she noted, was smooth and middle-of-the-road.

A moment later Andrew Scrivener stepped onto the porch and lifted a hand in greeting.

'Our host appears to have been looking out for us,' Gray murmured in Rebecca's ear. 'Just shows how keen he is.'

As if to confirm this, Scrivener came down the steps to meet them.

His heavy face, and the grizzled, crinkly hair brushed straight back from his forehead, were tolerably familiar. But this time, dressed informally in lightweight fawn trousers and a white open-necked shirt, he looked younger than she recalled, and somewhat less intimidating.

Even so, that powerful face, with its large, hooked nose and sensual mouth, sent a shiver down her spine.

'Gallagher... How are you? Nice to see you again.' He clapped Gray on the shoulder with a surprising show of bonhomie.

'Miss Ferris...' His hooded eyes lingering on her face, he lifted her hand to his lips in a gesture that, on a lesser man, might have appeared overdone. 'I'm pleased you could come.'

A glint in his eye, Gray said, 'Rebecca wouldn't have missed it for the world, would you, darling?'

Scrivener glanced at him sharply, before turning to escort them inside.

The large room, and the terrace beyond, seemed to be full of people standing in little groups, laughing and talking, all with glasses in their hands.

Along with their designer party clothes and Californian tans, they sported the unmistakable aura that success and money brought in their wake. Yet there was an atmosphere of informal friendliness that was very pleasant and welcoming.

A stunning blonde, dressed in gold harem trousers and a bra-top, detached herself from the crowd and, making a bee-line for Gray, took his arm.

'Hi! You must be Gray Gallagher. I'm Sue Collins, Jeff's sister, and the unofficial hostess.

'First of all, there's a senator here dying to meet you! Then I'll get you a drink and introduce you to the rest of the crowd.'

A second later, in one of the neatest manoeuvres Rebecca had ever witnessed, Gray was whisked away.

Finding herself left with Andrew Scrivener, she said the first thing that came into her head. 'I didn't realise you were travelling to the west coast quite so soon.'

Those obsidian eyes, set deep beneath almost black brows, looked straight into hers. 'Some business I considered urgent came up,' he said smoothly, 'so I changed my plans and flew in yesterday.'

Flustered by their almost hypnotic quality, she dragged her gaze away and, indicating the party going on around them, asked, 'How on earth did you manage to arrange all this in so short a time?'

'My manager, Jeff Collins, said if I didn't mind the whole thing being simple and informal, he and his sister would make all the arrangements, and he would do the barbecuing. So I left them to it.

'Now, how about a drink?'

Already regretting coming, she answered, 'Yes, please, I'd love one.'

Spreading a hand across the small of her back in what could only be described as a proprietary manner, he ushered her through the open French windows and onto the terrace.

An almost full moon, silver and ethereal-looking, was rising above the trees, and the air was fragrant with the scent of flowering shrubs and woodsmoke from the big barbecue.

A couple of well-stocked trestle tables covered with white cloths made up the bar, while a little way away two more stood empty, waiting for the food.

As her host had said, it was all quite informal, and guests drifted up to help themselves to whatever drink they fancied. Most of them, she noticed, were choosing wine.

'Now then, what would you like, Rebecca? I may call you Rebecca?'

Forcing a smile, she replied politely, 'Of course,' just as Gray, with Sue Collins in close pursuit, appeared by their sides.

Ignoring them, Scrivener said, 'And do call me Andrew. So what's it to be?'

About to say lemonade, she changed her mind. 'I'll have a glass of wine, if I may, please...'

'Andrew...' Scrivener prompted.

'Andrew,' she echoed obediently, avoiding Gray's mocking eyes.

'I can recommend the Cabernet Sauvignon,' he told her and proceeded to fill two glasses.

Gray chose a non-alcoholic drink on the grounds that he was driving, and then, accompanied by Scrivener and Sue Collins, they began to circulate.

As though to make his intentions abundantly clear, Scrivener always managed to put his bulk between Rebecca and Gray, and while he introduced her to a variety of people he curved his hand around her slim waist and left it there.

Though she was made uncomfortable by such close proximity, his touch was so light and easy that she could find no valid reason to object.

Deciding to ignore it as best she could, she did her utmost to concentrate on the interesting people she was meeting.

Though a lot of the guests were in the wine trade as growers or shippers, mingled with them was a world-famous author, the US senator that Sue Collins had mentioned earlier, and an ex-president.

There was also, causing a flutter of excitement among the ladies, a Hollywood director and a handsome male star, who were filming in the area.

Occasionally, caught up in separate conversations, the pairs moved from group to group at different times. But, despite all Sue Collins' efforts, Gray never left Rebecca's side for long, while Scrivener never left it at all.

Only when the ex-president came up and murmured, 'I'd like a word in your ear, Andrew,' did he reluctantly excuse himself and move away.

'Judging by our Andrew's manner,' Gray said in an undertone, 'you're home and dry...'

His cynical words hurt, and she bit her lip as he went on, 'I feel I ought to offer my congratulations, but I see my watchdog homing in.'

Almost as tall as he was, and curvaceous to the point where her bosom appeared to be inadequately restrained by the low-cut bra-top she was wearing, Sue Collins slipped a hand through his arm, and pressed herself against him.

'I need a big, strong man.' She fluttered her eyelashes at him. Getting no response, she pursued, 'Jeff's busy at the moment, so will you be a sweetie and bring up some more wine for me?'

'Certainly.' Gray gave Rebecca a droll look and allowed himself to be led away.

A moment later there was the dull boom of a gong being struck, and a shout of, 'Come and get it!'

Huge oval platters piled with steaks and chicken, sausages and ribs, corn on the cob and vegetable brochettes appeared on the empty tables along with rolls, various salads, plates, cutlery and napkins.

The guests milled about, helping themselves to food and topping up their drinks. Then while some stood around in little groups eating and talking, others sat on various chairs and loungers, or perched on the low wall surrounding the terrace.

Seeing Andrew Scrivener coming back, Rebecca glanced around anxiously. She could see no sign of Gray, and though she hated his cynicism she wanted him there as protection.

Looking pleased to see her alone, Scrivener said, 'I'm sorry to have had to leave you, my dear.'

She found her voice and assured him, 'That's quite all right.'

'Now, suppose we get something to eat while it's good and hot? What would you like?'

When he had filled two plates with chicken and salad, and refilled their glasses, indicating a table and two chairs set beneath one of the old cedar trees, he suggested, 'Let's get away from the crowd.'

Remembering Gray's warning, she hesitated. Had this been planned?

But they wouldn't be *alone*, she reassured herself, they

weren't that far away from the house, and there were plenty of people within sight.

All the same, she followed reluctantly as he led the way down the terrace steps and across the smooth green lawn.

As he pulled out a chair for her, she felt a cowardly urge to turn and run. But she was just being foolish, she told herself sternly, sitting down. If he showed any signs of doing anything she objected to, she could simply get up and walk away.

In the event, he behaved like a perfect gentleman, and while they ate, at his most charismatic, he talked easily about music and a series of symphony concerts he'd been to.

Deciding that, no doubt influenced by Gray, she must have been imagining some ulterior motive, she relaxed somewhat.

Even so, not wholly comfortable, she was wondering how soon she could suggest that they rejoin the others, when he queried casually, 'Do you like the Napa Valley?'

'Very much, what little I've seen of it.'

He nodded his approval. 'The west-coast climate suits me and, as I've every intention of living out here for at least part of the year, I'm having a house built.'

She could vaguely recall that the night they had dined together in Boston he'd mentioned it.

'Close to here?' she asked, for something to say.

'Just the other side of the garden, where the hill starts to climb. It's as good as finished, and they'll be starting on the pool next week. Come and take a look. I'd like to know what you think.'

Getting to his feet, he added with rather touching pride, 'I drew up the plans myself.'

Reluctant to appear churlish, she rose.

Even then, if he had touched her in any way, she would have made some excuse not to go, but he merely waited for her, smiling.

He was a big man, as tall as Gray, and heavily built. Very aware of his bulk looming by her side, she accompanied him along an unpaved path that skirted the garden.

It was a bright, moonlit night, the air still and balmy, the sky a deep, cloudless blue pricked with stars. A beautiful night for romance.

Only Gray didn't believe in romance.

She wondered what he and Sue Collins were doing, then wished she hadn't as a picture of the blonde's ample cleavage flashed into her mind.

'How is the holiday going?' Andrew Scrivener's voice broke into her thoughts.

'Very well,' she answered evenly.

After a moment, he went on, 'When we met in Boston you said you were still carrying a torch for young Beaumont, and the relationship between you and Gallagher was quite platonic.'

When she said nothing, he went on, 'I thought he might have managed to change your mind.'

Carefully avoiding his eyes, she asked, 'What makes you think that?'

'Two reasons. Where before you were merely beautiful, now you look alive...glowing...'

'I can explain that,' she said lightly. 'I've started to catch the sun.'

'I didn't mean that kind of glow. You look fulfilled. Like a woman who's quite recently been made love to. Can you explain that?'

For one mad moment she considered telling him the truth, but even to end his pursuit—if that was what it was—she couldn't bring herself to admit she'd been such a fool.

Shaking her head, she suggested, 'Perhaps you've had too many glasses of wine?' Then hastily, 'But you said *two* reasons.'

'Gallagher's Cerberus act.'

'I beg your pardon?'

'The way he's been guarding you. He's scarcely left your side, and when he has he's never taken his eyes off you. He appears to be as jealous as hell.'

'He certainly has no reason to be,' she said with perfect truth.

'I'm delighted to hear it.'

There was so much satisfaction in his voice that she felt a quiver of alarm.

They were quite a way from the house now and there wasn't a soul in sight. She could still hear the music faintly, but it only served to make her feel even more isolated.

Wishing she had had more sense than to come, she began a shade desperately, 'It's further than I expected. If Gray's waiting to go home, he'll wonder where I've got to.'

Scrivener laughed. 'If I know Sue Collins, he'll have his hands full. In any case we're almost there. You'll see it any second.'

They reached a gap in the trees, and there it was in front of them, a sprawling, split-level place built into the hillside.

For some reason she had expected it to be soulless and ultra-modern, all sharp angles and straight lines. Instead it was colour-washed and harmonious, with long, arched windows and a covered balcony that gave it a charming old-fashioned look.

Though the moonlight leached away the colours, leaving everything an eerie silvery blue, she could tell that in daylight it would be quite vibrant.

'Why, it's lovely!' she exclaimed, momentarily forgetting her apprehension.

He looked pleased by her enthusiasm. 'I'm glad you like it. Let me show you the inside.'

'No!' Then more moderately, 'No, thank you. Some other time perhaps.' *In broad daylight with at least one other person present.* 'Gray didn't want to be too late starting back,' she lied.

'Very well,' he gave in gracefully. 'Some other time. But

I'd like you to see it. I think you'll be impressed. It has some unusual features.'

'And you were able to design it all yourself?'

'When I was young, I trained as an architect. I wanted to create something lasting and beautiful.'

Seeing a sensitive side that she hadn't realised existed, for the first time she found something to like about him.

'Now it's merely a hobby I enjoy, along with music. Of course, I still have what amounts to a passion for beautiful things. Especially women.

'Though it takes more than mere beauty to touch my heart these days. I've had three wives, all of them beautiful, all of them with brains, but somehow it hasn't worked.

'None of them have had the qualities I've been hoping to find in a woman.'

Wary of the turn the conversation was taking, Rebecca began to walk determinedly back the way they had come, and of necessity Scrivener followed her.

'As well as being sexually attractive,' he pursued, 'I want my next wife to be honest, to have strength of character and a maternal streak, as well as a certain *je ne sais quoi* that sets her apart from other women.'

As they reached the edge of the trees he stopped abruptly and, gripping her upper arms, turned her to face him.

'After we met in London all those months ago, I found myself thinking about you, unable to get you out of my mind. I was convinced that, as well as brains and beauty, you had almost everything I'd ever wanted in a woman.

'I learnt as much as I could about your background and family life, and I was about to try to arrange another meeting, when I heard a whisper that you were engaged to young Beaumont… It was something of a blow.

'Seeing you again in Boston was not only a surprise but also a great pleasure, and when you said you would like children it confirmed my earlier impression that you're just the woman I've been looking for.

'I'm not a young man any longer and I can't afford to let the grass grow under my feet, so I'm taking this opportunity to ask you to marry me, Rebecca.'

Though she had been apprehensive, half waiting for something to happen, now it *had*, she was stunned and speechless, totally unprepared.

As she stood as though turned to ivory in the moonlight his grip tightened and, drawing her close, he bent to kiss her.

Coming to life, she cried, 'No, don't!'

His hold slackened a little, and she pulled away as far as his grip on her upper arms would allow. 'I can't marry you. I don't love you.'

'I don't expect you to love me,' he said decisively. 'I'm well aware that you're still carrying a torch for young Beaumont, but now he's no longer on the scene to complicate matters—'

'I could never marry a man I didn't love,' she burst out agitatedly.

'It doesn't matter a great deal whether you love me or not, so long as you make me the kind of wife I need. In return I'll give you everything you could possibly want. I'm good in bed, I can keep you happy and satisfied, take the best care of our children...'

As she began to shake her head, he went on, 'I'm a very rich man. I can provide the kind of lifestyle some women would kill for—'

'I don't want to marry you,' she broke in urgently, 'and I certainly don't want your money.'

'Don't you want what it could buy? Think! If you had unlimited money, what would you choose? Diamonds? Pearls? Mink? A yacht?'

'I don't want any of those,' she cried hoarsely.

His black eyes on her face, he persisted, 'There must be something you've dreamt of owning? Something you'd give your eye-teeth for?'

'Only one thing… Elmslee Manor. My family home.'

'Is it on the market?'

'It was.'

'Then consider it yours. I'll give you the deeds on the day you marry me.'

'You don't know what you're saying. It would cost a small fortune.'

'I have a large fortune. If it happens to be already sold I'll offer the buyer more. Double if necessary. Everyone has a price.'

Looking him straight in the eye, she said clearly, '*I* don't.'

His grip tightened and he dragged her against his big, heavy body, crushing her to him. 'Damn it, Rebecca, don't play games with me. You're what I want, and I intend to have you.'

'No! Let me go!'

But, holding her easily in spite of her struggles, he gripped her chin with a powerful hand and an instant later his hot, wet mouth was covering hers, the fierceness of his kiss stopping her breath and forcing her head back.

It was her worst nightmare come true.

Then suddenly he was plucked away from her as though he was a lightweight and sent staggering backwards. 'Perhaps you didn't hear the lady say no?' Gray's voice, though quiet, was full of menace.

Regaining his balance, Scrivener snarled, 'What the hell has it to do with you?'

'Rebecca happens to be my guest,' Gray said, putting an arm around her waist, 'and as such I feel responsible for her.'

'She's not a child.'

'As I don't have you down as a child molester, she'd no doubt be safer if she was.'

'Damn it, man, I wasn't molesting her. I've just asked her to marry me.'

'Yes, I heard. I also heard her refuse.'

'She may change her mind.'

'I very much doubt it.'

Rebecca had stood mute and frozen, listening to the two men, then all at once, reaction setting in, a wave of nausea washed over her and she began to tremble violently.

In response to that involuntary movement, Gray's arm tightened and he glanced down at her ashen face. 'We'd better get you straight home.'

Turning to the other man, he said coolly, 'Goodnight and thanks for the party.'

They were moving away when he added over his shoulder, 'Oh, by the way, Sue Collins seems to be looking for a rich husband. She's just assured me she would do *anything* for a man who could give her the kind of lifestyle she's set her heart on.'

Sketching a mocking salute, Gray led Rebecca across the garden to where his car was parked and, her knees feeling like jelly, she sank into it with relief.

He drove back to Santa Rosa without saying a word, while Rebecca shrank into herself, her mind refusing to let go of what had happened that evening.

As her skin crawled and nausea filled her, time and time again she unwillingly relived the moment when Andrew Scrivener had crushed her to him, and his mouth, with those thick, sensual lips had closed over hers.

As soon as they came to a halt by the veranda, before Gray could come round and help her, she stumbled out of the car, and the instant he had opened the front door of the house she made to brush past him.

He caught hold of her arm. 'Where are you off to in such a hurry?'

She turned large, unseeing eyes on him. 'I'd like to take a shower.'

His face softened. 'Very well. Don't be long, and I'll fix us a nightcap.'

Going straight to her bathroom, she stripped off her

things, stepped into the shower stall and for a long time stood under the flow of hot water, letting it run over her face and into her mouth, trying to wash away any last traces of that kiss.

A loud rap at the door made her jump. 'All right in there?' Gray called.

'Yes,' she answered in a muffled voice.

'I'll give you five more minutes.'

She turned off the shower, rubbed herself dry and, pulling on a towelling robe, took the pins from her hair and brushed out the damp, tangled mass.

Then, too tired to bother getting dressed again, she slipped her feet into mules and went out onto the moonlit patio just as she was.

He settled her into a chair and passed her a brandy. As she opened her mouth to protest, he said firmly, 'It's for medicinal purposes. You need it.'

'Perhaps I do.' She took a sip, and felt its smooth, fiery warmth slide down her throat to banish the last of the lingering nausea.

His eyes gleaming silver in the moonlight, he studied her face. 'Feeling somewhat better?'

She nodded.

'I'm sorry you had such an unpleasant experience.'

'It was partly my own fault,' she admitted. 'I should have had more sense than to go with him.'

Then anxiously, 'What if he withdraws from the deal now he's been humiliated?'

'My guess is, he won't. He's too good a businessman to let anything get in the way of making money.'

'Suppose you're wrong?'

He lifted broad shoulders in a shrug. 'If I am, Finance International will just have to weather it.'

'I'm only sorry things happened the way they did. Perhaps if I'd behaved differently...'

'You mean, if you'd agreed to marry him?' Gray asked with grim humour.

'It's no laughing matter. You may find yourself in serious trouble with Philip Lorne, and it will be all my fault for behaving so stupidly.'

'There's no need to start blaming yourself. If it hadn't been for you, Scrivener would have already pulled out.'

'I just wish you hadn't had to get involved,' she said miserably, 'then at least he couldn't have blamed *you.*'

Gray gave her an ironic smile. 'Are you suggesting that instead of riding up on my white charger I should have left you to defend your own honour?'

Repressing a shudder, she assured him, 'I'm very pleased you didn't.' Then guiltily, 'And I haven't even thanked you yet.'

'Think nothing of it. Any time you need rescuing just let me know and I'll make sure I'm on the spot.'

That sparked off a thought, and she asked curiously, 'How come you *were* on the spot? How did you know where to find me?'

'When I'd looked all over for you, I did what I should have had the sense to do in the first place; put pressure on Sue Collins.

'She admitted that the whole thing had been arranged, and that when she had got me safely out of the way Scrivener was planning to show you the house he's having built.

'I was hoping against hope that you wouldn't be fool enough to go inside, and it was a great relief when I reached the trees and saw the pair of you start to return.

'Everything seemed to be fine, so I decided that, rather than make an uncomfortable threesome, I would stay out of sight until you'd passed, and then cut across the garden back to the house.

'Fortunately, as it turned out, I found myself unwittingly

eavesdropping when you stopped fairly close to where I was standing.'

'But if you overheard everything, why didn't you…?' With a sudden unhappy realisation of what his answer would be, she faltered to a stop.

'Step in sooner? I can only apologise for not doing so. But I still wasn't one hundred per cent sure that you weren't playing hard to get, that you didn't *want* to be the fourth Mrs Scrivener.'

'So you *did* think I was just like the others…' she whispered, her hurt showing.

He shook his head. 'I didn't think that. I've never thought it since first meeting you. Though I must admit a few doubts had crept in.

'On the first occasion this marriage thing came up you didn't exactly dismiss it out of hand. In fact, if I remember rightly, you said something like, "I'll bear that in mind."

'And tonight, when I mentioned making hay while the sun shone, you answered, "I might just do that."'

'I only said those things because I was hurt by your attitude and what *you'd* said. I had no intention of doing anything of the kind.'

'Then why did you choose to go to Hillsden?'

'I didn't *want* to go, but I thought a party might help to ease the…the situation…'

'If only I'd realised that. But when I discovered you'd gone off with Scrivener quite happily in spite of my warning, it made me wary of interfering.

'Though I couldn't resist following to make sure you were all right.'

In a heartfelt voice, she said, 'I can only thank God you did.'

# CHAPTER TEN

AFTER a moment, his voice thoughtful, Gray said, 'I must admit that I was fascinated to learn what lengths he'd go to to try and persuade you.

'Knowing how much you love Elmslee Manor, I did wonder if offering you that might do the trick.'

Rebecca shook her head. 'Though I'd give the world to have Elmslee, I'd never marry Andrew Scrivener to get it.'

Jokingly, he asked, 'If *I* happened to be rich enough to offer you Elmslee, would you marry me?'

'No,' she answered unhesitatingly. And knew, even as she spoke, that if he wanted her for his wife she would marry him if he hadn't got a penny and could offer her nothing but a shack.

'So you put me in the same class as Scrivener?'

'You must know perfectly well I don't.'

'Then it's because you still love Jason?'

'I don't still love Jason,' she said flatly. 'I realised that the morning we left Boston.'

'If that's the case, as you've been willing to sleep with me, I'm intrigued to know why you wouldn't marry me if I was rich enough to give you Elmslee as a wedding present.'

'Because you'd always believe you'd bought me.'

'And you'd like your husband to respect you?'

She lifted her chin. 'Yes, I would.'

'Fair enough... But there's one important thing you haven't mentioned.'

When she just looked at him, he said, 'Love. I heard you tell Scrivener that you could never marry a man you didn't love.'

'No, I couldn't.'

'And of course you don't love me.' It was a statement not a question. All the same he seemed to be waiting for an answer.

About to assure him she didn't, she paused, knowing it was a lie. From the moment he had walked into the summer house she had been lost. In Boston she had warned herself not to let him become part of her life, *necessary* to her, but it had already been too late. She had loved him even then.

But she mustn't admit it. He'd made it plain that he didn't want any emotional entanglements, and if he learnt the truth now it would only embarrass him…

'Having trouble deciding?' he queried.

'N-no…'

'No, you're not having trouble deciding? Or no, you don't love me?'

'No, I don't love you.' Despite all her efforts her voice shook slightly.

'But what guarantee is there that love will make a marriage work? It would have been a terrible mistake to marry Jason.'

'Yes, I know,' she admitted quietly. 'Though, looking back, I can see now that I never really did love Jason. It was just infatuation.'

Sighing, she added, 'I suppose, never having been in love before, I couldn't tell the difference.'

They both fell silent, and after a moment, watching her stifle a yawn, Gray said abruptly, 'Time for bed, I think.'

All at once her breathing grew shallow and her pulses quickened. Now he was finally convinced that she wasn't a gold-digger, if he suggested moving back into her room she would welcome him with open arms.

But he made no such suggestion.

When they reached her bedroom door, he hesitated for a moment as though about to kiss her goodnight. Her lips had parted in eager anticipation, when he walked away with just a quiet, 'Sleep well.'

Sleep, however, proved to be elusive, and she tossed and turned restlessly for what seemed an age. When she did finally drop off, it was to dream that she was trapped in an underground maze with no way out, and Andrew Scrivener close at her heels.

He reached out of the darkness to grab hold of her and she awoke with a silent scream, drenched in perspiration and with a wildly beating heart.

Afraid to go back to sleep again, she lay with her eyes wide open, staring up at a ceiling dappled with moon shadows.

She wanted to be with Gray, wanted the comfort of his arms and the feel of his body next to hers. Wanted to lie with the man she loved.

But perhaps he no longer wanted her?

No, she couldn't believe that. Some instinct told her that, while he didn't love her, he *did* want her. So why hadn't he suggested moving back?

The answer came immediately. Because he was too proud. His leaving had been at her behest, so he was waiting for her to ask him to come back.

Or go to him.

He might be asleep, the hesitant part suggested.

If he was, which somehow she doubted, she could always wake him.

But after what she had said earlier in the evening, it would mean sinking her pride.

So what? Pride was a cold bedfellow. And after this holiday he would go back to the States and all she would have would be memories.

Barefoot, and in her thin cotton nightie, she padded to his door and knocked.

After a moment it opened, and he stood there naked.

Taking a deep breath, she said awkwardly, 'I seem to be making a habit of this.'

'I'm certainly not complaining.' Smiling at her, he added, 'Though you are a shade overdressed.'

The rest of the holiday proved to be sheer bliss and they enjoyed life to the full. Some days they took the car and went sightseeing, either inland or to the coast; others they walked hand in hand or just lazed in the sun.

Gray taught her how to swim with some degree of confidence, and even dive, and, having come across a pack of cards, she taught him how to play cribbage, a game she had often played with her father.

At times they shared a companionable silence, at others they talked freely, but by tacit consent they avoided all personal topics. They ate simply, and mostly out of doors, except for in the mornings, when, having made sweet love for most of the night, they breakfasted in bed before showering together.

It was the happiest time Rebecca had ever known and she wanted it never to end.

Then all too soon the last morning arrived, and with it Gloria Redford, who had popped in to return their clean laundry and resume her caretaking duties.

For once she said hardly anything, apparently made speechless by the huge tip Gray gave her, and the promise that he would do his best to find a job for her husband without delay.

Touched by his kindness, and battling against the feeling of sadness that the end of the idyll brought, Rebecca felt tears sting behind her eyes. But somehow she managed to keep smiling while they said their goodbyes, and set off to drive back to San Francisco. They were boarding the plane before she thought to ask, 'Will we be going straight through?'

'No, as it's such a long haul I thought it best to break

our journey in Boston, so I've booked a room at a hotel near the airport.'

Rebecca sighed. In less than twenty-four hours they would be home and parting company. But, as though they were both determined not to spoil their last day together, neither of them mentioned it.

When they reached London it was damp and overcast, and the contrast to the golden days they had just spent lowered her spirits even more.

As soon as the airport formalities were over, a uniformed chauffeur appeared as if by magic to deal with their luggage and lead them to where a sleek limousine was waiting for them.

As he began to load their cases into the boot, she braced herself and said to Gray, 'If it's out of your way to drop me, I can always get a taxi.'

'It isn't out of my way,' he answered evenly.

Handing her into the car, he followed her in and took a seat beside her, before adding, 'Though unless you insist, I wasn't intending to take you home just yet. There are still a lot of things to be settled.'

Her heart gave a little flip. 'Things?' she echoed.

He looked at her with those fascinating green eyes. 'I presume you won't be taking up Scrivener's offer of a job?'

'No, I certainly won't.'

'Then we still have your future to consider. I thought, if you're agreeable, you could stay at my house until we've had a chance to really talk?'

It was a wonderful, unexpected gift, and, choked by excitement, all she could do was nod.

'Good,' he said casually. 'Then we'll discuss the various possibilities as soon as I've dealt with the business that brought me back to London.'

*       *       *

The white-stuccoed town house they drew up in front of had a handsome portico, long windows and a basement guarded by black wrought-iron railings.

Situated in a quiet square near Regent's Park, it was much bigger and grander than anything she might have imagined.

While the chauffeur dealt with the luggage, Gray explained, 'It was my grandparents' house. Jason always referred to it as "the family mausoleum".'

'Why was that?'

'Come and meet the housekeeper, and you'll no doubt understand why. Mrs Sheldon is somewhere in her nineties. She's been with the family since the year dot, and she still runs the household with the proverbial rod of iron.

'I offered to have a stairlift installed, but she soon put me in my place. She said *when* she was too old to climb the stairs she would let me know.'

Grinning, he added, 'She called me *Master* Graydon until I was twenty. I'm quite fond of her. She's one of the reasons I keep the house on. I think it would kill her if she had to leave.'

Opening the door, he ushered Rebecca into a large wood-panelled hall with an elegant staircase and a crystal chandelier.

As he closed the door behind them a small, upright figure appeared, dressed neatly in black. Her silver hair was taken up in a bun, and the skin of her pale face stretched so tightly over the bones that it appeared translucent.

She could well have been a corpse, Rebecca reflected, if it hadn't been for the small, birdlike eyes that were so amazingly alive and intelligent.

'Mr Graydon. It's nice to have you back.'

'Thank you, Mrs Sheldon.'

'Did you have a good holiday?'

'Marvellous.' Gray put an arm around Rebecca's waist, and smiled at her.

Her heart in her eyes, she smiled back.

'Mrs Sheldon, this is Miss Ferris.'

'How do you do?' Rebecca turned to the old lady, whose sharp gaze had been assessing her.

After a moment, with what seemed to be a nod of approval, the housekeeper said, 'If you'd like to freshen up, Miss Ferris, I'll show you to your room.'

So Gray had made arrangements for her to stay before he'd even asked her!

As she glanced at him, he said easily, 'When you come down again you'll find me in the den.'

Mrs Sheldon, proving more sprightly than Rebecca would have expected, led the way upstairs and opened a door to the right. 'This is the Rose Room. I hope you'll be comfortable.'

'Thank you. I'm sure I will.'

'I'll get Watkins to bring up your luggage. If you need anything, just ring for Mary.'

Large and airy, the room had Regency wallpaper, a pale carpet and long windows that overlooked a walled garden. It smelled pleasantly of beeswax and lavender, and was furnished with antiques that wore the patina of age.

The first door she tried refused to open, the second led into an *en suite* bathroom that had all the trappings of the twenty-first century. It looked so inviting that she decided to have a quick shower before going down again.

There was a tap at the door, and the chauffeur carried in her case and put it on a low chest. When she thanked him with a smile, looking gratified, he gave her a smart salute.

As she opened her case and took out a change of clothing, she wondered why Gray had asked her to stay. What it was he wanted to talk about.

If it was something as impersonal as finding her a job, surely he could have given her any relative facts over the phone? She felt a heady rush of hope and excitement. Perhaps he was hoping to continue their affair?

But how could two people have an affair with the Atlantic

between them? Unless he was thinking of the odd times he came over on business?

If he was, she knew she wouldn't refuse. Seeing him, however infrequently, would be preferable to not seeing him at all…

When she had pulled on off-white trousers, a blue silky shirt and a pair of sandals, she fastened her hair into a loose knot and went downstairs.

There wasn't a soul in sight, and, having crossed the hall, she hesitated, unsure which of the several doors Gray had indicated.

She was approaching the first, which was slightly ajar, when a voice she knew, *Jason's voice,* cried in anguish, 'Oh, please, Uncle Pip, you can't do that…'

Then Gray's voice, quietly adamant, said, 'If you're going to keep behaving like a fool then I'll be forced to treat you like one.'

As she stood frozen to the spot, she heard Jason protest, 'But what the devil could I do? She assured me she was pregnant, and that mother of hers threatened to get hold of you and kick up a fuss.'

'It's a pity you didn't let her,' Gray said coldly.

'You said you'd wash your hands of me if I got into any more trouble.'

Gray sighed. 'That threat was intended as a deterrent; it wasn't meant to push you into marrying the first designing female that managed to get her claws into you.'

'I had no intention of marrying her—'

'Then why get involved?'

'It just started as a bit of fun,' Jason said sulkily. 'I'd been getting nowhere with—' He broke off abruptly.

'Rebecca?' Gray prompted.

Sounding startled, Jason asked, 'How do you know about Rebecca?'

'With so much at stake I like to keep a fatherly eye on you, so when I heard a whisper that you were seeing one of the Ferris girls, knowing how impecunious they were, I asked Billings to check.

'He sent me some nice pictures of you and a woman he named as Rebecca Ferris. Unfortunately, he failed to tell me when you decided to swop sisters.'

'I was a fool, I know, but I was hellish frustrated, and when Lisa came to my room that night... Well, she's quite something, and at first she seemed happy to keep things light.

'I can tell you it was a hell of a shock when she told me she was having a baby—'

'And you believed her?'

'Well, it was possible,' Jason admitted. 'That first night we had taken a chance...' Then angrily, 'Damn it, have you never made a mistake?'

'Yes, as you well know,' Gray said shortly. 'But I managed to learn from it. It's a pity you didn't. If you'd refused to marry her—'

'I might have done, but she wasn't just any little trollop, she was from a good family, and when she swore she was pregnant—'

'And was she?'

'While we were on honeymoon she "discovered" she wasn't. Though I was furious at the way she'd fooled me, I must admit it was a relief to know there was no baby on the way. I'm not cut out to be a father.

'I just wish I hadn't let myself be rushed into marrying the scheming little bitch.'

'If I'd found out about the wedding sooner I might have prevented it, but by the time Billings tipped me off it was too late. I can't say I was pleased that you'd gone behind my back.'

'The last ticking off you gave me you said it was time I settled down and got married.'

'I meant to a decent girl who loved you rather than your

money. Though it wouldn't be fair to any decent girl to have to put up with your lecherous ways.'

'Well, you're no saint!'

'That's quite true, but I've always stuck with one woman at a time. I suggest you do the same. Try to make something of your marriage.'

'But if you stop my allowance, how will I manage? What will I do for money?'

'Work for it. You've still got a good job with an excellent salary.'

'I'll never be able to manage on that.'

'Why not? You've no mortgage to find. The flat's paid for, though I took the precaution of keeping it in my name.'

Jason muttered something Rebecca didn't catch.

'Admittedly you won't be able to throw too much money away on other women,' Gray went on, 'and your wife will have to curtail her spending. But it should prove to be a salutary lesson. For both of you.

'After, say, a year, if you've no debts and you're still living together—and you might well be; it wouldn't be worth her while to divorce you—I'll be happy to reconsider.

'If not, I'll interpret your mother's will to the letter, and you'll never gain control of a penny.'

'Damn you, Uncle Pip, you can't do this to me. It was my father's money. I have a right to it.'

'It was not your father's money. The fortune came from your mother's side of the family. Your father was a charming but penniless ne'er-do-well when he married your mother.

'Though she was astute when it came to business, she was anything but when it came to personal relationships. She was mad about him. It took her a long time to discover that he was spending her money at a rate of knots, and mostly on other women.

'If he hadn't been killed when he was, she would have had very little left.

'That's why, knowing how like him you were, when she became terminally ill she made a will leaving everything to me, and asked me to do the best I could for you.

'Which, believe it or not, is what I've done for the past eight years and am still trying to do.

'Now, I suggest you go home to your wife and put her in the picture. If she decides to stay with you, there may yet be hope for you both...'

Wanting to hear no more, Rebecca turned and fled silently up the stairs. She had almost reached the top when Jason came rushing out. Without a glance in her direction he crossed the hall, and a second later the front door slammed behind him.

'So there you are.' Gray had followed him into the hall and was standing looking up at her. 'I was about to come up to see where you'd got to.'

Then, noting her pale face and utter stillness, 'How much did you overhear?'

'Most of it, I imagine,' she answered bitterly.

'I'm sorry you had to find out that way. I told Jason I wanted to see him in the office tomorrow, but, apparently scared by the message, he decided to call at the house to try and make his peace.'

Still scarcely able to believe it, she said, 'So *you're* Uncle Pip.'

'Yes.'

Even then she had half expected him to deny it.

'If you're Philip Lorne, why are you calling yourself Graydon Gallagher?'

'My full name is Philip Lorne Graydon Gallagher. But because I wanted some degree of anonymity, the ability to go out and about without being ''recognised'', I've always used Philip Lorne as a business name.

'It was one of the things I wanted to talk to you about. Come on down and I'll put you in the picture.'

With a feeling of utter despair, she shook her head. 'I'm going home.'

'If you still want to leave when you've heard what I have to say, I won't stop you. But first you're going to listen to me.'

When she just looked at him, her face set, he asked, 'What's it to be? Are you coming down? Or do I have to fetch you?'

She didn't doubt he meant every word, and rather than be ignominiously fetched she forced her unwilling feet to carry her down the stairs again.

When he would have put a hand at her waist, she flinched away from him. His jaw tightened and, his hand dropping to his side, he led the way back into the den.

It was a comfortable, homely room carpeted in Turkey red and lined with bookshelves. There was a desk with a swivel chair, a coffee-table and a suite in soft, natural leather. A log fire burnt cheerfully in the grate.

'Sit down,' Gray said shortly.

'I'd rather stand.'

He dropped into a chair, and, pulling her onto his lap, held her there despite her attempts to rise.

When, realising she was wasting her time, she stopped struggling, he said calmly, 'That's better.'

Sitting stiff and straight, her face averted, she demanded, 'Are you sure your wife won't walk in?'

Unruffled he said, 'Quite sure. To the best of my knowledge my ex-wife is married to an Australian businessman and living in Sydney.

'But I'd better start at the beginning. When I was born my mother was past middle age, and I already had a sixteen-year-old sister, named Anne.

'I was just a few months old when my parents were killed in a car crash and, as they hadn't altered their will to include me, Anne inherited everything.

'That didn't matter in the slightest as there was plenty of money in the family, but even so, she felt it wasn't fair.

'After the accident we came to live in this house with our paternal grandparents. They always called me Graydon, which was my grandfather's name. Only my sister ever called me Pip.

'Anne was twenty-two when she fell in love with, and married, Charles Beaumont.

'Beaumont, who was good-looking and charming and belonged to the peerage, hadn't a penny. That wouldn't have mattered at all, but unfortunately he turned out to be a wastrel and a womaniser.

'They moved into a house a few doors up from this one, and Jason was born two years later. Which made me an uncle at the tender age of eight.

'Realising that Jason was of the same mould as her late husband, when Anne found she was dying she named me as his legal guardian and gave me control of her money. I was twenty-three, to Jason's fifteen.

'Even then he was hardly ever out of trouble, and when he was barely seventeen he was expelled from boarding-school for having an affair with one of the teachers' wives.

'Rona and I had only been married a few weeks when he came to live with us. He brought a swift end to a marriage that was already doomed.

'She was very much like Lisa, beautiful, sexy, unscrupulous and from a good, but impoverished, family. Having set her sights on what she wanted, which was a rich husband, she lost no time in going to bed with me.

'She'd certainly got what it takes, and for a while I was on cloud nine. Then she told me she was pregnant, and if her mother found out she would make her have an abortion.

'We were married in the local register office as soon as it could be arranged. The day was cold and wet and the surroundings unappealing. But if the wedding was joyless, the honeymoon was even worse.

'Thinking to surprise her, I'd chosen to get away from it all in a villa in Tuscany. Rona hated everything about it—the isolation, the climate, the food—and couldn't wait to get back to London.

'Because she didn't want to live in the house my grandparents had left me, I'd bought a flat in Mayfair, and Jason came to stay with us there while I tried to find another school that would take him.

'One evening I'd arranged to work late at the office and then go on to a business dinner. At the very last minute my client rang to say he couldn't make it, so rather than have dinner alone I decided to go home.

'I got there to find the flat empty. As I was on my way to the kitchen to get a bite to eat, I noticed my study door was ajar and my small wall safe was standing open. When I checked, my grandmother's ruby ring was missing.

'Apart from being worth a great deal of money, it was a family heirloom. My intention had always been to give it to my wife, but something had held me back, and I'd bought her a diamond solitaire instead.

'I was about to call the police when I heard a sound from the master bedroom. Thinking the intruder might still be on the premises, I crept over and threw open the door.

'For days on end Rona had refused to let me touch her, saying she felt sick. Now she and Jason were in bed together, stark naked, and not only was my wife making the running, but she was also wearing my grandmother's ring.

'I lost my temper and hauled her out of bed. She'd obviously been drinking heavily; she was unsteady on her feet and she stank of gin. I called her a thief and a slut, and threatened to put her over my knee.

'She threw the ring in my face, and said if I laid as much as a finger on her she'd take me to court.

'It wasn't the threat that stopped me, but the knowledge that she was pregnant.

'When I said as much, she called me a poor sucker and

laughed in my face. She said only a fool would have fallen for that old trick.

'I spent the night in my study, and in the morning I told her to pack her bags and get out.

'Having sobered up, she tried to talk me round, but I was through. Still she proved difficult to get rid of, and in the end, because I didn't want to involve Jason, or have my dirty linen washed in public, I was forced to pay her off.'

After a moment he stroked a finger down Rebecca's cheek and asked, 'Have you listened to a word I've been saying?'

'Yes.' And it explained so much.

She turned her head to look at him, her golden eyes brimming with tears.

'Don't cry, little one.' He smiled at her with such tenderness that the tears spilt over.

'I'm sorry…' she whispered.

'For what?'

'That you've never found someone to love.'

'Oh, but I have. One day I walked into an old summer house and there was the woman of my dreams.'

'What?' She looked at him dazedly.

'The only problem is, she won't have me. I've tried to lure her with the promise of a manor house but…'

'You really would buy Elmslee?'

'The deed is done. It's signed, sealed and settled. As soon as I knew you wanted it, I contacted my agent and offered him a substantial bonus if he could push the sale through quickly.'

A thought struck her, and she said, 'I see now what you meant when you said Lisa should have set her cap at the organ-grinder.'

'Don't change the subject, woman.' He stroked a finger down her cheek caressingly. 'Now I've gone to all that trouble, won't you change your mind and agree to marry me?'

She shook her head. 'If I do, you'll believe it's only to get Elmslee.'

'That's where you're wrong. I'll believe you love me. And even if you keep saying no, I'll still believe you love me. You do, don't you?'

'Yes. But what makes you so sure?'

'When I asked you before and you said no, I watched your face. You're not a very good liar.

'Added to that, Mrs Sheldon thinks so, and she's never wrong.'

'Mrs Sheldon?'

'She's fey,' he said, as though that explained everything. 'When I mentioned I was bringing home the woman I loved and wanted to marry, she asked, "Does she love you?"'

'I told her I very much hoped so.

'She said, "I'll know for certain when I've seen the two of you together."

'When she'd shown you to your room, she came back and said very primly, "You'll be pleased to know I've put Miss Ferris in the Rose Room."'

When Rebecca looked blank, he added with a grin, 'The Rose Room is next to mine, and has a connecting door.'


Later that night as they lay in each other's arms, Gray said, 'You'll never know how jealous I was of Jason, and when Scrivener kissed you I could cheerfully have broken his neck.'

She shuddered. 'Don't remind me; it was horrible.' Lifting her face, she added, 'You'd better kiss me to take the memory away.'

'There's nothing I'd like better,' he said with satisfaction, 'especially when you think what a kiss can lead to.'

It did, and it was heavenly. Secure now in his love, she hit the heights and heard the angels singing, before floating gently back to earth.

Drawing her against him and cradling her head on his shoulder, he asked, 'How soon will you marry me?'

'Tomorrow.'

'Can't be too soon for me. But it might take a bit longer to arrange. You see, this time I want a proper wedding. I'd like us to be married in church with all the trimmings, and go on a romantic honeymoon.'

'I didn't think you believed in romance.'

'I've changed my mind… Then when we get back…' He stopped and asked seriously, 'Do you care where you live?'

'I don't care at all so long as you're there.'

That earned her a kiss. 'Well, we could spread ourselves a little. There's this place, I'm fairly certain you'll like New York, and we could go back to Napa from time to time.'

'It's going to be wonderful,' she said dreamily.

'And of course there's Elmslee, it'll be ideal for our children, and to retire to when we get old.'

She nestled even closer. 'It sounds like one of those fairy tales that end, ''And they lived happily ever after.'''

He kissed her again, and said contentedly, 'I'm quite sure we will.'

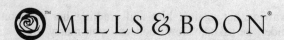